NATIONAL CERTIFICATE
MATHEMATICS
VOLUME III

THE TECHNICAL COLLEGE SERIES

General Editor

E. G. STERLAND
M.A., B.Sc., C.Eng., M.I.Mech.E., A.F.R.Ae.S.
Principal of the Bristol Aeroplane Technical College

A Selection of Books Published

Examples in Practical Mathematics for National Certificate
C. C. T. BAKER
B.Sc.

Applied Mechanics
J. D. WALKER
B.Sc., C.Eng., M.I.Mech.E.

National Certificate Mechanical Engineering Science
J. D. WALKER
B.Sc., C.Eng., M.I.Mech.E.

Electro-Technology for National Certificate
(In three volumes)

H. TEASDALE
B.Sc., C.Eng., A.M.I.Prod.E.

E. C. WALTON
B.Eng., Ph.D., C.Eng., F.I.E.E.

H. BUCKINGHAM
M.Sc., Ph.D., C.Eng., M.I.E.E.

E. M. PRICE
M.Sc. (Tech.), C.Eng., M.I.E.E.

National Certificate Workshop Technology
T. NUTTALL
M.I.Mech.E., A.M.I.Prod.E.

Laboratory Manual for Principles of Electricity and Electronics

E. C. HALLIDAY
B.Sc. (Eng.)

B. P. MORRIS
B.Sc., A.M.I.E.R.E.

National Certificate Electrical Engineering Science

E. C. HALLIDAY
B.Sc. (Eng.)

B. P. MORRIS
B.Sc., A.M.I.E.R.E.

NATIONAL CERTIFICATE MATHEMATICS

VOLUME III

By

G. E. MAHON, B.Sc., and P. ABBOTT, B.A.

Completely Revised by

W. E. FISHER, O.B.E., D.Sc., C.Eng., M.I.Mech.E.
*Formerly Principal, Wolverhampton and
Staffordshire College of Technology*

THE ENGLISH UNIVERSITIES PRESS LTD

ST. PAUL'S HOUSE   WARWICK LANE
LONDON EC4

First published	1938
Fifteenth impression	1957
Revised Edition	1962
Second impression (with corrections)	1963
Third impression	1965
Fourth impression	1967

Revised Edition
Copyright © 1962
The English Universities Press Ltd

Printed and Bound in Great Britain for the English Universities Press Ltd.,
by Richard Clay (The Chaucer Press), Ltd., Bungay, Suffolk

GENERAL EDITOR'S FOREWORD

THE last twenty years have seen far-reaching changes in technical education, changes whose objectives have been to meet the ever-increasing demands of technology. A new pattern of technical education is now emerging as a result of a series of Government Committees and White Papers. Initially, attention was directed perhaps more intensely to the education of technologists resulting in the expansion of the universities, a greater emphasis on the teaching of science in schools, and the establishment of the Colleges of Advanced Technology.

The training of technologists has hitherto fallen into two broad categories; university courses and National Certificate courses arranged on a part-time day-release basis for apprentices in industry. These part-time courses have become the route through which the majority of professional engineers have received their training. It is, however, unlikely that this state of affairs will continue in the future. The professional Institutions have rightly raised their entrance requirements to a level which the part-time day-release student will find extremely difficult to achieve; at the same time the greatly increased facilities for full-time and sandwich courses will provide a much more satisfactory educational system for those wishing to attain professional status.

Latterly, more attention has been given to the better training of technicians, craftsmen, and operatives. The Government White Paper " Better Opportunities in Technical Education " seeks to establish a new pattern for technical college courses at these levels. The very high failure rate in Ordinary and Higher National Certificate courses which has caused such concern in recent years is, it is hoped, to be avoided by the introduction of the new General Course. This is designed as a diagnostic course to

v

determine whether a student is best suited to continue with an Ordinary National Certificate course, a craft or operative course, or a technician course. The City and Guilds of London Institute are making radical changes in their existing courses, and designing new technician courses to fulfil these objectives.

The Technical College Series of books covers the National Certificate, the General Course in Engineering, and the very wide field of technician courses. Many of the books in the series are now standard works, having stood the test of time over a long period of years. Such books are reviewed from time to time and new editions published to keep them up to date, both in respect of new technological developments and changing examination requirements. New works are constantly being added to the list as new courses are arranged and new techniques developed. The Publishers are fully aware of the part that well-written up-to-date text-books can play in supplementing teaching, and it is their intention that the Technical College Series shall continue to make a substantial contribution to the development of technical education.

PREFACE

This volume is essentially the work of Mr. G. E. Mahon and is based on the lectures given by him for many years to engineering students at the Polytechnic, Regent St., W.1.

IT is now twenty years since the Authors of National Certificate Mathematics set out " to provide a systematic and progressive text-book in Mathematics for students taking mechanical or electrical engineering courses ". At that time National Certificates, though still a year or two short of their majority, were well established, and the success of the early schemes had made it clear that preparation for these certificates would be the central activity of the system of part-time technical education favoured in this country—the system of opportunity.

Since the first publication of this work there have been a world war and many years of troubled peace. The total of National Certificate students has increased twenty-fold. Part-time day students now outnumber evening students as greatly as once they were outnumbered. But the three volumes of National Certificate Mathematics still succeed in fulfilling the Authors' original purpose: to meet the immediate practical needs of the first-year no less than of the third-year technical student while providing at all stages a sound basis for more advanced studies.

Why, then, a new edition? Simply because advances in technology have been reflected in changes in courses. National Certificates themselves are responsible for a whole literature of new applications of age-old truths. The day-to-day experience of the typical student has changed. Because of this it has seemed desirable to introduce, here and there in the text, but more especially by way of exercises, matter taken from current National Certificate schemes and examinations.

Acknowledgments are again due to a number of examining bodies which now includes, as well as the City & Guilds of London Institute, the Union of Lancashire and Cheshire Institutes, the Union of Educational Institutions, the Northern Counties Technical Examinations Council, and the East Midland Educational Union, for permission to print questions which have been set in their examinations. The present edition contains also, by kind permission of many Principals of Colleges, and Chief Officers of Education Authorities, a large number of examples taken from the internal sessional examinations of courses approved for the award of National Certificates. This generous co-operation is highly appreciated, and the place of origin is given at the end of each question quoted. Such miscellaneous exercises occasionally anticipate the work of later chapters. This is not altogether accidental: these exercises test the alertness of the student and may provide an experimental introduction to studies which follow.

W. E. FISHER.

CONTENTS

CHAPTER 1

THE SOLUTION OF EQUATIONS

1. The Quadratic Equation

Every quadratic equation can be reduced to the form $ax^2 + bx + c = 0$, where a, b, c are real numbers. It may happen that either b or c is zero.

We shall assume that the student is familiar with the solution of quadratic equations, either by factorisation or by the use of the formula

$$x = \frac{-b \pm \sqrt{b^2 - 4ac}}{2a}$$

In addition, he will know that if the roots of any quadratic equation are α and β

$$\left. \begin{array}{l} \alpha + \beta = -\dfrac{b}{a} \\[2mm] \alpha\beta = \dfrac{c}{a} \end{array} \right\}$$

Further, the roots are real, coincident, or imaginary when $b^2 - 4ac$ is respectively positive, zero or negative. The graph of $y = ax^2 + bx + c$ cuts the x-axis in real points if $b^2 - 4ac$ is positive, touches the axis when $b^2 - 4ac = 0$, and, assuming a to be positive, lies above this axis when $b^2 - 4ac$ is negative.

Example 1

If one root of $x^2 - 6x + k = 0$ is 2, find k.
The sum of the roots is **6.**
∴ The other root is **4.**

$$k = \text{product of roots} = 8.$$

Example 2.

In drawing the graph of $y = x^2 - 3{\cdot}7x + 3{\cdot}12$, we find the curve cuts the x-axis where $x = 1{\cdot}3$. At what other point must it cut this axis?

The axis is cut where $x^2 - 3{\cdot}7x + 3{\cdot}12 = 0$. One root of this quadratic is $1{\cdot}3$.

The sum of the roots is $3{\cdot}7$.

∴ The graph again cuts the axis where $x = 2{\cdot}4$.

Also $2{\cdot}4 \times 1{\cdot}3 = 3{\cdot}12$, the constant term.

In Chapter 3 of Volume II (Revised Edition) of National Certificate Mathematics *will be found a useful discussion of the types of practical problems which lead to quadratic equations.*

EXERCISE 1

1. Solve $\dfrac{x^2}{2} - \dfrac{x(3 - 2x)}{4} = \dfrac{x}{3} - \dfrac{1}{4}$.   (N.C.T.E.C.)

2. Factorise (a) $x^2 - x - 20$, (b) $\pi R^2 - 4\pi r^2$, and (c) $R^3 + 6R^2 r + 8R r^2$.

Use the results of (b) and (c) to find the values of these expressions when $R = 6{\cdot}5$, $r = 1{\cdot}75$ and $\pi = 3{\cdot}14$.

(N.C.T.E.C.)

3. Given that $f = \dfrac{p(D^2 + d^2)}{D^2 - d^2}$, express d in terms of the other quantities, and find d when $D = 8$, $p = 1100$, and $f = 3200$.   (U.L.C.I.)

4. Given $f = \dfrac{Wx}{S(a + b)} + \dfrac{Wd}{2Sk^2}\left[x - \dfrac{bx^2}{L(a + b)}\right]$, find the values of x given that $f = 4{\cdot}2$, $W = 1{\cdot}5$, $S = 10$, $k^2 = 11$, $L = 240$, $a = 12$, $b = 60$, $d = 8$.   (U.L.C.I.)

5. The lengths of the sides of a triangle are $5{\cdot}6$ in., 5 in., and $3{\cdot}4$ in. Calculate the lengths of the two parts into which the longest side is divided by the perpendicular drawn to it from the opposite vertex.   (N.C.T.E.C.)

6. Fill in the blanks of

$$3a^2 + 5ab - 2b^2 = (3a^2 + 6ab) - (ab + \quad)$$
$$= 3a(\quad) - b(\quad)$$
$$= (\quad)(a + 2b)$$

and evaluate with as little labour as possible

$$3(8{\cdot}9)^2 + 5(8{\cdot}9)(25{\cdot}7) - 2(25{\cdot}7)^2.$$

(N.C.T.E.C.)

7. Without solving the equations, state whether the roots of the following equations are real, equal, or complex (imaginary):

 (a) $x^2 + 3x + 1 = 0.$ (b) $2x^2 - 3x + 4 = 0.$
 (c) $x^2 + 4x + 4 = 0.$ (d) $0{\cdot}2x^2 - 0{\cdot}1x - 3 = 0.$

8. Given that the area of a rectangle, whose sides are x and y, is A, and that its perimeter is P, find a quadratic equation whose roots give the side of length x.

Find the sides given A = 12 sq. in. and P = 18 in.

9. Solve $\dfrac{3}{x + 2} - \dfrac{1}{x - 3} = \dfrac{4}{x}.$

10. When a body moves with a uniform acceleration f, we get $s = ut + \frac{1}{2}ft^2$, where s is the distance gone in time t, and u is the velocity of the body at zero time. Find t if $s = 3$ miles, $u = 8$ ft/sec, and $f = 4$ ft/sec^2.

2. Equations Reducible to Quadratics

It will be found that there is but a single idea underlying the solution of the equations given in this section—viz., the use of a simple symbol for a group of symbols, or for a more complicated one.

Example 1

Solve $x^4 - 5x^2 + 4 = 0$ . . . . (1)

Writing z for x^2, the above becomes

$$z^2 - 5z + 4 = 0$$
$$(z - 4)(z - 1) = 0$$

Hence $\qquad z = 4$ or 1

i.e., $\qquad\qquad x^2 = 4$ or 1

giving $\qquad\qquad x = \pm\,2$ or $\pm\,1$.

The equation has four roots, $+\,2$, $-\,2$, $+\,1$, $-\,1$, all of which satisfy it.

Example 2

Solve $\qquad x^{\frac{1}{2}} - 5x^{\frac{1}{4}} + 4 = 0 \quad . \quad . \quad . \quad . \quad . \quad (2)$

If $\qquad\qquad\qquad x^{\frac{1}{4}} = z$

then $\qquad\qquad\qquad x^{\frac{1}{2}} = z^2$, and (2) becomes

$$z^2 - 5z + 4 = 0$$

and just as before, we get

$$z = 4 \text{ or } z = 1.$$

Hence $\qquad\qquad x^{\frac{1}{4}} = 4$ or 1

$$\therefore \quad x = 256 \text{ or } 1.$$

Example 3

Solve $\qquad\qquad x^2 = 4 + 5\sqrt{x^2 - 8} \quad . \quad . \quad . \quad (1)$

Subtracting 8 from both sides, we get:

$$x^2 - 8 = -4 + 5\sqrt{x^2 - 8} \quad . \quad . \quad . \quad (2)$$

Put $\qquad z = \sqrt{x^2 - 8}$.

Then $\quad z^2 = -4 + 5z$, by substituting for z in (2),

i.e., $\qquad\qquad z^2 - 5z + 4 = 0$

or $\qquad\qquad (z - 1)(z - 4) = 0$

Giving $\qquad\qquad\qquad z = 1$ or 4

i.e., $\qquad\qquad \sqrt{x^2 - 8} = 1$ or 4

Giving $\qquad\qquad x^2 - 8 = 1$ or 16

i.e., $\qquad\qquad\qquad x^2 = 9$ or 24

or $\qquad\qquad\qquad x = \pm\,3$ or $\pm\,2\sqrt{6}$.

Test if these roots satisfy equation (1).

They do so if $\sqrt{x^2 - 8}$ is regarded as positive.

Example 4

Solve $\dfrac{1}{y^4} - \dfrac{13}{y^2} + 36 = 0.$

Put $z = \dfrac{1}{y^2}.$

Then $z^2 - 13z + 36 = 0$

i.e., $(z - 4)(z - 9) = 0$

or $\dfrac{1}{y^2} = 4 \text{ or } 9.$

i.e., $y^2 = \tfrac{1}{4} \text{ or } \tfrac{1}{9}.$

Giving $y = \pm \tfrac{1}{2} \text{ or } \pm \tfrac{1}{3}.$

All four roots satisfy the original equation.

3. Trigonometrical equations are frequently simple examples of the quadratic.

Example 1

Solve for $\cos \theta$,

$$6 \cos^2 \theta - 5 \cos \theta + 1 = 0$$

We have $6x^2 - 5x + 1 = 0$ if $x = \cos \theta.$

Giving $(3x - 1)(2x - 1) = 0.$

$$\therefore \quad x = \tfrac{1}{3} \text{ or } \tfrac{1}{2}$$

i.e., $\cos \theta = \tfrac{1}{3} \text{ or } \cos \theta = \tfrac{1}{2}.$

Example 2

Solve $12 - 9 \cos \theta - 10 \sin^2 \theta = 0$.   .   (1)

(1) can be written:

$$12 - 9 \cos \theta - 10(1 - \cos^2 \theta) = 0$$

i.e., $10 \cos^2 \theta - 9 \cos \theta + 2 = 0$

$$\therefore \quad (5x - 2)(2x - 1) = 0.$$

where $x = \cos \theta$ as before.

Hence $\cos \theta = \tfrac{2}{5} \text{ or } \tfrac{1}{2}.$

Reference to a book of trigonometrical tables will give us the values of θ. Where $\cos \theta = \tfrac{1}{2}$, one value of θ is $60°$

,, $\cos \theta = \tfrac{2}{5}$,   ,,   ,, $66° 25'$

EXERCISE 2

Solve the following equations:

1. $x^4 - 5x^2 + 6 = 0$.

2. $\dfrac{1}{y^4} + \dfrac{1}{y^2} - 6 = 0$.

3. $3x^{\frac{3}{2}} + 8x^{\frac{1}{2}} - 3 = 0$.

4. $x^2 - 2x - 5\sqrt{x^2 - 2x} + 4 = 0$.

5. $z = 4\sqrt{z - 3} + 8$.

6. $12 \sin^2 \theta - 13 \sin \theta + 3 = 0$.

7. $4 \tan^2 \theta + 19 \tan \theta - 5 = 0$.

8. Solve for $\sin \theta, 8 - 7 \sin \theta - 6 \cos^2 \theta = 0$.

9. Find $\tan \theta$, if $3 \sec^2 \theta - 10 \tan \theta - 11 = 0$.

Solve:

10. $3^x + \dfrac{27}{3^x} - 12 = 0$.

11. $2^{2x+2} - 17 \cdot 2^x + 4 = 0$.

12. Given that $\cos 2\theta = 2 \cos^2 \theta - 1$, solve
$\cos \theta + \frac{2}{15} \cos 2\theta = 0$ for $\cos \theta$.

13. Solve   (i) $10^x(10^x - 2\cdot5) = -1\cdot5$,
(ii) $5 \sin^2 x - 3 \cos^2 x = 1$.   (U.L.C.I.)

4. Equations Involving the Square Root of the Unknown

Example 1

Solve $\sqrt{2x + 3} = 4$.
Squaring $2x + 3 = 16$
or $x = 6\frac{1}{2}$.

Strictly speaking, $\sqrt{2x + 3}$ should be taken to mean $\pm \sqrt{2x + 3}$, since any number has two square roots. When, however, the square root does not arise in the course of algebraic work, but is part of the data of a problem or example, the positive square root will always be understood.

Example 2

Solve $\sqrt{x+1} + \sqrt{x+8} = 7.$

We have $\sqrt{x+8} = 7 - \sqrt{x+1}$

Squaring, $x + 8 = 49 + x + 1 - 14\sqrt{x+1}$
$$= 50 + x - 14\sqrt{x+1}.$$

i.e. $14\sqrt{x+1} = 42$

$\sqrt{x+1} = 3$

Giving $x = 8,$

which will be found to satisfy the given equation.

Example 3

Solve $\sqrt{2x+6} + \sqrt{3x+1} = 8$ . . . (1)

Transposing, $\sqrt{3x+1} = 8 - \sqrt{2x+6}$

Squaring $3x + 1 = 64 + 2x + 6 - 16\sqrt{2x+6}$
$$= 70 + 2x - 16\sqrt{2x+6}$$

$\therefore\ \ 16\sqrt{2x+6} = 69 - x.$

Square again:

$$256(2x+6) = 69^2 - 138x + x^2$$

i.e., $512x + 1536 = 4761 - 138x + x^2$

$x^2 - 650x + 3225 = 0$ . . . . . . (2)

$(x - 5)(x - 645) = 0.$

Giving $x = 5$ or $645.$

It is clear that $x = 645$ does not satisfy the equation.

Hence $x = 5$ is the only solution. It will, however, be found that $x = 645$ satisfies the equation

$$-\sqrt{2x+6} + \sqrt{3x+1} = 8.$$

Whenever we have to square twice, as in the above example, one of the roots found will not satisfy the original equation. See note in Example 1. In every case the values found for the unknown should be tried in the original equation.

Example 4

Solve for M *the equation* $T_e = M + \sqrt{M^2 + T^2}$, *given that* $T = 4 \cdot 22$ *(tons-ft) and* $T_e = 18 \cdot 54$ *(tons-ft)*   (U.L.C.I.)

Substituting, we get

$$18 \cdot 54 = M + \sqrt{M^2 + (4 \cdot 22)^2}$$

$$\therefore \quad (18 \cdot 54 - M)^2 = M^2 + (4 \cdot 22)^2$$

i.e., $(18 \cdot 54)^2 - 2M \times 18 \cdot 54 + M^2 = M^2 + (4 \cdot 22)^2.$

i.e., $(18 \cdot 54)^2 - (4 \cdot 22)^2 = 37 \cdot 08M.$

$$\therefore \quad = M = \frac{22 \cdot 76 \times 14 \cdot 32}{37 \cdot 08} \left(\begin{array}{l} \text{factorising the difference} \\ \text{between two squares} \end{array} \right).$$

Notice that we could first solve the equation as given, *i.e.,* without replacing symbols by numbers, thus

$$(T_e - M)^2 = M^2 + T^2$$

i.e., $T_e^2 - 2M \cdot T_e + M^2 = M^2 + T^2$

i.e., $T_e^2 - T^2 = 2M \cdot T_e.$

Giving $$M = \frac{(T_e + T)(T_e - T)}{2T_e}.$$

With the given values $M = 8 \cdot 79$. From the other information given we know that M is a " moment " the magnitude of which is $8 \cdot 79$ tons-ft.

Note that, as in all such formulæ and equations, the symbols stand for numbers. The solution of the equation is thus also a number. The other conditions of the problem tell us how to complete the answer: in this case M is the *number* of tons-ft in a certain " moment." This particular equation tells us the Twisting Moment which is equivalent (*i.e.,* leads to the same maximum stress) to the combination of a bending and a twisting moment acting in the same member.

EXERCISE 3

Solve:

1. $\sqrt{3x - 4} = 5.$

2. $\sqrt[4]{x - 6} = 2.$

3. $\sqrt{x^2 - 8} = \sqrt{17}.$

4. $\sqrt{x - 2} = \sqrt{x} - 1$.

5. $\sqrt{3x + 1} + \sqrt{x + 3} = 2$.

6. $3\sqrt{y} + 2\sqrt{5 - y} = 8$.

7. $5\sqrt{z - 3} + 2\sqrt{z + 1} = \sqrt{z + 13}$.

8. $2\sqrt{x + 3} + \sqrt{x} = 5$.

9. $\dfrac{12}{\sqrt{x + 5}} + \sqrt{x + 5} = 7$.

10. A Board of Trade formula for determining the distances between the centres of rivets is

$$10c = \sqrt{(11p + 4d)(p + 4d)}.$$

Find p when $c = 1\frac{3}{8}$ and $d = \frac{3}{4}$.   (U.L.C.I.)

In regard to Question 10, refer to the note appended to Example 4, p. 20. The symbols p, c, and d, stand for numbers. It would be unusual to speak of $1\frac{3}{8}$ cm or $\frac{3}{4}$ cm, so we conclude that c and d are numbers of inches and that the answer gives us one rivet pitch in inches.

If, however, we simplify the equation by squaring, we obtain

$$100c^2 = 11p^2 + 16d^2 + 48pd$$

an equation in which each term has the dimension (length)^2. So the formula for the pitch is a " rational " one, and will apply whatever unit of length we adopt. With many formulæ in common use this is not the case, so that care is necessary.

5. Simultaneous Quadratic Equations

Case I.

When one equation is of the first degree.

Solve

$$\left. \begin{array}{l} x^2 + 3y^2 = 13 \\ 2x + y = 4 \end{array} \right\} \quad \begin{array}{l} \ldots \ldots \ldots \quad (1) \\ \ldots \ldots \ldots \quad (2) \end{array}$$

From (2) $y = 4 - 2x$.

Substitute in (1) and get:

$$x^2 + 3(4 - 2x)^2 = 13$$

i.e., $x^2 + 3(16 - 16x + 4x^2) = 13.$

Simplifying, this gives:

$$13x^2 - 48x + 35 = 0$$

i.e., $(13x - 35)(x - 1) = 0$

From which, $x = 1$ or $\frac{35}{13}$.

Now substitute each of the above values for x in (2).

Putting $x = 1$,   we get $y = 2$.
Putting $x = \frac{35}{13}$,   we get $y = -\frac{18}{13}$.

The values $(1, 2)$, and $(\frac{35}{13}, -\frac{18}{13})$, will be found to satisfy both equations.

The student will observe that the method of solution is to use the linear (first degree) equation to express y in terms of x (or vice versa). This value is then substituted in the other equation, and the resulting quadratic is then solved.

6. *Case II*.
Consider the equation

$$3x^2 + 2xy - y^2 = 0 \quad . \quad . \quad . \%. \quad (1)$$

Every term is of two dimensions in x and y, and the equation is said to be homogeneous.

(1) becomes $(3x - y)(x + y) = 0 \quad . \quad . \quad . \quad . \quad (2)$
when we factorise.

Hence, either $3x - y = 0 \quad . \quad . \quad . \quad . \quad (3)$
or $x + y = 0 \quad . \quad . \quad . \quad (4)$

From (3) we get:

$$3x = y, \quad i.e., \quad \frac{x}{y} = \tfrac{1}{3}$$

From (4), $x = -y, \quad i.e., \quad \frac{x}{y} = -1.$

Such an equation as (1) cannot be solved for either x or y, but it can be solved for the ratio $\dfrac{x}{y}$, or $\dfrac{y}{x}$.

If Equation (1) cannot be factorised, we can still find the ratio $\dfrac{x}{y}$.

For example, find the ratio $\dfrac{x}{y}$, if

$$x^2 - 2xy - 2y^2 = 0 \quad . \quad . \quad . \quad . \quad (5)$$

Dividing by y^2, we get:

$$\frac{x^2}{y^2} - \frac{2x}{y} - 2 = 0 \quad . \quad . \quad . \quad (6)$$

Put
$$\frac{x}{y} = z.$$

(6) becomes:

$$z^2 - 2z - 2 = 0$$

Giving
$$z = \frac{2 \pm \sqrt{12}}{2}$$

i.e.,
$$\frac{x}{y} = 1 \pm \sqrt{3}.$$

7. We can now apply the above method to the solution of a certain type of simultaneous quadratic equation.

Example 1

Solve
$$\left.\begin{array}{l} x^2 + y^2 = 5 \\ 2xy - y^2 = 3 \end{array}\right\} \quad \begin{array}{l} . \quad . \quad . \quad . \quad . \quad (1) \\ . \quad . \quad . \quad . \quad . \quad (2) \end{array}$$

Observe that there are no terms of the first degree in either of the given equations.

We have, by cross-multiplication,

$$3(x^2 + y^2) = 5(2xy - y^2)$$

i.e.,
$$3x^2 - 10xy + 8y^2 = 0.$$

Factorising, we get:

$$(3x - 4y)(x - 2y) = 0.$$

These give $\qquad\qquad x = 2y$ . . . . . . (3)

or $\qquad\qquad\qquad x = \dfrac{4y}{3}$ . . . . . . (4)

Substitute from (3) in (1) and get

$$5y^2 = 5$$
$$\therefore\ \ y = \pm 1, \text{ and}$$
$$x = 2y = \pm 2.$$

The values $(2, 1)$, $(-2, -1)$ will be found to satisfy both equations.

Now take (4) and again substitute in (1).

We get:

$$\frac{16y^2}{9} + y^2 = 5$$

i.e., $\qquad\qquad \dfrac{25y^2}{9} = 5$

or $\qquad\qquad\qquad y^2 = \tfrac{9}{5}$

and $\qquad y = \pm \dfrac{3}{\sqrt{5}} = \pm \dfrac{3\sqrt{5}}{5}$

$$x = \tfrac{4}{3}y = \pm \frac{4\sqrt{5}}{5}.$$

The values $\left(\dfrac{4\sqrt{5}}{5}, \dfrac{3\sqrt{5}}{5}\right)$ and $\left(-\dfrac{4\sqrt{5}}{5}, -\dfrac{3\sqrt{5}}{5}\right)$ satisfy both equations.

The methods used in Cases (1) and (2) are perfectly general, and will always solve simultaneous equations of the given types.

8. Notice the method used in solving the following:

Example 1

Solve $\qquad \left.\begin{array}{l} x + y = 7 \\ xy = 12 \end{array}\right\}$ . . . . . (1) $\newline$ . . . . . (2)

Squaring (1) $\qquad x^2 + 2xy + y^2 = 49$

Multiplying (2) by 4 $\qquad 4xy = 48$

Subtracting $\qquad x^2 - 2xy + y^2 = 1$

i.e., $\qquad\qquad\qquad (x - y)^2 = 1$

$$\therefore \quad x - y = \pm 1 \quad . \quad . \quad . \quad (3)$$

Combine (3) and (1)

$$\left.\begin{array}{r} x + y = 7 \\ x - y = 1 \end{array}\right\} \text{giving } x = 4, y = 3$$

$$\left.\begin{array}{r} x + y = 7 \\ x - y = -1 \end{array}\right\} \text{giving } x = 3, y = 4.$$

If the graphs of Equations (1) and (2) are plotted, the points (4, 3) and (3, 4) will be found to lie on both curves.

Example 2

Solve $\qquad\qquad \left.\begin{array}{r} x^2 + y^2 = 170 \\ xy = 13 \end{array}\right\} \quad . \quad . \quad . \quad . \quad \begin{array}{l}(1)\\(2)\end{array}$

$$x^2 + 2xy + y^2 = 170 + 26 = 196$$
$$\therefore \quad (x + y)^2 = 196 = 14^2$$
$$\therefore \quad x + y = \pm 14 \quad . \quad . \quad . \quad . \quad (3)$$

Similarly $\quad x^2 - 2xy + y^2 = 170 - 26 = 144$

i.e., $\qquad\qquad (x - y)^2 = 12^2$

$$\therefore \quad x - y = \pm 12 \quad . \quad . \quad . \quad . \quad (4)$$

We now solve

$$\left.\begin{array}{r} x + y = 14 \\ x - y = 12 \end{array}\right\} \qquad \left.\begin{array}{r} x + y = 14 \\ x - y = -12 \end{array}\right\}$$

$$\left.\begin{array}{r} x + y = -14 \\ x - y = 12 \end{array}\right\} \qquad \left.\begin{array}{r} x + y = -14 \\ x - y = -12 \end{array}\right\}$$

These give the four solutions:

$$\left.\begin{array}{r} x = 13 \\ y = 1 \end{array}\right\} \quad \left.\begin{array}{r} x = 1 \\ y = 13 \end{array}\right\} \quad \left.\begin{array}{r} x = -1 \\ y = -13 \end{array}\right\} \quad \left.\begin{array}{r} x = -13 \\ y = -1 \end{array}\right\}$$

9. Simultaneous Equations of the First Degree with Three Unknowns

The method of solution is to eliminate one unknown—say, z—and get two equations involving x and y only.

The method of solving this pair is known.

Example 1

Solve

$$x + y + z = 6 \quad \cdots \cdots \quad (1)$$
$$2x - y + 3z = 9 \quad \cdots \cdots \quad (2)$$
$$x + 3y - z = 4 \quad \cdots \cdots \quad (3)$$

Adding (1) and (3) we get:

$$2x + 4y = 10$$

or

$$x + 2y = 5 \quad \cdots \cdots \quad (4)$$

Now multiply (3) by 3 and add to (2).

Then

$$5x + 8y = 21 \quad \cdots \cdots \quad (5)$$

Solving (4) and (5), we get

$$x = 1, \quad y = 2.$$

Substitute these values in (1) and $z = 3$.

Example 2

It is known that the readings given below for x and y follow a law of the form $y = Ax^2 + Bx + C = 0$. *Find* A, B, *and* C.

x . . .	1	2	3
y . . .	1	3	12

Substituting the pairs of values for x and y in the given equation, we get:

$$A + B + C = 1 \quad \cdots \cdots \quad (1)$$
$$4A + 2B + C = 3 \quad \cdots \cdots \quad (2)$$
$$9A + 3B + C = 12 \quad \cdots \cdots \quad (3)$$

Eliminate C from (1) and (2) by subtraction. We get:

$$3A + B = 2 \quad \cdots \cdots \quad (4)$$

Subtract (2) from (3) and get:

$$5A + B = 9 \quad \cdots \cdots \quad (5)$$

Now eliminate B from (4) and (5), and

$$2A = 7$$
$$\therefore \quad A = \tfrac{7}{2}$$

Substitute in (4), giving B $= 2 - 3A = 2 - \frac{21}{2} = -\frac{17}{2}$.
From (1) C $= 1 - B - A = 1 + \frac{17}{2} - \frac{7}{2} = 6$.

Hence $$y = \frac{7x^2}{2} - \frac{17x}{2} + 6.$$

Other readings could be checked by the equation.

EXERCISE 4

1. Solve: $\left.\begin{array}{l} x^2 + y = 1 \\ y - 2x = 2 \end{array}\right\}$.

2. $\left.\begin{array}{l} x^2 - xy = 21 \\ x - y = 3 \end{array}\right\}$.

3. $\left.\begin{array}{l} x + y = 5 \\ xy = 6 \end{array}\right\}$.

4. $\left.\begin{array}{l} z^2 - 9w^2 = 28 \\ z - 3w = 2 \end{array}\right\}$.

5. $\left.\begin{array}{l} x^2 + xy = 3 \\ xy + y^2 = 6 \end{array}\right\}$.

6. $\left.\begin{array}{l} 3x^2 + 4xy + 5y^2 = 31 \\ \ x + 2y = 5 \end{array}\right\}$.

7. $\left.\begin{array}{l} x^2 + y^2 = 100 \\ \ xy = 14 \end{array}\right\}$.

(U.L.C.I.)

8. Find the values of $\frac{1}{x}$ and $\frac{1}{y}$ if $\frac{4}{x} - \frac{1}{y} = 13$ and $\frac{3}{x} - \frac{2}{y} = 6$.

(N.C.T.E.C.)

9. $\left.\begin{array}{l} 3x^2 - 5xy = -2 \\ 4xy - 3y^2 = 1 \end{array}\right\}$.

10. If $x = 4y$ and $\frac{1}{5}(2x + 7y - 1) = \frac{2}{3}(2x - 6y + 1)$, find x and y.

(N.C.T.E.C.)

11. Find the value of x and y which satisfy
$$v = \tfrac{1}{2}(x + \sqrt{y^2 + 4f^2})$$
$$\tan 2\theta = \frac{2f}{x}$$

Given that $\theta = 22\frac{1}{2}°$, $f = 50$, and $v = 150$.   (U.L.C.I.)

12. S and T are connected by a relation

$$S = aT^3 + bT^2 + cT,$$

where a, b, c are constants, and $S = 11\cdot4$ when $T = 2$, $S = 42\cdot3$ when $T = 3$, and $S = 202\cdot5$ when $T = 5$.   Find the values of a, b, c and deduce the value of S when $T = 4$.

(U.L.C.I.)

13. The equation to a parabola is given by

$$y = A + Bx + Cx^2.$$

The parabola passes through the points $(1\cdot4, 3\cdot19)$, $(2, 4)$ and $(5, 10\cdot75)$.   Find A, B, and C.   (U.L.C.I.)

10. Some Other Types of Equation

Example 1

Solve the simultaneous equations $3^x = 27^{y-2}$ *and* $25^y = 5^{x-2}$.

(U.L.C.I.)

Notice $25 = 5^2$ and $27 = 3^3$.

Hence

$$3^x = 3^{3\,(y-2)} \quad \cdots \cdots \quad (1)$$

and

$$5^{2y} = 5^{x-2} \quad \cdots \cdots \quad (2)$$

∴ Equating indices

$x = 3y - 6$ from (1)

and $2y = x - 2$ from (2).

Solving this pair of simultaneous equations we get:

$$x = 18 \text{ and } y = 8.$$

Example 2

If $5^x = 3^{x^2-4}$ *find the values of x.*   (U.L.C.I.)

Taking logs of both sides of the given equation we get:

$$x \log 5 = (x^2 - 4) \log 3.$$

$$\therefore \quad \frac{x \log 5}{\log 3} = x^2 - 4$$

whence $$x^2 - 1\cdot465x - 4 = 0$$

solving $\qquad x = \dfrac{1\cdot465 \pm \sqrt{(1\cdot465)^2 + 16}}{2}$

whence $\qquad x = 2\cdot862 \text{ or } -1\cdot397$

EXERCISE 5

1. The points $x = 2$, $y = 6\cdot49$, $x = 4$, $y = 15\cdot43$, and $x = 8$, $y = 40\cdot06$ lie on a curve whose equation has the form $y = a + bx^n$ where a, b, and n are constants. Find a, b, and n. (Note that the abscissæ form a G.P.)

(U.L.C.I.)

2. Three variables, p, v, T, are related by the formulæ $pv^{1\cdot3} = c$ and $pv = RT$, where c and R are constants. Given that $p = 150$ and $T = 500$ when $v = 31$, find the values of p and T when $v = 126$. (N.C.T.E.C.)

3. There is a root of $x^3 + 5x - 11 = 0$ between 1 and 2. Find it, by calculation, by putting $(1 + h)$ for x, neglecting h^3 and solving the resulting quadratic for h.

4. Solve $3^{x^2-3} = 9^x$.

5. Solve $\left.\begin{array}{l} 2^{3x-y} = 4^{x-2} \\ 4^{x+y} = 2^{x+3} \end{array}\right\}$.

6. Solve $3^{x^2-5} = 81^x$.

7. Solve $\left.\begin{array}{l} 3^{2x-y} = 9^{x+2} \\ 5^{x+y} = 25^{2x-3y} \end{array}\right\}$.

8. Two variables, x and y, are connected by a law of the form $y = a + bx^c$, where a, b, c are constants. When x has the values 0, $6\cdot33$, $9\cdot05$, the values of y are $2\cdot36$, $13\cdot46$, and $20\cdot66$, respectively. Find (1) the values of a, b, and c and (2) the value of y when $x = 16$. (N.C.T.E.C.)

9. (a) The diameter of the base of a right cone is 20 cm and the height of the cone is 30 cm. At what distance from the base must the cone be cut parallel to the base so that the volume of the frustum thus formed shall be 2000 c.c.?

(b) The parallel sides of a trapezium are 10 in. and 16 in. and the other sides are 5 in. and 7 in. Find the area of the

whole triangle obtained by producing the non-parallel sides
to meet at a point.   (N.C.T.E.C.)

10. (a) Use logarithms to evaluate $(32 \cdot 15)^{-0 \cdot 152}$.

(b) Solve for x the equation $x^{0 \cdot 06} = 1 \cdot 017$.

(c) Solve the simultaneous equations:

$$\left. \begin{array}{l} 3x + 4y + 5z = 15 \\ x - 2y - 3z = 1 \\ 2x - 3y + z = -8 \end{array} \right\}$$ (Coventry.)

11. (i) If

$$W = 1400 \left\{ (t - t_0) - t_0 \log_e \frac{t}{t_0} + L \left(1 - \frac{t_0}{t} \right) \right\},$$

find W when $t = 600$, $t_0 = 390$ and $L = 240$.

(ii) Solve the equation

$$2^{2x} + 12 = 2^{x+3}.$$ (Sunderland.)

12. (i) Using logarithms, evaluate the following:

$$\frac{27 \cdot 12 \times (0 \cdot 7065)^2}{0 \cdot 004729 \times \sqrt{987 \cdot 6}} - 7 \cdot 5$$

(ii) Solve the following equations:

(a) $\sqrt{3x - 2} + \sqrt{2x + 5} = \sqrt{7x + 11}$

(b) $3^{2x} - 2 \cdot 3^x - 2 = 0$ (Cheltenham.)

GRAPHS. THE DETERMINATION OF LAWS. THE GRAPHIC SOLUTION OF EQUATIONS

1. The reader will already have learned from many examples in Volumes 1 and 2 what is understood by " the equation of a line." The fact that there is an equation connecting the co-ordinates x and y means that for any chosen value of x the value of y is determined by the equation. We may think of a line graph as traced by a moving point, in which case we could translate the command " Draw the graph of $y = x^2$ " by the words, " Draw the path, on some suitable scale, of a point which moves so that its ordinate is always equal to the square of its abscissa."

We shall refer to the path of a point when it moves under a given law as the " locus " of the point; and if we can find an equation connecting the co-ordinates of the point with the law we impose on its motion, we call this equation the " equation of the path " or the " equation of the locus."

2. The Equation of a Straight Line

Find the equation of the path of a point which always moves in a given direction, and in so doing passes through a given point.

Case I.

The locus is a straight line, and we shall find an equation which is satisfied by the co-ordinates of every point on the line.

Suppose K is the given point. (Fig. 1.) Let the fixed

direction make θ with the positive sense of OX. Clearly the locus is the straight line KP. For simplicity take the *y*-axis through K. Take any point O on this axis as origin and draw the other axis X_1OX.

Suppose K is the point $(0, c)$. Let P be *any* point on the straight line; let its co-ordinates be (x, y).

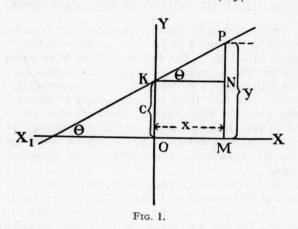

Fig. 1.

The law imposed on the moving point gives us the constants *c* and θ. We connect these with *x* and *y*, thus:

$$\frac{NP}{KN} = \tan \theta,$$

where KN is parallel to OX, and PN parallel to OY.

KN = *x* and NP = MP − MN = *y* − *c*.

$$\therefore \quad \frac{y - c}{x} = \tan \theta$$

i.e.
$$y = \tan \theta \,.\, x + c \quad . \quad . \quad . \quad . \quad (1)$$

This is the required equation, usually written

$$y = mx + c \quad . \quad . \quad . \quad . \quad . \quad (2)$$

In this equation m ($= \tan \theta$) is called the *gradient* of the straight line; c is the intercept on the y-axis.

Remember that P *is any point on the straight line.*

We make, then, the important inference that "*Every first degree equation in x and y* (*or any other two variables*) *represents a straight line.*"

This follows from the fact that any such equation can be put in the form (2).

3. Instead of taking the point K on the y-axis, take it anywhere in the plane—*i.e.*, let the co-ordinates of K be (x_1, y_1).   (Fig. 2.)

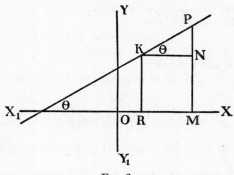

FIG. 2.

The equation of the straight line is got in exactly the same way as before—*i.e.*, we write down the value of $\tan \theta$ thus:

Let the co-ordinates of P be (x, y).

$$OR = x_1, \quad OM = x \qquad \therefore \ RM = KN = x - x_1$$
$$RK = y_1 = MN \qquad \therefore \ NP = y - y_1$$
$$\tan \theta = m = \frac{NP}{KN} = \frac{y - y_1}{x - x_1}$$

Hence

$$y - y_1 = m(x - x_1)$$

B

Example 1

The straight line through $(3, -4)$ inclined at $60°$ to the x-axis, is:

$$y + 4 = \sqrt{3}(x - 3),$$

since $\tan 60° = \sqrt{3}$.

Example 2

Find the equation to the straight line through $(-2, 3)$ *and* $(1, 4)$.

Let $y = mx + c$ be the straight line.

We must get values for m and c.

$(-2, 3)$ is on the line

$$\therefore \quad 3 = -2m + c \quad . \quad . \quad . \quad . \quad (1)$$

Similarly $\quad\quad\quad 4 = m + c \quad . \quad . \quad . \quad . \quad . \quad (2)$

since $(1, 4)$ is on the line.

Solving (1) and (2) as simultaneous equations

$$m = \tfrac{1}{3}, \; c = \tfrac{11}{3}$$

$$\therefore \quad y = \frac{x}{3} + \frac{11}{3} \text{ is the required equation.}$$

It may be written $x - 3y + 11 = 0$, by clearing fractions,

4. The Determination of Laws of Linear Form

When we are given equations like

$$y = 3x + 4$$
or $\quad\quad\quad y = 0\cdot2x^3$

it is a simple matter to get corresponding pairs of values of x and y, and so plot the graph.

The converse problem often confronts the student. He is given, or gets for himself in the laboratory, corresponding pairs of values of two variables—say, the extensions of a spring under various weights or corresponding values of the pressure and volume of a gas under certain constant conditions, or the values of the voltage drop as known currents are passed through a resistance.   From the data he is asked to find an equation connecting the two variables—*i.e.*, he must find the law connecting the variables.

In many cases we know the general form of the law. Thus Hooke's Law connecting the tension (y) of a spring with the extension x, is $y = kx$.   In the case of an expanding gas we may know that in general $pv^n = $ constant, though we do not know the index n.

In these cases we find k for our particular spring, and n together with the constant for the gas.

In other cases, however, we have no indication of what the law may be, and we must use the method of " trial and error "—*i.e.*, we invent various forms of equations and test each one to see if the data given satisfy it.

5. The following examples illustrate some of the ways in which a non-linear law is reduced to a linear form.

Example 1

The following corresponding values of x and y are thought to be connected by the law $y = a + bx^2$.   Test this and find the most probable values of a and b.

Note.—There may be slight experimental errors in the given values.   (U.L.C.I.)

x . .	1	1·5	2	2·3	2·5	2·7	2·8
y . .	11	15	21·4	25·3	29	32	34·6
$x^2 = t$.	1	2·25	4	5·29	6·25	7·29	7·84

If $y = bx^2 + a$
we can write $y = bt + a$
where $x^2 = t$.

The values of x and y in the table are those given.

We find the values in the bottom line by squaring the x-values.

Now plot y against t.   (Fig. 3.)

The points lie almost on a straight line, AD, in Fig. 3.

Take any two points on the line.

We take the points C $(4, 21)$, and D $(8\frac{1}{3}, 36)$.

These must satisfy the equation:

$$y = bt + a$$
$$\therefore \quad 21 = 4b + a \quad . \quad . \quad . \quad . \quad (1)$$
and $\quad\quad\quad\quad 36 = 8\frac{1}{3}b + a \quad . \quad . \quad . \quad . \quad (2)$

By subtraction $\quad 15 = 4\frac{1}{3}b$
$$\therefore \quad b = 3 \cdot 46$$

and by substituting for b in (1)

$$a = 7 \cdot 2 \text{ (nearly)}$$

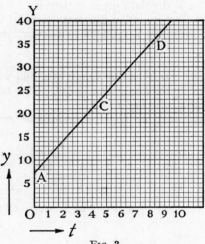

Fig. 3.

$\therefore$ The equation is

$$y = 7 \cdot 2 + 3 \cdot 46x^2.$$

For most practical purposes we could write

$$y = 7 + 3 \cdot 5x^2.$$

Example 2

The following table gives the sectional areas of Whitworth bolts at the bottom of the thread for various diameters of bolts.

A = area in sq in .	0·13	0·3	0·9	1·3	1·8	2·28
d = diam. in in. .	0·56	0·75	1·25	1·5	1·8	2

It is believed these figures are connected by a law in the form of $A = ad^2 + bd$. *Test this, and if correct find the most probable values of a and b.*

We have $\qquad\qquad A = ad^2 + bd$

i.e., $\qquad\qquad \dfrac{A}{d} = ad + b$

viz., $\qquad\qquad y = ax + b,$

where $\qquad\qquad y = \dfrac{A}{d}$ and $x = d.$

Now calculate $\dfrac{A}{d}$, and make the following table:

x = d . .	0·56	0·75	1·25	1·5	1·8	2
$y = \dfrac{A}{d}$ . .	0·24	0·4	0·72	0·87	1	1·14

The graph is shown in Fig. 4.

We have taken the line through the points (1·75, 1) and (0·6, 0·3).

These points are on $y = ax + b$.

Substituting, we get:

$$1 = 1\cdot75a + b \quad . \quad . \quad . \quad . \quad . \quad (1)$$
and $\qquad\qquad 0\cdot3 = 0\cdot6a + b \quad . \quad . \quad . \quad . \quad . \quad (2)$

Subtracting (2) from (1):

$$0 \cdot 7 = 1 \cdot 15a$$
$$\therefore \quad a = 0 \cdot 61$$
$$b = 0 \cdot 3 - 0 \cdot 366 \text{ (from (2))}$$
$$= - 0 \cdot 066$$
$$\therefore \text{ the law is } A = 0 \cdot 61d^2 - 0 \cdot 066d.$$

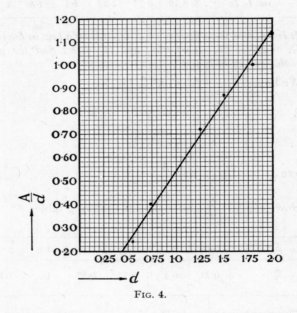

FIG. 4.

NOTE: *The engineering student can learn a great deal from study of Example 2. First of all he would be tempted to think of the cross-sections at the bottom of the thread as being similar figures for large and small bolts. On reflection he will see that this cannot be the case because it would require the number of threads per inch to be proportional to the diameter; and this is not so, because for manufacturing reasons the threads per* *inch are always denoted by a whole number. If the sections were similar figures the area would be proportional to the square of the diameter and the formula would bring in d^2 only. We can see that this is very nearly the case because the second term is comparatively small: it is only $- 0.066\,d$.*

Next refer to the note appended to No. 10 of Exercise 3, p. 21. We know that the figures given at the head of the present question will be numbers of INCHES *because Whitworth bolts are made to inch sizes. So the areas given by the formula and the graph must be taken as so many square inches. But in this case the formula is not rational and will only be true for diameters measured in inches. This is on account of the term in d whose dimension is not that of an area. It is easy to show discrepancy by working out the area for (say) a bolt of 1 in. dia., and then for the same bolt, taking d as 2.54 (cm).*

The actual formula has been devised in the knowledge that a formula such as $A = ad^2$ *would very nearly fit the facts. The addition of a term in d, which can have a small coefficient of either $+$ or $-$ sign, can be relied on to give a small adjustment to the values of the section areas. An actual value for the small coefficient of d, and its sign, have emerged in the working of the example.*

Example 3

Show that the following corresponding values of p and v can be represented by a law of the form

$$p = \frac{a}{v} + b$$

and find the most suitable values for a and b.   (U.L.C.I.)

p	100	120	140	160	180
v	4.29	3.57	3.16	2.75	2.49
$y = \dfrac{1}{v}$ . . .	0.233	0.28	0.316	0.364	0.402

Put $\dfrac{1}{v} = y$, and find the third row in the table.

Then: $\qquad\qquad\qquad p = ay + b$ . . . . (1)

Now plot y against p. See Fig. 5.

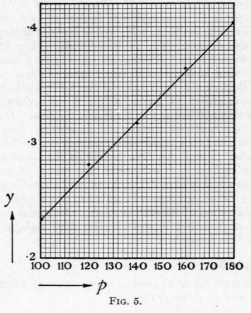

FIG. 5.

The line drawn passes through the points $p = 100$, $y = 0.236$ and $p = 150$, $y = 0.34$.

Hence, substituting in (1) we get:

$$100 = a \times 0.236 + b$$
$$150 = a \times 0.34 + b.$$

Solving, $a = 481$ and $b = -13.5$.

The approximate law is:

$$p = \frac{481}{v} - 13.5.$$

6. Exponential equations such as

$$y = ax^n \qquad \cdots \cdots \cdots \quad (1)$$

whether n be positive or negative, can be reduced to the linear form by taking logarithms of both sides to base 10.

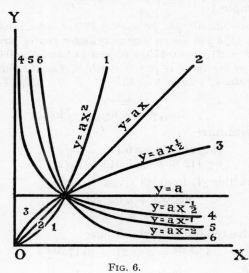

FIG. 6.

Clearly

$$\log y = n \log x + \log a$$

i.e.,
$$z = nt + c \qquad \cdots \cdots \cdots \quad (2)$$

where $z = \log_{10} y$, $t = \log_{10} x$, and $c = \log_{10} a$.

We thus plot $\log y$ against $\log x$.

The following points concerning the curves given by (1) above, might be noticed.

    (1) They all pass through the point $(1, a)$.

    (2) Two of them are straight lines—viz.,
        $y = a$, $(n = 0)$, and $y = ax$, $(n = 1)$.

    (3) $y = ax^2$, a parabola, is a member of the family.

(4) pv^n = constant, is also a member, and so is the rectangular hyperbola $xy = c$, $(n = -1)$.

A few of the curves are sketched in Fig. 6, for + values of x.

Example 1

A curve showing the pressure p lb per sq in. and volume v cu ft, of a gas in an engine cylinder passes through the points $p = 21$, $v = 0\cdot175$, and $p = 112$ and $v = 0\cdot045$. If the law of the curve is pv^n = constant, find the value of n, (2) the value of v when $p = 45$.   (N.C.T.E.C.)

Let
$$pv^n = c$$
$$\therefore \ \log_{10} p + n \log_{10} v = \log_{10} c$$

i.e., substituting

$$\log 21 + n \log 0\cdot175 = \log c \quad . \quad . \quad . \quad (1)$$
and
$$\log 112 + n \log 0\cdot045 = \log c \quad . \quad . \quad . \quad (2)$$

Subtracting (1) from (2) gives:

$$\log \tfrac{112}{21} + n \log \tfrac{45}{175} = 0$$
giving
$$n = 1\cdot232.$$

To solve the second part, we have:

$$45v^{1\cdot232} = c = 21 \times (0\cdot175)^{1\cdot232}$$

Hence

$$\log 45 + 1\cdot232 \log v = 21 + 1\cdot232 \log (0\cdot175).$$

This is a simple equation for $\log v$.

Solving, we get $\log v = \bar{2}\cdot974$
and $v = 0\cdot094.$

Notice once more that the numerical value assigned to " c " depends upon the units in which p and v are measured. The " constant " c cannot therefore be determined in one example and used in another without confirming that the units in which pressure and volume are measured remain unchanged. A note dealing with this point can be found at the head of Exercise 17A in Volume II (Revised Edition) of this work.

Example 2

The following values of d and W *were obtained in a series of experiments on the strength of pillars.*

d	2·5	2·35	2	1·55
W	58,900	46,800	26,600	10,900

Test whether the law connecting d and W *is of the form* W $= kd$, *where k and n are constants; and find values for k and n which give a line closely approximating to the graph of experimental results.* (U.L.C.I.)

If $\quad\quad\quad\quad\quad$ W $= kd^n$

$$\log W = n \log d + \log k \quad . \quad . \quad . \quad (1)$$

i.e., in form, $\quad\quad\quad y = nx + c \quad . \quad . \quad . \quad . \quad (2)$

Make the following table:

$x = \log d$ . .	0·398	0·371	0·301	0·190
$y = \log W$ . .	4·770	4·670	4·425	4·037

Take the origin at (0, 4). Unit on x-axis $= 100$ squares, on y-axis 10 squares.

Plotting y against x, it will be found that the points are almost co-linear. See Fig. 7.

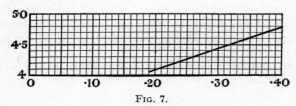

FIG. 7.

The line drawn passes through (0·25, 4·25) and (0·35, 4·60).

Substituting in (2) above:

$$4 \cdot 25 = n \times 0 \cdot 25 + c$$
$$4 \cdot 60 = n \times 0 \cdot 35 + c.$$

These give $n = 3 \cdot 5$ and $c = 3 \cdot 375 = \log k$ and the approximate law is

$$W = 2371 d^{3 \cdot 5}.$$

EXERCISE 6

1. Find the equations to the straight lines:

    (a) Through (2, 3) inclined at 30° to the x-axis.

    (b) Through (− 1, 1) inclined at 120° to the x-axis.

    (c) Through (− 3, − 2) inclined at 37° to the x-axis.

    (d) Through (− 2, 3) and (5, 6).

    (e) Through (4, − 1) and (− 2, 0).

2. In a certain experiment it is required to show that the product of two variables x and y is constant. In observing the value of y there is a constant error in the reading. The following table gives the experimental reading, y_1, for each value of x.

x . .	15	17	20	25	30	34	40
y_1 . .	5·00	4·34	3·60	2·76	2·20	1·87	1·5

Using squared paper find the most probable value of the constant error, on the assumption that the product is in fact constant.

3. In certain experiments the following results were obtained:

y	26·6	22·5	17·8	12·5	7·9	0·1
x	0	5	9·3	13	15·8	17·3

It is believed that the relation between y and x can be represented by a formula

$$y = + \sqrt{a - bx},$$

where a and b are constants. Test this graphically, and find the best values for a and b.   (U.L.C.I.)

4. The following results are found to obey, allowing for errors of observation, the law $x(y + n) = m$. Determine the values of the constants n and m.

y . . .	3	4	5	6	7	8	9	10
x . . .	2·35	2·1	1·9	1·75	1·58	1·45	1·35	1·25

(U.L.C.I.)

5. The following values of x and y were found in a certain experiment:

x . . .	5·5	6·0	6·5	7·0	7·5	8·0	8·5	9·0
y . . .	5·13	4·91	4·71	4·52	4·36	4·20	4·04	3·91

Show that the figures follows a law of the form $y = \dfrac{b}{1 + ax}$ and find the values of the constants a and b.

(U.L.C.I.)

6. The air resistance to the motion of a flat vane is given in the following table, where R = resistance in lb and V = speed in ft/sec.

R . . .	30	105	163	230	313
V . . .	10	20	25	30	35

Determine whether these values are connected by a law of the form $R = a + bV^2$, and if so find this equation.

7. The student should train himself to recognise symmetry in a curve from its equation.

Take $$y = x^2.$$

We get the same value of y for $+$ or $-$ values of x. Hence the curve is symmetrical about the y-axis.

Similarly, if we have only even powers of y, there is symmetry about the x-axis.

Where both powers are even, we have symmetry about both axes as in the circle $x^2 + y^2 = a^2$.

In $y = x^3$, if any point, say $(2, 8)$, is on the curve, then $(-2, -8)$ is on the curve, and the curve lies only in the first and third quadrants. We need only find points in the first quadrant. The corresponding points in the third quadrant are obtained by a change of sign.

8. The Ellipse

The curve $\dfrac{x^2}{a^2} + \dfrac{y^2}{b^2} = 1$ is clearly symmetrical about both axes.

Since
$$y^2 = b^2\left(1 - \frac{x^2}{a^2}\right)$$
$$= \frac{b^2}{a^2}(a^2 - x^2)$$

and
$$x^2 = \frac{a^2}{b^2}(b^2 - y^2)$$

x can never be greater than a; otherwise y^2 would be negative, and y imaginary. Similarly y can never be greater than b. The curve is an ellipse, whose semi-axes are a and b. If $a > b$, $2a$ is the major axis and $2b$ the minor axis.

The curve is readily drawn with the help of a trammel—say, the straight edge of a piece of paper.

Draw AB and CD (Fig. 8), the major and minor axes, each bisected at right angles at O.

KL is the edge of a sheet of paper.

Take any point E on the edge and make EG = a = OB and EF = b = OC.

Keep G and F on the minor and major axes respectively, and mark the varying positions of E.

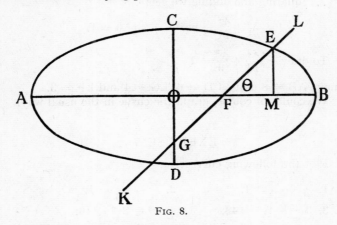

FIG. 8.

The locus of E is the ellipse:

$$\frac{x^2}{a^2} + \frac{y^2}{b^2} = 1$$

with O as origin.

Proof.—In any position of the trammel with G and F on the axes, let KL make θ with OB.

Then OM = x = the projection of GE on OB.
         = GE cos θ

i.e., $x = a \cos \theta$ . . . . . . (1)

   Similarly,

         $y =$ ME = EF sin θ
i.e., $y = b \sin \theta$ . . . . . . (2)

   From (1)

         $\frac{x}{a} = \cos \theta.$

From (2)
$$\frac{y}{b} = \sin \theta$$

$\therefore$ Squaring and adding we get:

$$\frac{x^2}{a^2} + \frac{y^2}{b^2} = \cos^2 \theta + \sin^2 \theta = 1.$$

To draw $\dfrac{x^2}{16} + \dfrac{y^2}{9} = 1$

make AB $= 8$ units, CD $= 6$, EG $= 4$ and EF $= 3$.

We could, of course, graph the curve in the usual way.

EXERCISE 7

Plot the following curves:

1. $\dfrac{x^2}{9} + \dfrac{y^2}{4} = 1.$ 2. $\dfrac{x^2}{9} + \dfrac{y^2}{16} = 1.$

3. $3x^2 + 4y^2 = 48.$ 4. $x^2 + 2y^2 = 16.$

9. Graphic Solution of Equations

Notice the following method of solving a given equation graphically.

Example 1

Solve $x^3 - 8x - 5 = 0.$

This may be done by plotting $y = x^3 - 8x - 5$, and finding the points where the curve cuts the x-axis.

Or we may solve thus:

$$x^3 - 8x - 5 = 0$$
$$\therefore \quad x^3 = 8x + 5.$$

Now plot $y = x^3$

and $y = 8x + 5.$

The scale on the x-axis is ten times that on the y-axis.

The graph is shown in Fig. 9.   The points common to the two curves are A, B, C and their abscissæ are $3\cdot1$, $-0\cdot65$, and $-2\cdot5$, respectively, true to two figures.   These are the roots required.

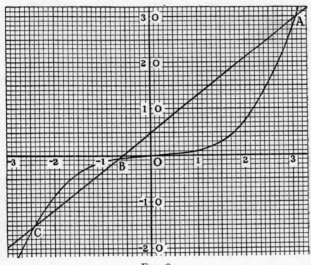

FIG. 9.

Example 2

Solve graphically

$$(x^2 - 6)(4 + x^2) = 32x$$

(Slightly adapted from N.C.T.E.C.)

Clearly $\qquad\qquad x^2 - 6 = \dfrac{32x}{4 + x^2}.$

Now graph $\qquad\qquad y = x^2 - 6$

and $\qquad\qquad\qquad y = \dfrac{32x}{4 + x^2}$

These are shown in Fig. 10.

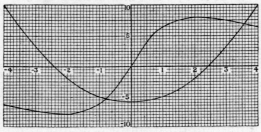

Fig. 10.

The abscissæ of the points of intersection give two of the roots.

These are $x = 3 \cdot 6$ and $x = -0 \cdot 75$.

10. The Cubic and Other Equations

The accurate graphing of a cubic function is more readily done when one knows how to get the turning-points on the curve, a matter which is dealt with in Chapter 7.

In solving any equation graphically, say $f(x) = 0$, we are merely concerned with finding the points where the curve $y = f(x)$ cuts the x-axis—*i.e.*, the points where $y = 0$. For this purpose it is not necessary to draw the whole curve.

Suppose, in the curve $y = f(x)$, that when $x = 3$, y is positive, and when $x = 4$, y is negative.

Clearly the curve must cut the axis between $x = 3$ and $x = 4$. Hence we infer a root of $f(x) = 0$ between these two values. To find this root we need only plot values of x and y between these numbers. We may similarly limit our plotting for any further roots.

Example 1

Solve graphically the equation

$$x^3 - 1 \cdot 87x^2 - 4 \cdot 54x + 6 \cdot 41 = 0,$$

by plotting between $x = \pm 3$.

First, make the usual table

x . . .	0	1	2	3	−1	−2	−3
x^3 . .	0	1	8	27	−1	−8	−27
$-1 \cdot 87 x^2$.	0	−1·87	−7·48	−16·83	−1·87	−7·48	−16·83
$-4 \cdot 54 x + 6 \cdot 41$	6·41	1·87	−2·67	−7·21	10·95	15·49	20·03
y . . .	6·41	1	−2·15	2·96	8·08	0·01	−23·8

Noting the changes in the sign of y, we see that there are roots between 1 and 2, 2 and 3, whilst the third root is − 2 (nearly).   Hence we need not plot for a series of negative values of x.

Take 10 squares = 1 unit horizontally, 5 squares = 1 unit vertically.   Fig. 11 (a).

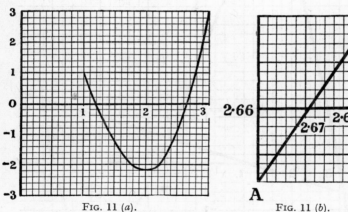

FIG. 11 (a).   FIG. 11 (b).

To get the root between 2 and 3:
The curve cuts the x-axis between $x = 2 \cdot 6$ and $x = 2 \cdot 7$.

When $x = 2 \cdot 64$, $y = - 0 \cdot 2$
  ,, $x = 2 \cdot 66$, $y = - 0 \cdot 08$ . . . . . (A)
  ,, $x = 2 \cdot 68$, $y = + 0 \cdot 07$ . . . . . (B)

The root is between 2·66 and 2·68.

Plot the last two points, A and B, on the diagram. Fig. 11 (b). The short line AB can reasonably be taken as straight.

50 squares = 1 unit on x-axis, 100 squares = 1 unit on y-axis.

The root is clearly 2·67 correct to three figures.

The other roots will be found to be 1·2 and −2, very nearly.

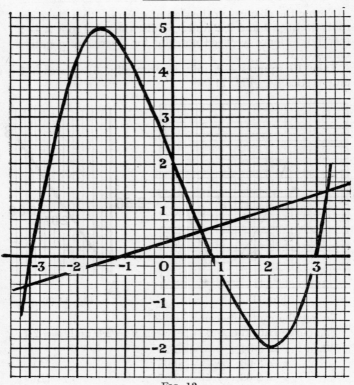

Fig. 12.

Example 2

Graph the functions $0{\cdot}08(4x - 3)(x^2 - 9)$ *and* $\frac{1}{3}(x + 1)$
for values of x from $-3\frac{1}{4}$ *to* $+3\frac{1}{2}$, *using the same scales and
reference axes for both graphs. By means of the graphs
estimate to two significant figures the roots of*

$$0{\cdot}24(4x - 3)(x^2 - 9) - x = 1.$$

(N.C.T.E.C.)

Plot $\qquad y = 0{\cdot}08(4x - 3)(x^2 - 9)$ . . . . (1)

i.e., $\qquad y = 0{\cdot}08(4x - 3)(x - 3)(x + 3)$ . . (2)

and the straight line

$$y = \tfrac{1}{3}(x + 1) \qquad . \quad . \quad . \quad . \quad . \quad . \quad (3)$$

Plot the straight line first.

Where (1) cuts (3) we have, by equating ordinates,

$$0{\cdot}08(4x - 3)(x^2 - 9) = \tfrac{1}{3}(x + 1)$$

i.e., $\qquad 0{\cdot}24(4x - 3)(x^2 - 9) - x = 1.$

Hence, the common abscissæ give the roots.
The graphs are shown in Fig. 12.
The roots are $-3{\cdot}1,\ 0{\cdot}56,$ *and* $3{\cdot}3.$

Example 3

Solve graphically the following equation

$$x^3 - 2x^2 - 2x + 1 = 0. \qquad \text{(U.E.I.)}$$

Put $y = x^3 - 2x^2 - 2x + 1$ and draw up the table below.

x	0	1	2	3	-1
y	1	-2	-3	4	0

From the table, one root is clearly $x = -1$.
Since y changes sign between $x = 0$ and $x = 1$ there is a
root between these values.
Similarly, y changes from negative to positive between
$x = 2$ and $x = 3$; we thus infer a root between 2 and 3.

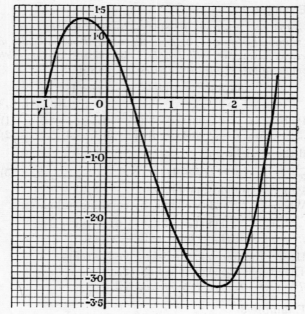

Fig. 13.

Actually we need only plot the curve between $x = 0$ and $x = 1$, and between $x = 2$ and $x = 3$, but the full curve is drawn in Fig. 13 between $x = -1$ and $x = 2\cdot7$.

x .	0	0·2	0·4	2	2·2	2·4	2·6	2·7
y .	1	0·528	−0·056	−3	−2·432	−1·5	−0·15	0·703

The student should make the above table, plotting the relevant portions to a larger scale and joining the points (0·2, 0·528) and (0·4, − 0·056) to get one root and the points ($2\cdot6$, $-0\cdot15$) and ($2\cdot7$, $0\cdot703$) to get the other (because short lengths of the curve can be treated as straight),

the roots are seen to be -1, $0\cdot38$, and $2\cdot62$.

Example 4

Show that $x^2 - 4 \log_e x = 2\cdot86$ is satisfied by a value between $x = 2$ and $x = 3$, and by a graphic method or otherwise find this value correct to three significant figures.

(U.L.C.I.)

Put $\qquad y = x^2 - 4 \log_e x - 2\cdot86$ . . . . . (1)

or $\qquad y = x^2 - 9\cdot212 \log_{10} x - 2\cdot86$ . . . (2)

since $\log_e x = 2\cdot303 \log_{10} x$.

If a table of naperian logarithms is available use (1) above; otherwise use (2).

Putting $x = 2$ in (1) above we get

$$y = 4 - 2\cdot77 - 2\cdot86 = -1\cdot63$$

Put $x = 3$,

$$y = 9 - 4\cdot39 - 2\cdot86 = +1\cdot75.$$

Hence a root lies between $x = 2$ and $x = 3$.
Draw up the following table:

x . . .	$2\cdot2$	$2\cdot3$	$2\cdot4$	$2\cdot5$	$2\cdot6$
$x^2 - 2\cdot86$ . . $- 4 \log_e x$ . .	$1\cdot98$ $-3\cdot15$	$2\cdot43$ $-3\cdot33$	$2\cdot90$ $-3\cdot50$	$3\cdot39$ $-3\cdot67$	$3\cdot90$ $-3\cdot82$
y . . .	$-1\cdot17$	$-0\cdot90$	$-0\cdot60$	$-0\cdot28$	$+0\cdot08$

The root lies between $x = 2\cdot5$ and $x = 2\cdot6$.
Now join the points given by the last pairs of co-ordinates

in the above table and find $x = 2.58$ correct to three figures. (Fig. 14.)

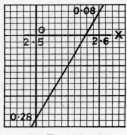

Fig. 14.

EXERCISE 8

1. Plot $\qquad y = x^2$
and $\qquad y = 5.2x - 6.4$.

Hence solve $x^2 - 5.2x + 6.4 = 0$.

2. Solve $x^2 - 6.4x + 9.43 = 0$ graphically.

3. On the same axes and to the same scale graph the functions $y = 2x^2$ and $y = 3x + 1$, and hence solve the quadratic $x^2 - \dfrac{3x}{2} - \tfrac{1}{2} = 0$.

4. Plot $y = x^3$ and $y = 9x - 3.5$, and hence find one root of $x^3 - 9x + 3.5 = 0$.

5. Graph each of the functions $\{0.2x^3(4 - x)\}$ and $\{0.5(x - 2)^2 + 1\}$ for values of x from $x = 0$ to $x = +4$, showing accurately the turning-point of each graph and using the same scales and references axes for both graphs. By means of these graphs estimate within limits ± 0.05 the roots of the equation $x^3(x - 4) + 2.5x^2 - 10x + 15 = 0$.

{Take the x-axis parallel to the longer side of your sheet of squared paper, and use a length of 8 in. for the range $x = 0$ to $x = 4$, and a length of 6 in. for the range $y = 0$ to $y = 6$.} (N.C.T.E.C.)

EXERCISE 8A—MISCELLANEOUS

Many of the questions which follow relate to the work of Chapters 1 and 2 preceding; others are given for use in general revision. For methods, etc., not given in this volume refer to Volume II of this work. The questions are taken by permission from Final Year examinations for Ordinary National Certificates.

1. The horizontal thrust, P lb wt, required to drive an engine at a speed of v m.p.h. is given in the following table:

v . . .	1·68	2·43	3·18	3·60	4·03	4·66
P . .	76	150	240	310	370	500

(i) By drawing a suitable graph show that P and v are connected by a law of the form $P = av^n$ and use your graph to determine the values of a and n.

(ii) Estimate the thrust when the speed is 3 m.p.h.: (1) by reading from your graph, (2) from the formula you have obtained.   (West Riding.)

2. The following table shows the volume v cu ft and the corresponding pressure p lb/in.^{2} of steam.

p . . .	21·9	25·7	30·6	35·3	41·6
v . . .	22	19	16	14	12

By means of a suitable graph show that p and v are connected by an approximate equation of the form $pv^n = c$, where n and c are constants. Find the best values of n and c. Deduce the corrected value of p when $v = 19$.

(E.M.E.U.)

3. The quantity of water W lb per minute and the corresponding depth of water, H, when water flows over a weir, are given by the following table:

W . . .	1535	3152	5504	8682	12760
H	3	4	5	6	7

Show that the relationship between W and H is of the form $W = aH^n$ and find values for a and n. Use your result to calculate W when $H = 10 \cdot 5$.   (Shrewsbury.)

4. A force of P lb per ton is required to pull a canal boat at a speed of V m.p.h., and the following table gives corresponding values of P and V.

Show by means of a suitable graph that the relationship between P and V is of the form $P = aV^n$, and find from the graph the approximate values of a and n.

P	1·58	2·08	2·62	3·20
V	2·5	3	3·5	4

(Cannock.)

5. (i) The currents x, y, z amp. respectively in three branches of an electrical network are given by:

$$2x + 3y - z = 5$$
$$3x - 4y + 2z = 1$$
$$4x - 6y + 5z = 7.$$

Calculate the current in each branch of the network.

(ii) Solve the equations:

(a) $x^2 + 4xy - 3y^2 = 9$; $x - y - 1 = 0$;
(b) $\log_e (x^2 - x - 1 \cdot 2) = 0 \cdot 47$.

(Cheltenham.)

6. (a) The length of a parabolic arc of perpendicular height h, on a chord of length c, is given by

$$L = \frac{c}{2} \left[\sqrt{(n^2 + 1)} + \frac{1}{n} \log_e \left\{ \sqrt{(n^2 + 1)} + n \right\} \right]$$

where $n = \dfrac{4h}{c}$.

Find L, if $h = 6$ and $c = 4\frac{1}{2}$.

(b) The equation relating temperature rise $\theta°$ C., and time t hours for an electrical machine is

$$\theta = \theta_m \left(1 - e^{-\frac{t}{T_0}} \right)$$

where θ_m is the maximum temperature rise and T_0 is the thermal time constant in hours.   Find θ after 0·9 hour, if $\theta_m = 40°$ C. and $T_0 = 1·5$ hours.   (Handsworth.)

7. (i) If $\dfrac{1}{x} + \dfrac{1}{y} + \dfrac{2}{z} = 21$,

$$\dfrac{2}{x} - \dfrac{3}{y} + \dfrac{2}{z} = -6,$$

$$\dfrac{3}{x} - \dfrac{4}{y} + \dfrac{4}{z} = -1,$$

find x, y and z.

(ii) Solve the equation $3^{x+5} = 2^{4x}$, giving x correct to three significant figures.

(iii) Find the values of θ between $0°$ and $360°$ (in degrees and minutes) which satisfy the equation:

$$8 \sin^2 \theta - 2 \cos \theta = 5.$$

(Halifax.)

8. (a) The value of a machine costing £800 depreciates every year by 5% of its value at the beginning of that year. Find: (i) an expression for its value after n years; (ii) the value of the machine after 7 years.

(b) After how many years is the machine worth less than half its original value?

(c) Solve the equation $4^x . 3^{x+1} = 122·7$, giving x correct to two decimal places.   (Rugby.)

9. (i) If

$$L = (D + d)\left\{\frac{\pi}{2} + \theta + \frac{1}{\tan \theta}\right\}^{-\frac{1}{4}}$$

and $\sin \theta = \dfrac{D + d}{2C},$

where $0 < \theta < \dfrac{\pi}{2}$, find L when $C = 20$, $D = 6$ and $d = 3$.

(ii) Solve the equation

$$3^x + 1 = 4 \cdot 3^{1-x}.$$

(Sunderland.)

10. In the table below, p and v are corresponding values of the pressure and volume respectively of air in adiabatic expansion.

v . . .	2	4	6	8	10
p . . .	18·8	7·07	4	2·66	1·95

Confirm that p and v are connected by a law of the form $pv^y = c$, where y and c are constants.

Use your graph to determine the values of y and c.

(Coventry.)

11. (i) The oscillations of a pendulum are damped in such a way that successive amplitudes are in Geometric Progression. If the first amplitude is 2 in. and the second 1·4 in., find the magnitude of the fifth amplitude correct to the nearest thousandth of an inch. Find also the total distance moved by the bob of the pendulum.

(ii) Prove that

$$\frac{1 - \tan^2 (45° - \theta)}{1 + \tan^2 (45° - \theta)} = \sin 2\theta.$$

(Sunderland.)

12. The pressure P of the atmosphere at various heights H is given below:

H . .	0	5,000	10,000	20,000	35,000
P . .	30	27·14	24·56	20·11	14·90

Verify by a graph that these values are consistent with a law of the form $P = ae^{kH}$ and find approximate values for the constants a, k.

(Nuneaton.)

13. (*a*) Show that if a circle is inscribed in a triangle having sides *a*, *b* and *c*, the radius of the circle

$$r = \frac{2 \times \text{Area of triangle}}{a + b + c}.$$

(*b*) A cam A rotates about a point O and lifts a follower B by means of a roller C (Fig. 1).   The radius of the base circle of the cam OR = 0·6 in., the radius PS = 0·1 in. and the radius of the roller C is 0·4 in.   The motion of the follower is in a straight line which passes through C and the sides of the cam are straight.   The straight side RS is 0·8 in.   Find the lift of the follower when the point S lies on line BO, and the angle turned through.   Rotation is anti-clockwise.

(Stafford.)

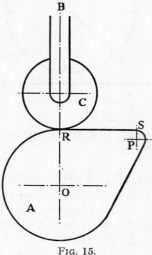

FIG. 15.

14. (*a*) The expansion curve for a gas is given by the equation $pv^{1\cdot32} = 1725$.   Plot the curve for all values of *v* from 4 to 16 cu ft at intervals of 2 cu ft.

(*b*) By using a suitable graphical method determine the roots of the equation $x^3 - 8x - 5 = 0$.   All the roots are in the range $x = -4$ to $x = +4$.   (Stafford.)

15. (*a*) Solve the equation $(\cos \theta + 1)^2 + \frac{1}{2}\cos 2\theta = 3$ for values of θ between 0° and 360°.

(*b*) Given that $\tan (A - B) = 0\cdot6924$, and $\tan B = 1\cdot2088$, find the value of tan A, without using trigonometrical tables.

(c) Express $3.6 \sin x + 1.5 \cos x$ in the form R sin $(x + \alpha)$, giving the value of α in radians.   (Dudley.)

16. The diagram represents a great wheel at a fun-fair. The radius OA is 40 ft. and the hub O is 48 ft above the

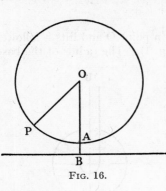

ground. The angle POA is θ. Find an expression for the height of P above the ground in terms of θ. The wheel is revolving at the rate of one revolution every 50 sec. Find the rate at which the height of P above the ground is increasing after (a) 10 sec, (b) 30 sec.

(S.W. Essex.)

FIG. 16.

17. (a) The pulls T_1 and T_2 at the ends of a taut rope which is sliding round a circular post are related by the formula

$$T_2 = T_1 e^{\mu\theta}$$

where $e = 2.718$, $\mu = 0.22$ and θ radians is the angle through which the rope turns.

Find (a) θ, given that $T_2 = 3T_1$; (b) T_1 and T_2, given that $\theta = 3.1$ and $T_2 - T_1 = 745$ lb wt.

(b) The curve

$$y = ax^3 + bx^2 + cx + d$$

passes through the four points $(1, 5)$; $(2, 5)$; $(-1, -1)$; $(-2, -19)$. Rewrite the equation of the curve giving a, b, c, d their numerical values.   (Halifax.)

18. (a) State and prove the rule used for finding the third side of a triangle when given the other two sides and the included angle.

(b) A casement window can be secured in several positions when open by means of a horizontal bar 7.5 in.

long, in which 4 small holes are punched at intervals of
1·5 in. from each other, the first being 1·5 in. from the end
of the bar.   One end of the bar is attached to the window
5 in. away from the line of hinges, and a small peg on the
frame of the window which fits the holes, is 6 in. from the
line of hinges.   Find the greatest and least angles which
the window can make with its frame when fastened open.

(S.W. Essex.)

19. Solve the equations:

(a) $\sqrt{x} + \sqrt{x + 3} = \dfrac{4}{\sqrt{x + 3}}$;

(b) $7^x = 4^{x+1} \div 3^{x-2}$;

(c) $x^3 - 1·5x^2 - 9x + 13·5 = 0$ (by   an   algebraic
method).   (Dudley.)

20. (a) Draw a rough sketch and find the angles of intersection of the curves $y = x^3$ and $y = 2x^2 - 2x + 1$.

(b) A vessel, in the form of an inverted cone, has a
semi-vertical angle of $\dfrac{\pi}{6}$ and water is poured into it at the
rate of 1 cu ft per min.   At what rate is the depth of
water increasing when the depth is 18 in.?

(Worcester.)

21. (a) In the formula $i = \dfrac{E}{R}(1 - e^{-Rt/L})$, t is the time
taken for the current to build up to a value i.   Make t the
subject of the formula.   Calculate the value of t when
$i = 10·2$, $R = 25$, $L = 5·0$ and $E = 350$.

(b) Solve the equation $(1·5)^{x+2} = 4^{5x+1}$.   (U.L.C.I.)

22. In an experiment to test the efficiency of the lubrica-
tion of a bearing the following results were obtained for the
rise in temperature ($t°$ F.) for various velocities (v ft/sec).

v .	7·86	10·76	13·04	15·90	18·88	22·04	25·70
t .	52·8	67·6	78·6	91·2	103·5	116·8	126·4

Show by drawing a graph that these values obey a law of the form $t = av^n$ and find the best values of a and n.

(West Riding.)

23. (*a*) If the value of a machine depreciates each year by 20% of its value at the beginning of the year, show that the values at the beginnings of successive years form a geometrical progression and calculate the value of a machine costing £500, at the end of 12 years. At the end of which year will the value of the machine be written off as less than £5?

(*b*) The illumination of a surface varies directly as the candle-power of a source of light and inversely as the square of its distance from the source. A 25 candle-power lamp is placed 4 ft from a screen. If the lamp is now replaced by one of 36 candle-power, find in feet how much further from the screen it must be placed in order to give the same illumination. (E.M.E.U.)

24. The cost of repairs to a certain machine is £10 during the first year, and it is estimated that the cost will increase by 20% per annum. On the basis of this estimation, find the cost of repairs during the eighth year. If it is decided to write off the machine after a total sum of £100 has been spent on repairs, find the approximate " life " of the machine. (Cheltenham.)

25. (i) Two circles of diameter 1 in. and 2 in. respectively touch one another externally. Show how to construct a third circle of 3 in. diameter to touch the two given circles externally.

(ii) Three circles 3 in., 2 in., 1 in. diameter respectively touch externally. Find the area enclosed by the parts of the circumferences between the points of contact.

(N.C.T.E.C.)

CHAPTER 3

PERMUTATIONS. COMBINATIONS. THE BINOMIAL THEOREM

1. No special mathematical knowledge is required to understand the method of finding the permutations or combinations of a given number of different things.

We must first understand the words " permutation " and " combination."

A " *Permutation* " is an arrangement.

A " *Combination* " is a group.

Thus *bac, abc, cab*, are different permutations of the same group *abc*.

Hence in arrangements order is the essential thing.

In groups or combinations the order of the things is of no importance.

If there are three members of a permutation or combination, we shall speak of it as a three-permutation or a three-combination.

Thus *pqr, rpq*, are three-permutations of the same three-combination.

2. The Fundamental Principle

Suppose there are four bus routes to a certain place but only three services convenient for the return journey. We can clearly go out and home in 4×3 ways, never using the same route on both journeys.

This is a simple illustration of a principle that is fundamental in dealing with the subject of permutations.

This principle is enunciated thus:

Suppose there are *m* ways of performing a certain action, and when it has been done in any one of these ways, there are n ways of doing a second action, then the numbers of ways of performing the two actions in succession is $m \times n$.

The principle is almost self-evident, and can be extended to any number of consecutive actions.

Example 1

Take the popular pastime of filling in a football coupon. Suppose we have to predict the results of 7 matches. Three results are possible in each match. Each may be associated with the three results of any other match. Hence the number of columns we require to make certain that one column is correct is 3^7 or 2187. We see at once that we are touching upon the theory of probability.

Example 2

How many possible sets of three letters are there available for the registration of motor cars, assuming that the twenty-six letters of our alphabet can be used?

The first letter may be chosen in 26 ways. Since we may repeat any letter, the second and third letters may also be chosen in 26 ways each.

The required number is 26^3 or 17,576.

3. To find the number of ways of arranging n different things, using all of them in each arrangement

Suppose we have n different things, and we wish to find how many different ways they can be arranged, using all of them in each arrangement.

The problem is identical with that of seating n people on n chairs, in every possible way.

The first chair may be filled in n ways.

When this has been done the second chair may be filled in $(n - 1)$ ways since we must leave one person on the first chair.

∴ Using our fundamental principle, the two chairs may be filled in $n(n - 1)$ ways.

We go on in this way, until there is but one person to fill the last chair.

∴ The number of ways of arranging *n* things using all of them in each arrangement is

$$n(n-1)(n-2) \ldots 3 \cdot 2 \cdot 1 \quad . \quad . \quad . \quad (1)$$

This is the product of the first *n* integers, and is denoted by $\lfloor n$ or *n*!, and read " factorial *n*."

Thus $\lfloor 5 = 1 \cdot 2 \cdot 3 \cdot 4 \cdot 5 = 120 = $ " factorial five."

4. To Find ^nP_r

It often happens that we want to find how many *r*-permutations we can make from *n* different things.

Clearly *r* can never be greater than *n*.

This problem is stated shortly thus: " Find ^nP_r."

The " *n* " refers to the number of different things, whilst " *r* " tells us how many of them appear in each arrangement.

We now see that our problem is to find how many different arrangements of people we can get on *r* chairs if we have *n* people at our disposal.

The first chair can be filled by any one of the *n* people—*i.e.*, it can be filled in *n* ways.

When it has been filled in any one of these ways the second can be filled in $(n-1)$ ways—*i.e.*, in $(n-2+1)$ ways.

The third can be filled in $(n-2)$ ways—*i.e.*, in $(n-3+1)$ ways, and reasoning in this way we see that the *r*th can be filled in $(n-r+1)$ ways.

Hence, using the fundamental principle we find:

$$^nP_r = n(n-1)(n-2) \ldots (n-r+1) \quad . \quad . \quad (2)$$

The number of factors is the same as the number of chairs —viz., *r*.

5. The problem solved in § 3 may now be stated as " Find ^nP_n "—*i.e.*, find the number of ways in which *n* different things may be arranged, using all of them in each arrangement.   Putting n for r in (2) above we get:

$$^nP_n = n(n - 1)(n - 2) \ldots 3 \cdot 2 \cdot 1 = \underline{|n}.$$

Example 1

The number of arrangements of three coins which can be made from a penny, a shilling, a florin, and a half-crown is:

$$^4P_3 = 4 \cdot 3 \cdot 2 = 24.$$

Example 2

The number of three-permutations which can be made from a complete pack of cards is

$$^{52}P_3 = 52 \times 51 \times 50 = 132,600.$$

Example 3

Express $10 \times 9 \times 8 \times 7$ in factorial notation.
We have

$$10 \times 9 \times 8 \times 7 = \frac{10 \cdot 9 \cdot 8 \cdot 7 \cdot (6 \cdot 5 \cdot 4 \cdot 3 \cdot 2 \cdot 1)}{(6 \cdot 5 \cdot 4 \cdot 3 \cdot 2 \cdot 1)}$$

$$= \frac{\underline{|10}}{\underline{|6}}.$$

EXERCISE 9

1. Evaluate (a) $^7P_3$, (b) $^8P_4$, and (c) $^6P_6$.
2. Express (a) $^6P_2$, (b) $^5P_4$, and (c) $^8P_2$ in factorial notation.
3. Show that $^nP_r = \dfrac{\underline{|n}}{\underline{|n - r}}$.

4. If there are nine horses in a race, how many possible ways are there of nominating the first three horses?

5. How many terms are there in the product

$$(a + b + c)(p + q + r)(x + y + z + w)?$$

6. A stretch of railway line covers six stations. How many different kinds of single second-class tickets must be printed so that one may book from any station to any other?

7. How many numbers each containing three different digits can be made from 2, 3, 4, 5, 6? How many numbers of three digits can be made?

8. In how many ways may eight people sit on eight chairs arranged in a line, if two of them insist on sitting next to each other?

6. To Find ^nC_r

The notation ^nC_r means the number of groups (or combinations) each containing r things which we can get if we have n different things from which to choose them.

The problem is identical with that of finding how many different groups of r people we can get from n people.

Observe that any group of r people can be arranged in $\lfloor r$ ways. Thus a group of four people can arrange themselves in $\lfloor 4$, or 24 ways.

Putting $x = {}^nC_r$, we see that $x \lfloor r$ represents the number of ways in which the n people can form r-arrangements, since every group of r can arrange themselves in $\lfloor r$ ways.

Hence $\quad x \lfloor r = {}^nP_r$

$$= n(n-1)(n-2) \ldots (n-r+1)$$

$$\therefore \quad x = {}^nC_r = \frac{n(n-1)(n-2) \ldots (n-r+1)}{\lfloor r}$$

i.e., $\quad {}^nC_r = \frac{n(n-1(n-2) \ldots (n-r+1)}{1 \cdot 2 \cdot 3 \ldots r}$

The above formula is very important. Notice that the number of factors in both numerator and denominator is r.

e.g., $\qquad 5C_3 = \frac{5 \cdot 4 \cdot 3}{1 \cdot 2 \cdot 3} = 10.$

7. If we take a group of r from n things, we have a group of $(n - r)$ things left.   Hence the number of r-combinations equals the number of $(n - r)$-combinations.

i.e., $$^nC_r = {}^nC_{n-r}$$

Use of this relation may save labour in computation.

Thus $$^{12}C_{10} = {}^{12}C_2 = \frac{12 \cdot 11}{1 \cdot 2} = 66.$$

Similarly,

$$^nC_{n-3} = {}^nC_3 = \frac{n(n - 1)(n - 2)}{1 \cdot 2 \cdot 3}.$$

Example 1

The number of soccer teams that can be picked from 14 people is

$$^{14}C_{11} = {}^{14}C_3 = \frac{14 \cdot 13 \cdot 12}{1 \cdot 2 \cdot 3} = 364.$$

Example 2

Reverting to Example 1 above, find in how many of the teams a particular man, say Brown, appears, and in how many he does not appear:

   (1) if he is in the team, pick 10 men from the remaining 13 men,
      $\therefore$ he is in $^{13}C_{10}$—*i.e.,* 286 of the teams.
   (2) He is not in $^{13}C_{11}$ of them—*i.e.,* he is not in $\frac{13 \cdot 12}{1 \cdot 2} = 78$ teams; since when he is excluded, we just pick 11 men from 13.

Observe that the number of teams Brown is in together with those he is not in $= 364$.

This example can be generalised; and it follows that

$$^nC_r = {}^{n-1}C_{r-1} + {}^{n-1}C_r$$

since the groups of r may be divided into (1) those in which a particular thing appears and (2) those in which it does not.

EXERCISE 10

1. Find (a) $^7C_4$, (b) $^8C_6$, (c) $^{10}C_1$, (d) $^5C_5$.

2. Express each of the above examples in factorial notation.

3. Show that $^8C_5 + {}^8C_4 = {}^9C_5$.

4. How many different triangles can be formed from sixteen points in a plane, if no three of the points are in a straight line?

5. How many points of intersection have

    (a) eight straight lines in a plane, no two of which are parallel,

    (b) eight intersecting circles in a plane?

6. From eight white and six coloured balls in how many ways may three white and four coloured balls be selected?

7. In how many ways may seventeen articles be packed into two parcels one containing ten of them and the other seven?

8. If $^8C_r = {}^8C_{2r-7}$, find r.

8. The study of permutations and combinations is much more than a frivolous matter of football pools or musical chairs—though such familiar illustrations are not to be despised by the student. The notation (symbols ^nP_r, $\lfloor r$, etc.) is a great convenience to mathematicians, for without it many algebraic expressions would be too cumbersome. Question 5, in Exercise 9 above, shows the immediate and easy application of the study to products, and thence to powers, as in the Binomial Theorem with which paragraph No. 9 (following this one) deals. Example 1 on p. 66 introduces the important subject of probability. Unless special knowledge or skill is available the probability of a correct prediction of the results of 7 matches is seen to be

1 in 2187. "Probability" is itself a branch of mathematics of great importance in science and industry alike. Laws of physics are frequently valid statistically, but not so where individual particles are concerned. The system of inspection of engineering products by sampling, known as statistical control, centres on analysis of measurements in such a way as to separate significant from random variations.

9. The Binomial Theorem

When n is a positive integer, we are now in a position to show that

$$(1 + x)^n = 1 + {}^nC_1 x + {}^nC_2 x^2 + \ldots$$
$$+ {}^nC_r x^r + \ldots + {}^nC_n x^n \quad (1)$$

i.e., that $(1 + x)^n = 1 + nx + \dfrac{n(n-1)}{1 \cdot 2} x^2 + \ldots + x^n \quad (2)$

The expansion in (2) above is known as the Binomial Theorem.

By actual multiplication we see that

$$(1 + x)^2 = (1 + x)(1 + x) = 1 + 2x + x^2 \quad . \quad . \quad (A)$$
$$(1 + x)^3 = (1 + x)(1 + x)(1 + x) = 1 + 3x + 3x^2 + x^3 \quad (B)$$
$$(1 + x)^4 = (1 + x)(1 + x)(1 + x)(1 + x)$$
$$= 1 + 4x + 6x^2 + 4x^3 + x^4 \quad (C)$$

Proceeding in this way, we observe that

(1) Each expansion is in ascending powers of x.

(2) Each expansion starts with x°—*i.e.*, 1—and finishes with a power of x indicated by the particular index.

(3) The number of terms in the expansion is one more than the number expressed by the index.

We thus infer that, when n is a positive integer,

$$(1 + x)^n = 1 + a_1 x + a_2 x^2 + \ldots + a_n x^n \ldots (3)$$

All we require to find is the value of each of the a's—viz., a_1, a_2, etc.

This is a simple problem in combinations.

When n is a positive integer

$$(1 + x)^n = (1 + x)(1 + x)(1 + x) \ldots \text{to } n \text{ factors.}$$

The term in the product on the right-hand side which contains, say, x^3, is formed by taking x from three of its factors in every possible way. Since we have n factors, this may be done in $^nC_3$ ways. Similarly, for every other power of x; the coefficient of x^5 is, then, $^nC_5$, and that of x^r is ^nC_r.

Substituting for a_1, a_2, etc., in (3) we get:

$$(1 + x)^n = 1 + {}^nC_1 x + {}^nC_2 x^2 + \ldots + {}^nC_r x^r$$
$$+ \ldots + {}^nC_n x^n \quad . \quad . \quad . \quad . \quad (4)$$

$$= 1 + nx + \frac{n(n-1)}{1 \cdot 2} x^2 + \ldots + x^n \quad . \quad (5)$$

The forms (4) and (5) above for the Binomial Theorem should be remembered.

Example 1

Expand fully $(1 + x)^6$.

We have

$$(1 + x)^6 = 1 + {}^6C_1 x + {}^6C_2 x^2 + {}^6C_3 x^3 + {}^6C_4 x^4$$
$$+ {}^6C_5 x^5 + {}^6C_6 x^6$$

Notice that $^6C_6 = 1$, and that $^6C_5 = {}^6C_1$, etc. So that the coefficients of terms equidistant from the beginning and end of the series are equal.

Writing out the coefficients fully, we get:

$$(1 + x)^6 = 1 + 6x + 15x^2 + 20x^3 + 15x^4 + 6x^5 + x^6.$$

From (4) above, the coefficient of any particular power of x may readily be written down.

Thus, in $(1 + x)^8$ the term involving x^5 is $^8C_5 x^5$—*i.e.*, $56x^5$.

10. Now notice that:

$$(1 - x)^n = \{1 + (-x)\}^n$$

$$= 1 + n(-x) + \frac{n(n-1)}{1 \cdot 2}(-x)^2 + \ldots$$

$$= 1 - nx + \frac{n(n-1)}{1 \cdot 2}x^2 -, \text{ etc.}$$

viz.—the terms are alternately positive and negative. Thus the first four terms of $(1 - x)_7$ are:

$$1 - 7x + 21x^2 - 35x^3$$

$(1 + 2x)^9$ is expanded thus:

$$(1 + 2x)^9 = 1 + {}^9C_1(2x) + {}^9C_2(2x)^2 + {}^9C_3(2x)^3 +, \text{ etc.}$$
$$= 1 + 18x + 144x^2 + 672x^3 +, \text{ etc.}$$

11. The form

$$(1 + x)^n = 1 + nx + \frac{n(n-1)}{1 \cdot 2}x^2 + \frac{n(n-1)(n-2)}{1 \cdot 2 \cdot 3}x^3 + \ldots$$

we shall call the " Standard form of the Binomial Theorem." Any other form can be reduced to this one.

Example 1

Expand $(a + x)^n$.

$$(a + x) = a\left(1 + \frac{x}{a}\right)$$

$$\therefore (a + x)^n = a^n\left(1 + \frac{x}{a}\right)^n$$

$$= a^n\left[1 + {}^nC_1\frac{x}{a} + {}^nC_2\frac{x^2}{a^2} + \ldots + {}^nC_r\frac{x^r}{a^r} + \ldots\right]$$

i.e. $(a + x)^n = a^n + {}^nC_1 a^{n-1} x + {}^nC_2 a^{n-2} x^2 + \ldots$
$$+ {}^nC_r a^{n-r} x^r + \ldots \quad (6)$$

This expansion is more general than the one in standard form, but is not so useful.

Example 2

Expand $\left(3 + \dfrac{x}{2}\right)^6$ *as far as the term in* x^2.

$$\left(3 + \frac{x}{2}\right) = 3\left(1 + \frac{x}{6}\right)$$

$$\therefore \quad \left(3 + \frac{x}{2}\right)^6 = 3^6\left(1 + \frac{x}{6}\right)^6$$

$$= 3^6\left(1 + 6 \cdot \frac{x}{6} + \frac{6 \cdot 5}{1 \cdot 2} \cdot \frac{x^2}{36} + \ldots\right)$$

$$= 3^6\left(1 + x + \frac{5x^2}{12}\right).$$

12. The expansion of $(1 + x)^n$ preserves the same form when n is not a +ve integer, provided that x is real and is numerically less than unity. The proof of this proposition is beyond the scope of this book.

Thus if $x < 1$ (numerically)

$$(1 + x)^{-4} = 1 + (-4)x + \frac{(-4)(-5)}{1 \cdot 2}x^2$$
$$+ \frac{(-4)(-5)(-6)}{1 \cdot 2 \cdot 3}x^3 + \ldots$$

$$= 1 - 4x + 10x^2 - 20x^3 + \ldots$$

N.B.—(i) We cannot use the form involving $^nC_1$, etc., since this is meaningless unless n is a +ve integer.

(ii) In the above, observe that the series on the right-hand side is unending.

Similarly,

$$(1 - x)^{-\frac{1}{2}} = 1 + (-\tfrac{1}{2})(-x) + \frac{(-\tfrac{1}{2})(-\tfrac{3}{2})}{1 \cdot 2}(-x)^2$$
$$+ \frac{(-\tfrac{1}{2})(-\tfrac{3}{2})(-\tfrac{5}{2})}{1 \cdot 2 \cdot 3}(-x)^3$$

$$= 1 + \frac{x}{2} + \frac{3x^2}{8} + \frac{5x^3}{16} +, \text{ etc.}$$

13. We summarise our results thus:

$$(1 + x)^n = 1 + nx + \frac{n(n-1)}{1 \cdot 2}x^2 + \frac{n(n-1)(n-2)}{1 \cdot 2 \cdot 3}x^3 + \cdots$$

(a) *If n is a positive integer, the series terminates after* $(n + 1)$ *terms have been written down, and the series gives the exact value of* $(1 + x)^n$ *for all values of x.*

(b) *If n is a negative integer, or a positive or negative fraction, the " form " of the series is preserved, but gives the true value of* $(1 + x)^n$ *only when x is numerically less than unity.*

Example

$$\frac{1}{(1 + 2x)^3} = (1 + 2x)^{-3}$$

$$= 1 + (-3)(2x) + \frac{(-3)(-4)}{1 \cdot 2}(2x)^2 + \cdots$$

$$= 1 - 6x + 24x^2 -, \text{ etc., always provided}$$
that $2x < 1$ (numerically),

i.e., $x < \frac{1}{2}$ (numerically).

N.B.—When we wish to refer merely to the numerical value of x, we write it thus: $|x|$ —*e.g.,*
if
$$x = -2.$$
$$|x| = 2.$$

$|x|$ is then read " the numerical value of x."

In the above example, we have, then:

$$|2x| < 1$$
$$|x| < \tfrac{1}{2}.$$

14. The following examples are typical of many which involve a knowledge of the Binomial Theorem.

Example 1

Find the term independent of x, i.e., the constant term, in the expansion of $\left(x - \dfrac{2}{x}\right)^8$.

$$\left(x - \frac{2}{x}\right) = x\left(1 - \frac{2}{x^2}\right)$$

$$\therefore \ \left(x - \frac{2}{x}\right)^8 = x^8\left(1 - \frac{2}{x^2}\right)^8$$

The required term will be the one containing $\frac{1}{x^8}$ in the binomial expansion of $\left(1 - \frac{2}{x^2}\right)^8$—i.e., the fifth term. Thus the value of the term independent of x is

$$x^8 \cdot {}^8C_4\left(-\frac{2}{x^2}\right)^4 = 1120.$$

Example 2

Write down the expansion of $(x + a)^n$ where n is a positive integer. Give in full the $(r + 1)$th term. Find the constant term in the expansion of $\left(x^3 - \dfrac{2}{x^4}\right)^{14}$.   (U.L.C.I.)

$$(x + a)^n = x^n\left(1 + \frac{a}{x}\right)^n$$

$$= x^n\left(1 + {}^nC_1\frac{a}{x} + {}^nC_2\frac{a^2}{x^2} + \ldots + {}^nC_r\frac{a^r}{x^r} + \ldots + {}^nC_n\frac{a^n}{x^n}\right)$$

$$= x^n + {}^nC_1 x^{n-1}a + {}^nC_2 x^{n-2}a^2 + \ldots$$
$$+ {}^nC_r x^{n-r}a^r + \ldots + a^n.$$

The $(r + 1)$th term

$$= {}^nC_r x^{n-r}a^r$$
$$= \frac{n(n-1)(n-2) \ldots (n-r+1)}{1 \cdot 2 \cdot 3 \ldots r}x^{n-r}a^r.$$

Also $\qquad \left(x^3 - \dfrac{2}{x^4}\right)^{14} = x^{42}\left(1 - \dfrac{2}{x^7}\right)^{14}.$

Hence (see Example 1 above) the constant term is the seventh and is:

$$x^{42} \cdot {}^{14}C_6\left(-\frac{2}{x^7}\right)^6$$
$$= {}^{14}C_6 \cdot 2^6.$$

Example 3

$$\frac{1}{1 + x} = (1 + x)^{-1}$$

$$= 1 + (-1)x + \frac{(-1)(-2)x^2}{1 \cdot 2} +, \text{ etc.}$$

$$= 1 - x + x^2 - \ldots$$

If x is so small that x^2 and higher powers may be neglected, we get that:

$$\frac{1}{1 + x} = 1 - x.$$

Similarly,

$$\frac{1}{\sqrt{1 + x}} = (1 + x)^{-\frac{1}{2}} = 1 - \tfrac{1}{2}x$$

neglecting higher powers of x than the first.
Thus:

$$\frac{1}{\sqrt{0 \cdot 998}} = \frac{1}{\sqrt{1 - 0 \cdot 002}} = (1 - 0 \cdot 002)^{-\frac{1}{2}}$$

$$= 1 + \tfrac{1}{2} \times 0 \cdot 002 = 1 \cdot 001.$$

Example 4

Let $E = \dfrac{(1 + x)^4}{\sqrt{1 - x}}$

$$= (1 + x)^4 (1 - x)^{-\frac{1}{2}}$$

$$= (1 + 4x + \ldots)(1 + \tfrac{1}{2}x + \ldots)$$

$$= 1 + 4x + \tfrac{1}{2}x + \ldots$$

Thus $E = 1 + \dfrac{9x}{2}$, provided x^2 and higher powers may be neglected.

Now evaluate $\dfrac{(1 \cdot 02)^4}{\sqrt{0 \cdot 98}}$

Here $x = 0 \cdot 02$

An approximate value is, therefore, as above:

$$1 + \frac{9}{2} \times 0 \cdot 02 = 1 \cdot 09.$$

Example 5

Consider the formula $\frac{pv}{T} = $ constant, where p is the pressure of a gas in lb/sq in., v the volume in cu in., and T the absolute temperature.

Suppose v increased by 3%, T diminished by 2%, what is the percentage change in p?

We know that v becomes $v(1 + 0 \cdot 03)$,
and that   T becomes $T(1 - 0 \cdot 02)$,
so let p become $p(1 + x)$.

Then since the $\frac{pv}{T}$ fraction has a constant value,

$$\frac{pv}{T} = \frac{p(1 + x)v(1 \cdot 03)}{T(1 \cdot 0 - 0 \cdot 02)};$$

and dividing this equation by $\frac{pv}{T}$ we have

$$1 = \frac{(1 + x)(1 \cdot 03)}{1 - 0 \cdot 02},$$

which gives $1 + x = \dfrac{1 - 0 \cdot 02}{1 + 0 \cdot 03}$

$$= (1 - 0 \cdot 02)(1 + 0 \cdot 03)^{-1}.$$

Now since, in comparison with the other magnitudes concerned, we can neglect $(0 \cdot 02)^2$ and $(0 \cdot 03)^2$ we can equally well neglect the product of $0 \cdot 02$ and $0 \cdot 03$.   Thus

$$1 + x = 1 - 0 \cdot 02 - 0 \cdot 03$$
$$= 1 - 0 \cdot 05.$$

Hence $x = - 0 \cdot 05$ and p decreases by 5%.

15. From these examples and the earlier work of the chapter it can be seen that if fractions such as $0 \cdot 01$, $0 \cdot 02$,

0·03 occur, their squares and higher powers may be regarded as negligible compared with unity. Expansions by the Binomial Theorem can clearly be used to justify a rule commonly accepted and used in quite elementary examples. According to this rule a variation (or error) of, say, 1% in some magnitude can be expected to appear as 2% in the square of that magnitude, and as 3% in the cube, and so on.

EXERCISE 11

Expand to four terms, putting where necessary each binomial in " standard form."

1. (a) $(1 + z)^{\frac{1}{2}}$, (b) $(1 - h)^{-1}$, (c) $(1 + y)^{\frac{3}{2}}$, (d) $(1 - x)^{-\frac{5}{4}}$,

(e) $\dfrac{1}{1 + x}$, (f) $\dfrac{1}{\sqrt{1 - x}}$, (g) $\dfrac{1}{\sqrt[4]{1 + x}}$, (h) $\dfrac{1}{(1 + x)^3}$,

(k) $(a + x)^{-2}$, (l) $(a + 2h)^{\frac{1}{2}}$, (m) $(2 - 3x)^{-4}$.

2. Find approximately, using the Binomial Theorem,

(a) $(1·02)^5$,   (b) $(0·997)^4$,   (c) $\sqrt{1·006}$,   (d) $\dfrac{1}{0·996}$,

(e) $\dfrac{1}{3·015}$, (f) $\sqrt[3]{1·021}$.

3. Supposing h is small compared with x find values for
$$\frac{(x + h)^8 - x^8}{h}, \quad \frac{(x + h)^{\frac{1}{2}} - x^{\frac{1}{2}}}{h}.$$

4. Using the Binomial Theorem, find the first five terms in the expansion of $\sqrt{1 + 2x}$.   (U.E.I.)

5. If x is so small that its third and higher powers may be neglected, show by the Binomial Theorem that the values of $\sqrt[n]{\dfrac{1 + x}{1 - x}}$ and $\dfrac{n + x}{n - x}$ may be considered equal.

                                        (N.C.T.E.C.)

6. Expand $\dfrac{(1 - x)^{\frac{2}{3}}}{(1 - x^2)^{\frac{1}{3}}}$ in ascending powers of x as far as the term containing x^2.

Prove that $\dfrac{(1-x)^{\frac{1}{2}}}{(1+x)^{\frac{1}{3}}} = \dfrac{(1-x)^{\frac{5}{6}}}{(1-x^2)^{\frac{1}{3}}}$ and hence deduce that,

when $x = 0 \cdot 12$, $\dfrac{(1-x)^{\frac{1}{2}}}{(1+x)^{\frac{1}{3}}}$ is approximately equal to $0 \cdot 9033$.

(N.C.T.E.C.)

7. Find the coefficient of the seventh term in the expansion of $\left(\dfrac{2}{7} - \dfrac{x^3}{3}\right)^{10}$.   (U.L.C.I.)

8. Expand $(1 - 3x)^9$ for five terms and find the values of the fourth and fifth terms when $x = 0 \cdot 06$.   (U.L.C.I.)

9. Find the middle term in the expansion of $\left(x + \dfrac{a^2}{x}\right)^{12}$.

(U.L.C.I.)

10. Expand $(x - y)^{\frac{1}{2}}$ to the first four terms, and when $x = 3$ and $y = -0 \cdot 1$ find the numerical value of each of the first three terms of our result to four significant figures.

(U.L.C.I.)

11. Find the term containing x^{22} in the expansion of $\left(\dfrac{x^2}{2} - \dfrac{3}{4}\right)^{14}$.   (U.L.C.I.)

12. Given $F_1 = \dfrac{m}{(d-l)^2}$ and $F_2 = \dfrac{m}{(d+l)^2}$ find by using the Binomial Theorem the approximate value of $F_1 - F_2$, when l is so small compared with d that powers of $\dfrac{l}{d}$ above the first can be neglected.   (U.L.C.I.)

CHAPTER 4

FUNCTION. LIMIT. INFINITESIMAL. DEFINITION OF A DIFFERENTIAL COEFFICIENT

1. Functions of One Variable

In plotting $y = x^2$, we give a value to x, and then calculate a value of y. The two values, x and y, determine a point on the graph.

Both x and y are termed variables. In the above case we make x the independent variable and can assign any value whatsoever to it. y becomes the dependent variable because its value depends on that given to x.

Definition

When a value given to x determines a value of y, y is called a function of x.

Either x, or y, or any other symbol can represent an independent variable. But when we plot graphs (perhaps of experimental results) it is common to plot the quantity which we can most easily regard as a *cause* along the x-axis. This might be the brake load in an engine trial, or the suspended weight in a test of a spring. The fuel consumption at various loads, or the extensions of the spring, in fact the *effect*, can then be plotted upwards from the base line.

In such cases there is a natural distinction between the dependent and the independent variable; but when x and y are merely connected algebraically we can think of either as dependent upon the other. It is in general simplest to write the dependent variable standing alone as in " $y = x^2$." A common exercise consists in choosing some other variable and making it the " subject of the formula." This we could write " $x = \pm \sqrt{y}$." Many examples and exercises on thus changing the subject of a formula are given in Volume II of this work.

2. Notation

Instead of saying in words that y is a function of x, we often express the fact by writing $y = f(x)$ or $y = F(x)$, and sometimes by $y = \phi(x)$. In this book we shall use one or other of the first two forms.

Thus $\qquad y = f(x) = 3x^2 - 5x + 2$

and $\qquad y = F(\theta) = 3 \sin \theta + 2 \cos \theta$

are examples of functions of x and of θ. Both the above functions are called explicit functions, because one variable is expressed solely in terms of the other. In both cases we know the " form " of y.

On the other hand, if we merely know $y = f(x)$—i.e., that y is some function of x—the only knowledge we get from the relationship is that values given to x determine values of y. We cannot calculate values of y, but can only say that when $x = 2$, $y = f(2)$, when $x = 0$, $y = f(0)$, etc.

Example 1

If $\qquad y = f(x) = 3x^2 - 4x + 2$

$\qquad f(2) = 3 \cdot 2^2 - 4 \cdot 2 + 2 = 6$

$\qquad f(-1) = 3(-1)^2 - 4 \cdot (-1) + 2 = 9$

$\qquad f(\tfrac{1}{2}) = 3(\tfrac{1}{2})^2 - 4(\tfrac{1}{2}) + 2 = \tfrac{3}{4}.$

Example 2

If $\qquad y = \sin 2\theta°$

we have $\qquad F(\theta°) = \sin 2\theta°$

$\qquad F(15°) = \sin 30° = \tfrac{1}{2}$

$\qquad F(30°) = \sin 60° = \dfrac{\sqrt{3}}{2} = 0 \cdot 866.$

The student will now realise that all the formulæ he uses define functions.

Thus: $V = \frac{4}{3}\pi r^3$

—the volume of a sphere is a function of the radius.

Again, if $f = \dfrac{Ex}{l}$,

the intensity of stress, f, is a function of the strain, x.

In the last two examples we are conscious of the physical connection between the two variables as well as of the numerical relation expressed by the algebraic formula. The physical connection may not however apply for the complete range of values of the independent variable. We could plot the graph of $V = \frac{4}{3}\pi r^3$ for all values of r: we cannot however easily picture a sphere having a negative radius. Again although stress may always be *some* function of strain the function is only represented by the above formula for values of x between the elastic limits. Thus, calculated values should be frequently checked against given facts.

Notice that $y = \dfrac{1}{x}$ is meaningless when $x = 0$, so that for $x = 0$ y is not the given $f(x)$.

Perhaps the student has been accustomed to state that $\frac{1}{0}$ is equal to " infinity," whatever he may mean by that word. He should, however, remember that we cannot divide by zero; and will convince himself of this fact if he tries to divide both sides of the equation $2 \times 0 = 3 \times 0$ by zero.

EXERCISE 12

1. Given that $f(x) = 3x^2 - 5x + 2$, find (a) $f(2)$, (b) $f(0)$, (c) $f(-3)$, (d) $f(\frac{1}{2})$.

2. If $f(\theta°) = 3 \sin 2\theta° + 4 \cos \theta°$, find (a) $f(0°)$, (b) $f(15°)$, (c) $f(30°)$.

3. If $F(x) = 3x^3 - 4x + 2$, find (a) $F(3) - F(2)$, (b) $F(-1) - F(-3)$.

4. If $f(x) = 2x^2 - x - 4$, find (a) $f(x + 2) - f(x)$, (b) $f(x + h) - f(x)$.

5. If $\phi(t) = 3t^2 + 2t - 1$, find $\phi(t + 2) - \phi(t + 1)$.

3. The Notion of a " Limit "

The use of the word limit in mathematics is closely allied to many of the ways in which we use the word in everyday speech.

When we speak of " working to the limit," or say that a person has reached the " limit of endurance " we imply: (a) a boundary to the amount produced by, or to the possible endurance of, say, an individual, and (b) that the boundary has not quite been reached, otherwise the person could neither work nor endure.

This notion of " not quite reaching the boundary " is inherent in the mathematical notion of a limit.

Consider $$y = \frac{1}{x}.$$

Case I.

Let x increase progressively.

If $$x = 10^4, \quad y = \frac{1}{10^4} = 0 \cdot 0001.$$

If $$x = 10^5, \quad y = \frac{1}{10^5} = 0 \cdot 00001.$$

As x gets larger and larger, we see that y gets smaller and smaller.

To express this progression of x through greater and greater values we shall use the symbol ∞, and call it infinity.

We then write:

$$\underset{x \to \infty}{\text{Lt}} \left(\frac{1}{x} \right) = 0.$$

Lt is an abbreviation of the word " limit." " $x \longrightarrow \infty$ " should be read as " x tends to infinity " and the statement

$$\underset{x \to \infty}{Lt} \left(\frac{1}{x}\right) = 0,$$

means that as x progresses through greater and greater values $\frac{1}{x}$ approaches nearer and nearer to zero.

Case II.

Let x decrease indefinitely.

When $x = 0.001,$ $y = \dfrac{1}{0.001} = 10^3$

When $x = 0.0001,$ $y = \dfrac{1}{0.0001} = 10^4$

and again we see that as x gets smaller $\dfrac{1}{x}$ becomes greater—*i.e.*, that

$$\underset{x \to 0}{Lt} \left(\frac{1}{x}\right) = \infty \quad \cdot \quad \cdot \quad \cdot \quad \cdot \quad (2)$$

We do not mean that ∞ (infinity) is a number, but the statement (2) is a short way of saying that no matter how great a number N may be named by some hypothetical person, we can always choose x so small that $\dfrac{1}{x} > N$.

All we need do is to choose x smaller than $\dfrac{1}{N}$. Further, notice that we never contemplate x as *having* the value zero.

If we graph $y = \dfrac{1}{x}$ for positive values of x we get a curve that approaches the x-axis as $x \longrightarrow \infty$, and approaches the y-axis as $x \longrightarrow 0$.

Example 1

$$y = f(x) = \frac{(3 - x)(x - 1)}{x - 1} \quad . \quad . \quad . \quad (1)$$

When $x = 1, y = \dfrac{2 \times 0}{0} = \dfrac{0}{0}.$

If we are asked " what is the value of y when $x = 1$?," we must reply that nobody knows, or, which means the same thing, that its value is indeterminate.

Now, in (1) put $x = 1 + h$

Then
$$y = \frac{(2 - h) \cdot h}{h}$$
$$= 2 - h,$$

provided h is not zero.

If, after dividing by h, we now make $h = 0$, we get $y = 2$.

We write this result:

$$\underset{x \to \infty}{Lt} \frac{(3 - x)(x - 1)}{(x - 1)} = 2$$

Thus, although we cannot find a value of y when $x = 1$, the result shows that if some hypothetical person names any small number ε, we can find a value of x that differs very little from unity, which will make y differ from 2 by less than ε.

In the above example, if 0·00001 should be the number named, we merely choose h smaller than this—say, 0·000001.

Example 2

Evaluate $\underset{x \to 2}{Lt} \dfrac{x^2 - x - 2}{x - 2}$

It is at once clear that $(x - 2)$ is a factor of the numerator.

If the student will adopt the following method, he will have difficulty neither in evaluating examples similar to the above nor in understanding them.

Let $$f(x) = \frac{x^2 - x - 2}{x - 2}$$

If $x = 2$, $f(x)$ takes the form $\frac{0}{0}$.

Put $$x = (2 + h)$$

Then:

$$f(2 + h) = \frac{(2 + h)^2 - (2 + h) - 2}{h}$$

$$= \frac{4 + 4h + h^2 - 2 - h - 2}{h}$$

$$= \frac{h^2 + 3h}{h}$$

$$= h + 3.$$

Now put $h = 0$, and we see that the required limit is **3**.

EXERCISE 13

1. Evaluate $\underset{x \to 1}{Lt} \dfrac{(x + 4)(x - 1)}{x - 1}$.

2. Find $\underset{x \to 2}{Lt} \dfrac{x^2 + x - 6}{x - 2}$.

3. Find $\underset{x \to 3}{Lt} \dfrac{2x^2 - 5x - 3}{x - 3}$.

4. Find $\underset{x \to 0}{Lt} \dfrac{x^2 + 3x}{x}$.

5. Find $\underset{x \to 3}{Lt} \dfrac{2x^2 - x - 15}{x^2 + 2x - 15}$.

6. Evaluate $\underset{x \to 2}{Lt} \dfrac{x^2 - x - 2}{2x^2 - 3x - 2}$.

7. Find $\underset{t \to 5}{Lt} \dfrac{3t^2 - 13t - 10}{2t^2 - 9t - 5}$.

8. Show that $\underset{x \to 0}{Lt} \dfrac{(x + h)^3 - x^3}{h} = 3x^2$.

5. The Differential Notation and Infinitesimals

Suppose ABK is any curve whose equation is $y = f(x)$.

Let $OM = x$ $\therefore$ $MA = f(x)$.

MN is a positive increment of x. It will be written Δx. {Not $\Delta \times x$.} This is simply a notation, and may be read as " an increment of x " or " a bit of x," or " Delta x."

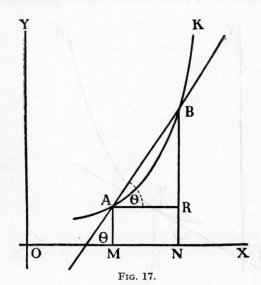

Fig. 17.

Δ is the Greek capital D, and is named Delta.

ON is then $= x + \Delta x$
      $\therefore$ $NB = f(x + \Delta x)$.

If AR is parallel to OX, we see that

$$MA = NR = f(x)$$
$$\therefore\quad RB = f(x + \Delta x) - f(x) \ldots$$
and $AR = \Delta x.$

It is clear that the gradient of the chord AB is tan θ, where

$$\tan\theta = \frac{f(x + \Delta x) - f(x)}{\Delta x}, \; i.e., \; \frac{RB}{AR}.$$

Now let $\Delta x \longrightarrow 0$—*i.e.*, let N approach M so that no matter how small a number, ε is named, we can make Δx smaller than ε. We thus observe that although we never

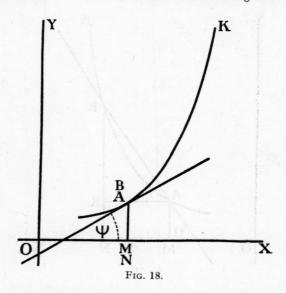

Fig. 18.

contemplate the actual arrival of N at M, it is impossible for the approach of N to M to be halted, since no matter how small a number is named, we can make Δx smaller than this number.

As N approaches M, B approaches A, and the chord AB approaches coincidence with the tangent at A, as in Fig. 18 above.

The gradient of the tangent at A is tan ψ. In the above

work, Δx is an example of an *infinitesimal*, which we define as "*a variable whose limit is zero.*"

Δx may now also be read as "*the differential* of x."

We shall often use the letter "h" instead of the symbol Δx.

Referring to Fig. 17 of this chapter, we see that

$$MA = NR = f(x) = y,$$

and $\therefore$ $NB = NR + RB = y + \Delta y,$

for by our definition RB is an infinitesimal, and may be regarded as the differential of y, or the increment of y.

6. We summarise the ideas of the last paragraph thus:

(1) For any curve, $y = f(x)$, if θ is the angle made by a chord AB with the positive sense of OX.

(2) The gradient of this chord is $\tan \theta$, where

$$\tan \theta = \frac{f(x + \Delta x) - f(x)}{\Delta x} = \frac{f(x + h - f(x)}{h}$$

$$= \frac{\Delta y}{\Delta x}$$

(3) Fig. 17 is what Fig. 18 becomes as $h \longrightarrow 0$, and we infer that the gradient of the tangent at any point A of the curve $y = f(x)$ is $\tan \psi$, where

$$\boldsymbol{\tan \psi} = \underset{\Delta x \to 0}{\textbf{Lt}} \frac{\Delta y}{\Delta x} = \underset{h \to 0}{\textbf{Lt}} \frac{f(x + h) - f(x)}{h} \qquad . \quad (1)$$

We shall refer to this expression as formula (1).

Example 1

Consider $y = f(x) = x^2$. *Find the gradient of the chord joining* $(1, 1)$ *and* $(2, 4)$.

If $\tan \theta$ is the gradient, we get:

$$\tan \theta = \frac{\text{Difference between the two ordinates}}{\text{Difference between the two abscissæ}}$$

$$= \frac{4 - 1}{2 - 1}$$

$$= 3.$$

The gradient of the chord joining two points on a curve is sometimes called the average gradient of the curve between the points.

Example 2

If $f(x) = 2x^2 + x + 1$, find the average gradient of the graph between the points where $x = \frac{1}{2}$ and $x = 2$.

In this example we take the average gradient of the graph between the two points as that of the chord which joins them.

$$\text{Average gradient} = \frac{f(2) - f(\frac{1}{2})}{2 - \frac{1}{2}}$$

$$= \frac{11 - 2}{\frac{3}{2}}$$

$$= 6.$$

Example 3

Find the gradient of the tangent at the point $(2, 4)$ on the curve $y = f(x) = x^2$.

This example shows how we apply to a particular curve formula (1), which is fundamental in much of the work of this book.

From formula (1), if $\tan \psi$ is the gradient we have:

$$\tan \psi = \underset{h \ \ 0}{Lt} \frac{f(x + h) - f(x)}{h}$$

In our example

$$f(x) = x^2, \text{ and } x = 2$$

$$\therefore \quad \tan \psi = \underset{h \to 0}{Lt} \frac{(2 + h)^2 - 2^2}{h}$$

$$= \underset{h \to 0}{Lt} \frac{4h + h^2}{h}$$

$$= Lt \ (4 + h)$$

$$= 4.$$

Example 4

Find the gradient of the tangent to the curve, $y = 2x^2 + x - 1$, at the point where $x = 3$.

Here, $f(x) = 2x^2 + x - 1$

$$\tan\psi = \underset{h \to 0}{Lt} \frac{\{2(3 + h)^2 + (3 + h) - 1\} - \{2.3^2 + 3 - 1\}1}{h}$$

$$= Lt \frac{\{2(9 + 6h + h^2) + 3 + h - 1 - 20\}}{h}$$

$$= Lt \frac{13h + 2h^2}{h}$$

$$= Lt\,(13 + 2h)$$

$$= 13, \text{ if we put } h = 0.$$

Example 5

Find the equation to the tangent at the point $(3, 20)$ on the curve in the above example.

We have just found the gradient of the tangent—viz., $\tan\psi$ to be 13. Also, the tangent passes through the point $(3, 20)$.

Hence its equation is

$$y - 20 = 13(x - 3) \quad i.e.,\ 13x - y - 19 = 0.$$

EXERCISE 14

1. If $y = 3x^2$, find the average gradient between the points where $x = 1$ and $x = 2$.

2. If $y = x^2$, find the gradient of the chord joining the points where—

    (a) $x = 3$, and $x = 4$.
    (b) $x = -1$, and $x = 2$.
    (c) $x = 1$, and $x = 1 + h$.

3. Using the result of (c) above, find the gradient of the tangent at the point $(1, 1)$ on the curve $y = x^2$. Write down the equation to the tangent at this point.

4. Find the equation of the tangent at the point where $x = 2$ on the curve $y = 4x^2$.

5. Find the equation to the tangent at the point where $x = 2$ on the curve $y = 2x^2 + x + 1$.

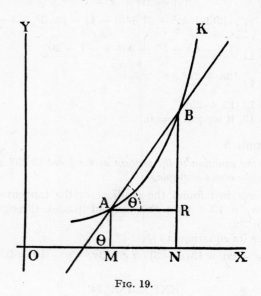

FIG. 19.

7. Differential Coefficient, or Derivative

The above figure is Fig. 17 of this chapter reproduced.

The equation of the curve is $y = f(x)$; $OM = x$ and $MN = h = \Delta x$.

Notice that A represents any point on the curve, and in order to get the gradient of the tangent at A, we let N approach M and use formula (1) from paragraph (6)

$$\tan \psi = \underset{h \to 0}{\mathrm{Lt}}\ \frac{f(x + h) - f(x)}{h}$$

This limit is called " the differential coefficient of y or $f(x)$ with respect to x."

We write it $\dfrac{dy}{dx}$. It is also frequently known as the first derivative of the function $f(x)$, with respect to x.

Similarly, if $z = f(\theta)$, $\dfrac{dz}{d\theta}$ is the differential coefficient of z, or $f(\theta)$, with respect to θ.

The relationship

$$\frac{dy}{dx} = \operatorname*{Lt}_{h \to 0} \frac{f(x + h) - f(x)}{h}$$

is fundamental, and must be remembered.

It has already been used by the student, when finding the gradients of the tangents to the curves given in the last set of examples.

Geometrically, a differential coefficient is the gradient of the tangent at any point (x, y) of the curve $y = f(x)$.

Clearly the differential coefficient of $y(= f(x))$ is itself a function of x; it is often known as the *derived* function.

Example 8

If $y = x^2 + x$, *find* $\dfrac{dy}{dx}$.

$$\begin{aligned}
\frac{dy}{dx} &= \operatorname*{Lt}_{h \to 0} \frac{\{(x + h)^2 + (x + h)\} - \{x^2 + x\}}{h} \\
&= \operatorname{Lt} \frac{(2hx + h^2 + h)}{h} \\
&= \operatorname{Lt} (2x + h + 1) \\
&= 2x + 1, \text{ when } h \longrightarrow 0.
\end{aligned}$$

$2x + 1$ is then the gradient of the tangent at any point whose abscissa is x. Thus if $x = 2$, then $y = 6$, and $\tan \psi = 5$.

Hence the equation to the tangent at $(2, 6)$ is

$$y - 6 = 5(x - 2).$$

8. The Calculus

The preceding paragraphs and examples give an introduction to the study of the " calculus," a study which will be pursued in subsequent chapters. One later chapter is devoted to " applications of the calculus "; part of another deals with " physical applications of integration " and so on. Such passages do indeed apply earlier work. But they should not be taken as suggesting that the calculus was first thought out independently of any actual problem, and then applied. A distinguished physicist * recently referred in a public lecture to the " special language invented by Newton and Leibniz, called calculus." That language was not invented and subsequently applied to the solution of Newton's problems: it is the expression of the way in which these problems *had been* attacked and solved. The calculus is not just a discipline invented by professors of mathematics but a method of expression which takes the place of arithmetic when it is necessary to deal with quantities which are changing—whether with time, or position, or anything else. We know that displacement is velocity multiplied by time, and arithmetic can deal with the multiplication so long as the velocity remains constant: but when in fact is velocity constant? If velocity is changing we can use arithmetic and algebra to deal with it by means of averages, and for the special case of constant acceleration; but we cannot deal with it generally. Again, WORK is force multiplied by distance moved under the action of the force; but what if the motion itself is leading to change in the force? The student of engineering or physics will find that the language of the calculus helps him to think clearly about his problems because it enables him to make definite statements about quantities although they may be changing. Calculus is a most practical study for the National Certificate student.

* *Lighthill on Shock Waves.*   Memoirs of the Manchester Lit. and Phil. Soc., 1958–59.

EXERCISE 15

1. Find the differential coefficients with respect to x of (a) x^2, (b) $3x^2 + x$, (c) x^3.

2. Get $\dfrac{d}{dt}(4t^2)$ and $\dfrac{d}{dz}(2z^2 + 3)$.

3. If $y = 3x^2 + 2x + 4$ find $\dfrac{dy}{dx}$. Then write down the equation to the tangent at the point where $x = 1$.

4. Find the gradient of the tangent where $t = 2$ on the curve $y = t + t^2$.

CHAPTER 5

DIFFERENTIATION OF FUNCTIONS OF A SINGLE VARIABLE

1. The Differentiation of x^n

It must be recalled that if $y = f(x)$, the gradient at any

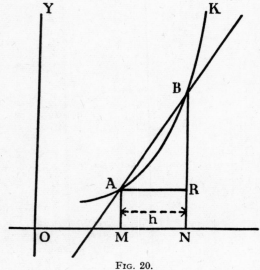

FIG. 20.

point A, where $OM = x$ and $MA = y = f(x)$, is calculated from the equation:

$$\frac{dy}{dx} = \underset{h \to 0}{Lt} \frac{f(x + h) - f(x)}{h} \quad . \quad . \quad . \quad (1)$$

If
$$y = f(x) = x^n$$
$$f(x + h) = (x + h)^n = x^n \left(1 + \frac{h}{x}\right)^n$$

Hence

$$\frac{dy}{dx} = \underset{h \to 0}{\mathrm{Lt}} \frac{x^n \left(1 + \dfrac{h}{x}\right)^n - x^n}{h}. \quad . \quad . \quad (2)$$

Before proceeding to evaluate (2), it is advisable to note the following points:

(1) The letter "f" standing for "function" is omitted from (2), since we have been given the function explicitly.

(2) $(x + h)^n$ has been put in "standard form," *i.e.*, $x^n \left(1 + \dfrac{h}{x}\right)^n$.

(3) Since $h \longrightarrow 0$, $\dfrac{h}{x}$ may be taken as a proper fraction and therefore the expansion of $\left(1 + \dfrac{h}{x}\right)^n$ is true for all values of n, positive or negative, integral or fractional.

(4) We are dealing with a function of x; that is, our independent variable is x: but in finding the gradient at A we are confining ourselves to a *single* value of x, namely, OM. In this particular discussion therefore the independent variable which moves towards a limiting value nothing, is MN, *i.e.*, h or Δx.

Hence

$$\frac{dy}{dx} = \underset{h \to 0}{\mathrm{Lt}} \frac{x^n \left(1 + \dfrac{h}{x}\right)^n - x^n}{h}$$

$$= x^n \, \mathrm{Lt} \frac{\left(1 + \dfrac{h}{x}\right)^n - 1}{h} \quad \text{[Taking out the common factor, } x^n]$$

$$= x^n \, \text{Lt} \, \frac{\left(1 + \frac{nh}{x} + \text{terms in higher powers of } h\right) - 1}{h}$$

$$= x^n \cdot \frac{n}{x}.$$

The two unit terms disappear; and the only term without h after division is $\frac{n}{x}$

i.e.,
$$\frac{d}{dx}(x^n) = nx^{n-1} \quad \cdots \quad (3)$$

This result holds for all values of n.

Further, if $y = ax^n$

$$\frac{dy}{dx} = nax^{n-1} \quad \cdots \quad (4)$$

This will be clear by reference to (2). Instead of x^n in the numerator, we have ax^n and this expression will be carried through the whole of the subsequent work.

N.B.—If $y = $ a constant, $\frac{dy}{dx} = 0$.

Example 1

If $\qquad y = x^{-3}, \quad \frac{dy}{dx} = -3x^{-4}.$

Example 2

If $\qquad y = x^{-\frac{1}{2}}, \quad \frac{dy}{dx} = -\frac{1}{2} \cdot x^{-\frac{3}{2}}.$

Example 3

$$\frac{d}{dx}(4x^3) = 12x^2.$$

Example 4

$$\frac{d}{dt}(3t^{-\frac{2}{3}}) = -2t^{-\frac{5}{3}}.$$

Example 5

If
$$y = \frac{2}{\sqrt[3]{z^4}} = \frac{2}{z^{\frac{4}{3}}} = 2z^{-\frac{4}{3}}$$

then
$$\frac{dy}{dz} = -\tfrac{8}{3}z^{-\frac{7}{3}}.$$

EXERCISE 16

1. Differentiate

   (i) x^7, (ii) $2x^{-4}$, (iii) $3x^{-2}$, (iv) $\dfrac{5}{x^3}$.

2. Evaluate $\dfrac{d}{dt}\left(\dfrac{2}{t^5}\right)$, $\dfrac{d}{dy}\left(\dfrac{5}{\sqrt{y}}\right)$, $\dfrac{d}{dz}\dfrac{3}{\sqrt[3]{z^2}}$.

3. In the following examples find $\dfrac{dy}{dx}$:

   (a) $y = \dfrac{4}{x}$, (b) $y = \dfrac{5}{x^3\sqrt[3]{x}}$, (c) $y = 6x^2\sqrt[5]{x}$.

4. Differentiate the following functions with respect to the appropriate variable:

   (i) $2x^{-\frac{3}{2}}$, (ii) $5\theta^{\frac{3}{2}}$, (iii) $2z^{-4}$, (iv) $\dfrac{5t^3}{\sqrt[4]{t}}$.

5. Differentiate

   (i) $2x^{3\cdot2}$, (ii) $x^{0\cdot13}$, (iii) $\dfrac{5}{x^{2\cdot14}}$, (iv) $\dfrac{3}{\sqrt[3]{2x^{1\cdot5}}}$, (v) $\dfrac{5x^{1\cdot3}}{\sqrt{x^{3\cdot6}}}$.

See also Exercise 28A—Miscellaneous.

2. The Differential Coefficient of a Sum

The differential coefficient of a sum of a number of terms is *the sum of their separate differential coefficients.*
Thus:

$$\frac{d}{dx}(x^3 + 3x^2 + 2x + 4) = 3x^2 + 6x + 2.$$

The proposition remains true if some of the terms are negative.

Example 1

If $\qquad y = 2t^{1\cdot3} - 3\sqrt{t} + 6, \text{ find } \dfrac{dy}{dt}.$

We put $\qquad y = 2t^{1\cdot3} - 3t^{\frac{1}{2}} + 6$

$\qquad\qquad \dfrac{dy}{dt} = 2\cdot6t^{0\cdot3} - 1\cdot5t^{-\frac{1}{2}}.$

Example 2

$$y = \frac{z^4 - 3z^2 + 2z - 1}{z^3}$$

Write $\qquad y = z - 3z^{-1} + 2z^{-2} - z^{-3} \text{ (by division)}$

$\qquad\qquad \dfrac{dy}{dz} = 1 + 3z^{-2} - 4z^{-3} + 3z^{-4}.$

EXERCISE 17

1. Find $\dfrac{d}{dx}(2x^3 - 3x^2 + 4x - 2)$ and

$$\frac{d}{dt}\left(2t^{1\cdot3} - 4t^{-2} + \frac{3}{t}\right).$$

2. Differentiate with respect to the independent variable used:

(i) $\dfrac{x^3 - 2x^2 + 3}{x^4}$,   (ii) $\dfrac{3t^{2\cdot6} - 4t^{0\cdot3} + 2}{t}$,

(iii) $(x + 4)(x - 5)$,   (iv) $(3x + 1)^2$.

3. Give the derivatives with respect to x of:

(a) $(2x^3)^3$,   (b) $1 - \dfrac{1}{3x^2}$,   (c) $x^{-1\cdot5}(x^2 - 4^2)$,

(d) $\dfrac{x^6 - x^2}{2x^3}$,   (e) $(2x^2 - x^3)^2$.   (N.C.T.E.C.)

4. Give the derivatives of

$$\text{(i) } \left(\frac{4^3}{x}\right)^2, \quad \text{(ii) } x^2(2x^2 - 8^4), \quad \text{(iii) } \sqrt[5]{x^3}.$$
$$\text{(iv) } -2^7 x^{0\cdot4}, \quad \text{(v) } \frac{x^{12} - x^3}{x^6}.$$

Find, without using tables or slide rule, the values of the first four of these derivatives when $x = 2^5$.

(N.C.T.E.C.)

5. Find $\dfrac{dy}{dx}$ when $y = 3\sqrt[3]{x^2} + \dfrac{2}{x^{1\cdot5}} - \dfrac{5}{x^3}$. (U.E.I.)

6. Find $\dfrac{dy}{dx}$ if

$$\text{(a) } y = x^3 + 2x^2 + 4, \quad \text{(b) } y = 6x^{3\cdot2} - \frac{2}{x},$$
$$\text{(c) } y = x(x^2 + 3)(x - 4).$$

(U.L.C.I.)

7. (a) Find from first principles the value of $\dfrac{dy}{dx}$ if $y = 3x^2 + 2x + 6$.

(b) Write down the value of $\dfrac{dp}{dv}$ at the point where $v = 6$, if $pv^2 = 100$. (U.L.C.I.)

8. (a) Find $\dfrac{dy}{dx}$ in the following cases:

$$\text{(i) } y = 4x^2 + x, \quad \text{(ii) } y = \frac{3(x + 2)^2}{x}.$$

(b) At what points on the curve $y = 3x^3 - 36x + 20$ is the slope $\left(\dfrac{dy}{dx}\right)$ equal to (i) 2, (ii) 0? (U.L.C.I.)

9. From first principles find $\dfrac{dy}{dx}$ if $y = x^2 + 2x$.

Write down $\dfrac{dy}{dx}$

$$\text{(i) when } y = 29x^{0\cdot7} + 5, \quad \text{(ii) when } y = \frac{3x^2 - 2}{x^3}.$$

(U.L.C.I.)

10. The equation to a curve is $y = Kx^{\frac{1}{3}}$. Find K so that $x = 8$, $y = 3$ is a point on the curve. Find the gradient of the curve at this point.   (U.L.C.I.)

11. The equation of a curve is given by

$$y = \frac{x^3}{3} - 3x^2 + 5x + 4.$$

Find an expression which will give the slope of the curve at any point on it.

What are the co-ordinates of the points on the curve (i) where the curve is horizontal, (ii) and one point where it is inclined at 45°?   (U.L.C.I.)

12. The curve $y = \dfrac{a}{x} + bx^2$ passes through the point $x = 3$, $y = 16\cdot5$, and the value of $\dfrac{dy}{dx}$ at this point is (-1). Find the values of the constants a and b.   (U.L.C.I.)

13. Find from first principles the value of $\dfrac{dy}{dx}$ when $y = 3x^2$.

Find $\dfrac{dy}{dx}$ when:

$$(a)\ y = + \frac{1}{x}, \quad (b)\ y = A\left(\frac{l}{2} - x\right)\left(\frac{l}{2} + x\right).$$

(U.L.C.I.)

See also Exercise 28A—Miscellaneous.

3. Repeated Differentiation

If $y = 3x^3 - 2x^2 + 1$ . . . . (1)

we have $\dfrac{dy}{dx} = 9x^2 - 4x$ . . . . . (2)

Observe that $\dfrac{dy}{dx}$ is itself a function of x. Hence like y it may be differentiated.

For two differentiations we use the notation $\dfrac{d^2y}{dx^2}$. This is called the second derivative.

From (2) above we have:

$$\frac{d^2y}{dx^2} = 18x - 4. \quad \cdot \quad \cdot \quad \cdot \quad \cdot \quad \cdot \quad (3)$$

Continuing from (3) we see that:

$$\frac{d^3y}{dx^3} = 18, \text{ which is a constant,}$$

so that $\dfrac{d^4y}{dx^4} = 0$

as are all subsequent derivatives.

Example 1

$$y = 5x^2 + 3x + 4$$
$$\frac{dy}{dx} = 10x + 3,$$
$$\frac{d^2y}{dx^2} = 10,$$
$$\frac{d^3y}{dx^3} = 0.$$

Another notation for derivatives of $y = f(x)$ is $f'(x)$ for $\dfrac{dy}{dx}$, $f''(x)$ for $\dfrac{d^2y}{dx^2}$, etc.

Example 2

If $f(x) = 3x^3 - 4x + 1$
$$f'(x) = 9x^2 - 4$$
$$f''(x) = 18x.$$

EXERCISE 18

1. If $y = 3x^4 - 6x^2 + 2x - 1$, find $\dfrac{dy}{dx}$ and $\dfrac{d^2y}{dx^2}$.

2. Given $f(t) = \dfrac{3t^3 - 5t^2 + 2t - 3}{t}$, find $f''(t)$.

3. If $y = 3\theta^2 - 5\theta + 6$, find $\dfrac{d^2y}{d\theta^2}$.

4. Find the first differential coefficient to vanish if:

(a) $y = 5x^4 - 3x^2 + 7x + 1$.

(b) $y = \dfrac{3x^5 - 7x^4 + 3x^2}{2x^2}$.

5. If $f(x) = 3x^3 - 4x^2 + 3x - 6$, find the point on the curve where $f''(x) = 0$.

4. Function of a Function of x

Example 1

Suppose that we have to differentiate a function y, where

$$y = (x^2 - 4)^6$$

We might of course raise $(x^2 - 4)$ to the sixth power. We should obtain a long expression commencing with a term x^{12}. This we could differentiate term by term, and so obtain the desired differential coefficient. In so doing we should be ignoring the help which the **form** of the expression (see p. 108) might give us. Let us then think first of all of the function as a sixth power, an aspect of the problem which is emphasised if we write

$y = z^6$, where, of course,
$z = x^2 - 4$.

We may now think of z as an independent variable, this giving

$$\frac{dy}{dz} = 6z^5,$$

and we know that

$$\frac{dz}{dx} = 2x.$$

The rule for differentiating " a function of a function " tells us that

$$\frac{dy}{dx} = \frac{dy}{dz} \times \frac{dz}{dx};\, *$$

that is, in the case which we are considering

$$\frac{dy}{dx} = 6z^5 \times 2x$$
$$= 12x(x^2 - 4)^5.$$

As a slight check notice that the first term of the differential is $12x^{11}$, which is also the first term of the expression which we should obtain by expanding $(x^2 - 4)^6$ as $x^{12} + \ldots$, and differentiating each term in turn with regard to x.

A **function** of a **function** is one of the useful forms, and the " z substitution " for a function of x is very commonly employed.

Example 2

$$y = (x^2 - 5x + 2)^3. \quad \text{We require } \frac{dy}{dx}.$$

Put
$$z = x^2 - 5x + 2$$

$$\therefore \quad \frac{dz}{dx} = 2x - 5$$

$$y = z^3$$

and
$$\frac{dy}{dx} = \frac{dy}{dz} \cdot \frac{dz}{dx} = 3z^2 \cdot (2x - 5)$$
$$= 3(x^2 - 5x + 2)^2(2x - 5).$$

* The rule is self-evident if we consider Δz as a small change in z following upon Δx a small change in x. Let Δz lead to a small change Δy.

Then
$$\frac{\Delta y}{\Delta x} = \frac{\Delta y}{\Delta z} \times \frac{\Delta z}{\Delta x}$$

since the increments Δz cancel. Proceeding to the limit when Δx and consequently Δz approaches 0, as also does Δy,

$$\frac{dy}{dx} = \frac{dy}{dz} \times \frac{dz}{dx}.$$

5. The " Formal " Aspect of Differentiation

Here the word " formal " is not used to indicate a style, but in its literal sense, in reference to the **form** of the expression to be differentiated.

There is no necessity for the substitution employed in the last paragraph if the formal aspect of differentiation is recognised.

Consider

$$y = x^n \\ \frac{dy}{dx} = nx^{n-1} \Bigg\} \quad \cdot \quad \cdot \quad \cdot \quad \cdot \quad \cdot \quad (1)$$

The formal meaning of (1) will be clear if we write:

$$y = (\quad)^n \\ \frac{dy}{d(\quad)} \cdot = n(\quad)^{n-1} \Bigg\} \cdot \quad \cdot \quad \cdot \quad \cdot \quad (2)$$

where any function of x may be written in the bracket. —*i.e.*, the " form " of (1) holds no matter what expression be put for x.

Hence if

$$y = (x^2 - 4)^6$$

$$\frac{dy}{dx} = \frac{dy}{d(\quad)} \cdot \frac{d(\quad)}{dx} = 6(x^2 - 4)^5 \cdot 2x.$$

With a little practice examples like the above may be done very readily, and the second step—putting in the brackets—may be omitted.

Example 3

$$y = \frac{1}{x^2 + a^2} = (x^2 + a^2)^{-1}$$

$$\frac{dy}{dx} = -1 \cdot (x^2 + a^2)^{-2} \cdot 2x$$

In the above

$$\frac{dy}{d(\quad)} = -1(x^2 + a^2)^{-2}$$

and

$$\frac{d(\quad)}{dx} = 2x.$$

EXERCISE 19

Differentiate the following functions of x:

(a) By first putting each bracket $= z$, finding $\dfrac{dz}{dx}$, and then using the equation

$$\frac{dy}{dx} = \frac{dy}{dz} \cdot \frac{dz}{dx}.$$

(b) Without using the above substitution of z.

1. $(x^2 + x)^3$.
2. $(3x^2 - 5x + 6)^4$.
3. $(x^2 + 3)^5$.
4. $\dfrac{1}{(x^2 + 3x + 4)}$.
5. $\dfrac{1}{(x + 3)}$.
6. $\dfrac{1}{(x^2 + 3)^2}$.
7. $\dfrac{4}{(x^3 - 3x + 1)^4}$.
8. $(x^2 - 1{\cdot}3x + 4)^3$.
9. $\dfrac{1}{\sqrt{x^2 + 3}}$.
10. $\dfrac{4}{\sqrt[3]{2x^2 + x + 1}}$.

See also Exercise 28A—Miscellaneous.

6. Differentiation of a Product

If $y = (x^2 + 4)^3 \cdot (x + 2)^2$, it would be very tiresome to expand each bracket and then perform the multiplication before differentiating.

We now establish a formula which enables us to differentiate products such as this.

Let $y = u \cdot v$, where u and v are functions of x.

Let x increase to $x + h$, i.e., to $x + \Delta x$.

Then u and v become $(u + \Delta u)$ and $(v + \Delta v)$ respectively, whilst y becomes $y + \Delta y$.

Since $\qquad y = uv \; . \; . \; . \; . \; . \; . \; . \; . \; . \quad (1)$

$\therefore \quad y + \Delta y = (u + \Delta u)(v + \Delta v)$

$\qquad\qquad = uv + v\Delta u + u\Delta v + \Delta u \cdot \Delta v \quad . \quad (2)$

Subtract (1) from (2) and get:

$$\Delta y = v\Delta u + u\Delta v + \Delta u \,.\, \Delta v$$

$$\therefore \quad \frac{\Delta y}{\Delta x} = v\frac{\Delta u}{\Delta x} + u\frac{\Delta v}{\Delta x} + \frac{\Delta u}{\Delta x} \,.\, \Delta v \quad . \quad . \quad (3)$$

Notice that the last term involves the product of $\frac{\Delta u}{\Delta x}$ and a differential Δv.

Now let $\Delta x \longrightarrow 0$. Then $\Delta v \longrightarrow 0$, and the last term on the right-hand side of (3) $\longrightarrow 0$, and (3) becomes

$$\frac{dy}{dx} = v\frac{du}{dx} + u\frac{dv}{dx}.$$

$$\therefore \quad \frac{d(uv)}{dx} = u\frac{dv}{dx} + v\frac{du}{dx} \quad . \quad . \quad (4)$$

(4) may be remembered thus:

(D.C. product) = (First factor × D.C. second)
            + (Second factor × D.C. first).

Either of the two factors of uv may be called the " first factor," since $uv = vu$.

This rule is rather more easily remembered by sound; *i.e.*, by saying " Diff. Co. of a product uv equals $w\frac{dv}{dx} + v\frac{du}{dx}$."

Example 1

$$y = x^3(x^2 + 6x + 3)$$

$$\frac{dy}{dx} = 3x^2(x^2 + 6x + 3) + x^3(2x + 6) \quad . \quad (5)$$

$$= 5x^4 + 24x^3 + 9x^2.$$

Example 2

$$y = x^3 \,.\, (x^2 + 4)^4$$

$$\frac{dy}{dx} = 3x^2(x^2 + 4)^4 + x^3 \,.\, 4(x^2 + 4)^3 \,.\, 2x \quad . \quad (6)$$

$$\left[\text{N.B.} \quad \frac{d}{dx}(x^2 + 4)^4 = 4(x^2 + 4)^3 \,.\, 2x \right]$$

Simplifying (6) we get:

$$\frac{dy}{dx} = x^2(x^2 + 4)^3\{3(x^2 + 4) + 8x^2\}$$
$$= x^2(x^2 + 4)^3(11x^2 + 12).$$

Example 3

$$y = \frac{2x^2}{(x + 5)}.$$

Notice　$y = 2x^2 \times (x + 5)^{-1}$

$$\therefore \quad \frac{dy}{dx} = 4x \times (x + 5)^{-1} + (-1)(x + 5)^{-2} \times 2x^2$$

$$= \frac{4x}{x + 5} - \frac{2x^2}{(x + 5)^2}$$

This example shows how a quotient may be treated as a product.

EXERCISE 20

Differentiate the following products:

1. $x^2(x^2 + 3x + 6)$.　　　　2. $x^{\frac{3}{2}}(x^2 + 5x - 2)$.
3. (i) $x^2(x^2 + 3x + 6)^2$, (ii) $x^5(x - 1)^4$.
4. (i) $3x^{-3}(x^2 + 2)^4$, (ii) $t^{-\frac{1}{2}}(t + 3)^3$.
5. (i) $x^4(x^2 + 3)^{-2}$, (ii) $2x^2(1 - x^2)^{-2}$, (iii) $3x(2 - x)^{-4}$.
6. (i) $\dfrac{x}{(x + 2)^2}$,　　(ii) $\dfrac{3x^2}{1 - x}$,　　　(iii) $\dfrac{1}{x^2(x + 3)}$,

　　(iv) $\dfrac{x^2 + x + 2}{(x + 1)^2}$,　(v) $\dfrac{t^2 + 3}{(1 + t + t^2)^2}$.

See also Exercise 28A—Miscellaneous.

7. The Differential Coefficient of a Quotient

The formula for differentiating a quotient could be obtained from that for a product.

We will, however, get it directly.

Let　$y = \dfrac{u}{v}$, where u and v are functions of x.

Let x change to $x + \Delta x$. Then, proceeding as for the product, we get

$$y + \Delta y = \frac{u + \Delta u}{v + \Delta v}$$

$$\therefore \quad \Delta y = \frac{u + \Delta u}{v + \Delta v} - \frac{u}{v}$$

$$= \frac{v(u + \Delta u) - u(v + \Delta v)}{(v + \Delta v)(v)}$$

$$= \frac{v\,\Delta u - u\,\Delta v}{(v + \Delta v)v}$$

$$\therefore \quad \frac{\Delta y}{\Delta x} = \frac{v\dfrac{\Delta u}{\Delta x} - u\dfrac{\Delta v}{\Delta x}}{(v + \Delta v)\,.\,v} \quad . \quad . \quad . \quad . \quad . \quad (1)$$

Now let $\Delta x \longrightarrow 0$. Then $(v + \Delta v) \longrightarrow v$

and (1) becomes $\dfrac{dy}{dx} = \dfrac{v\dfrac{du}{dx} - u\dfrac{dv}{du}}{v_2}.$

i.e., $$\frac{d}{dx}\left(\frac{u}{v}\right) = \frac{v\dfrac{du}{dx} - u\dfrac{dv}{dx}}{v^2} \quad . \quad . \quad . \quad . \quad . \quad (2)$$

This formula may be remembered in words, thus:

(D.C. quotient) =

$$\frac{(\text{Denom.} \times \text{D.C. numerator}) - (\text{Numerator} \times \text{D.C. Denom.})}{(\text{Denom.})^2}$$

or, as for the product, by voicing the formula:

" Diff. Co. of a quotient $\dfrac{u}{v} = v\dfrac{du}{dx} - u\dfrac{dv}{dx}$, all over v^2."

Example 1

$$y = \frac{x - a}{x + a}$$

$$\frac{dy}{dx} = \frac{(x + a) - (x \times a)}{(x + a)^2}$$

$$= \frac{2a}{(x + a)^2}.$$

Example 2

$$y = \frac{(a-x)^2}{a^2+x^2}$$

$$\frac{dy}{dx} = \frac{(a^2+x^2) \cdot 2(a-x) \cdot (-1) - (a-x)^2 \cdot 2x}{(a^2+x^2)^2}$$

$$= \frac{-2(a-x)\{a^2+x^2+x(a-x)\}}{(a^2+x^2)^2}$$

$$= \frac{-2(a-x)(a^2+ax)}{(a^2+x^2)^2}$$

$$= \frac{-2a(a^2-x^2)}{(a^2+x^2)^2}.$$

EXERCISE 21

Differentiate the following quotients:

1. $\dfrac{x}{x+a}$.

2. $\dfrac{x^2-a^2}{x^2+a^2}$.

3. $\dfrac{x^2+2x+2}{x+1}$.

4. $\dfrac{\sqrt{x}}{x+2}$.

5. $\dfrac{3x^2}{x+2}$.

6. $\dfrac{5x^2}{(x^2+1)^2}$.

7. $\sqrt{\dfrac{1+x}{1-x}}$.

8. $\sqrt[3]{\dfrac{5x^2+3}{x+2}}$.

See also Exercise 28A—Miscellaneous.

8. Differentiation of an Implicit Function of x

If we consider the two equations:

$$y = 3x^2 + 2x + 1 \quad . \quad . \quad . \quad (1)$$

and $\qquad x^2 + y^2 = 9 \quad . \quad . \quad . \quad . \quad . \quad . \quad (2)$

we notice that in (1), the two variables x and y appear on opposite sides of the equation; they are not mixed together, as in equation (2).

In (1) y is given as an explicit function of x.

In (2) it is " implicit " that y is a function of x.

In the simple case considered above in (2) it is seen that we could write:

$$y^2 = 9 - x^2$$

i.e.,
$$y = \pm \sqrt{9 - x^2}$$

where y becomes an explicit function of x which can readily be differentiated.

In other cases it may become tedious to express y explicitly in terms of x, yet we may require the value of $\frac{dy}{dx}$: we may then proceed as follows:

If
$$z = y^2$$

$$\frac{dz}{dx} = \frac{dz}{dy} \cdot \frac{dy}{dx} = 2y \cdot \frac{dy}{dx}$$

i.e.,
$$\frac{d}{dx}(y^2) = 2y\frac{dy}{dx} \quad . \quad . \quad . \quad . \quad . \quad . \quad (3)$$

Similarly,
$$\frac{d}{dx}(y^3) = 3y^2 \cdot \frac{dy}{dx} \quad . \quad . \quad . \quad . \quad . \quad (4)$$

Return now to (2),

$$x^2 + y^2 = 9.$$

If we differentiate with respect to x, we get:

$$2x + 2y\frac{dy}{dx} = 0, \ i.e., \ \frac{dy}{dx} = -\frac{x}{y}.$$

Again, suppose we require $\frac{d}{dx}(x^2 y^2)$, where y is regarded as some function of x.

Differentiating as a product, we get:

$$\frac{d}{dx}(x^2 y^2) = x^2 \cdot 2y\frac{dy}{dx} + 2x \cdot y^2 \quad . \quad . \quad (5)$$

Example

The point $(1, 1)$ clearly lies on the circle whose equation is:

$$x^2 + y^2 + 2x + 4y - 8 = 0 \quad . \quad . \quad (6)$$

Find the gradient of the tangent at this point.

Differentiating (6) we get:

$$2x + 2y\frac{dy}{dx} + 2 + 4\frac{dy}{dx} = 0$$

i.e., $\frac{dy}{dx}(2y + 4) = -2x - 2 = -2(x + 1)$

$$\therefore \ \frac{dy}{dx} = -\frac{x + 1}{y + 2}.$$

Now put $x = 1$, $y = 1$, and we see that the required gradient is $-\frac{2}{3}$.

EXERCISE 22

Differentiate with respect to x:

1. $3x^{1\cdot2} - 4\sqrt{x} + \dfrac{3}{x^3}$.   2. $(2x - 3)^3$.

3. $\sqrt{x - 4}$.

4. $\dfrac{1}{(x + a)^2}$.

5. $\dfrac{5}{\sqrt{4x - 2}}$.

6. $\sqrt{5 - 6x}$.

7. $(3 - x^2)^4$.   8. $(3x^2 - 2x + 2)^4$.

9. $x\sqrt{x + a}$.   10. $x^3(x + a)^3$.

11. $2x^5(x^2 + 2x + 3)^2$.   12. $\sqrt[4]{(x^2 - a^2)^3}$.

13. $\dfrac{1}{\sqrt[3]{x^2 + x + 1}}$.   14. $\dfrac{3x^2 + 2x + 1}{x + 2}$.

15. $\dfrac{x^3}{\sqrt{x + 1}}$.   16. $\dfrac{2x^2 - 1}{x^2 + 3}$.

17. $\sqrt{\dfrac{3 - x}{2 + x}}$.

Find the gradients of the tangents at the points indicated on the following curves:

18. $y = 3x^2 - x + 1$ at $(1, 3)$ and $(2, 11)$.

19. $y = \dfrac{x^2}{x + 1}$ at $(2, \frac{4}{3})$ and $(1, \frac{1}{2})$.

Find $\dfrac{dy}{dx}$ from the following equations:

20. $x^2 + y^2 = 6$.
21. $x^2 + 3xy + 4 = 0$.
22. $x^2 + y^2 + 3x + 4y + 1 = 0$.

See also Exercise 28A—Miscellaneous.

9. This chapter has been devoted to the general problem: " given a function, how can we obtain its differential coefficient? " In all the examples so far considered, the way in which the function was related to the independent variable could be expressed by an algebraic formula; and we have now learned to use such formulæ in finding the differential coefficient or *derived* function. If the relation between the function, or dependent variable, y, and the independent variable x, is not a simple algebraic one, there are other functional relations which can be expressed in symbols, *e.g.*, $y = \log x$, $y = \sin x$, etc. For all such ways of defining a functional relation we shall learn (as we have already learned for $y = x^m$, etc.) how to find by means of paper work, the differential coefficient of y with respect to x.

Often, however, a quantity y is a function of an independent variable x, but does not depend upon it according to any such rule as we have been discussing. In this event, although, we may not be able to express y as an algebraic function of x, and thus arrive at an *expression* (a formula, if you like) for the derivative, the derived function will exist, and have its customary significance.

An example may be found in the volume V cu ft of water stored in a reservoir provided with a single connection through which it is sometimes filling, sometimes emptying. Here time elapsed is the independent variable. We know that $V = f(t)$, but in any practical example we are unable to define $f(t)$ more closely. We just know that as time goes on the volume of water in store is likely to be changing continually.

Now suppose that in the single connection to the reservoir
a water meter is inserted to indicate the rate of flow—in or
out as the case may be.   It should be clear that although

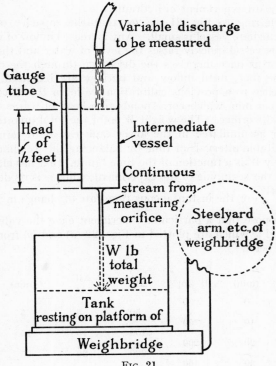

Variable discharge
to be measured

Gauge
tube

Head
of
h feet

Intermediate
vessel

Continuous
stream from
measuring
orifice

Steelyard
arm, etc., of
weighbridge

W lb
total
weight

Tank
resting on platform of

Weighbridge

Fig. 21.

we have no expression for the function $f(t)$ the meter reading
is the derivative: it is in fact $\dfrac{dV}{dt}$.   Thus we know a particular value of a derived function without any process of
algebra, but instead by direct observation.

It may be easier to follow a diagram of laboratory apparatus than a drawing of an actual reservoir, so Fig. 21 is a diagram of apparatus set up to measure by weight some discharge of water—perhaps from a steam-engine test, or maybe an experiment in hydraulics.

Referring to Fig. 21 we see that the capacity of the intermediate vessel is small.   Any increased inflow of water to this vessel quickly raises the level of water and thereby almost at once increases the discharge through the orifice at the foot, until inflow and outflow are balanced.   By reference to a previous calibration we learn the discharge w lb per min, which corresponds to a head of water h feet over the orifice.   The weight W lb of the total quantity of water accumulated in the lower tank can be determined at suitable intervals of time by balancing the weighbridge. Clearly W is a function of the time t (min.) that has elapsed since the beginning of the experiment, while w is its derivative $\dfrac{dW}{dt}$, or the instantaneous time rate of change in W.

Suppose that a particular experiment gave the values of W and w which are plotted in Figs. 22 (a) and (b) from the table below.

t (min)	W (lb)	ΔW	$\dfrac{\Delta W}{\Delta t}$	t (min)
0	0			
		50	5	5
10	50			
		150	15	15
20	200			
		200	20	25
30	400			
		200	20	35
40	600			
		225	22·5	45
50	825			
		275	27·5	55
60	1100			

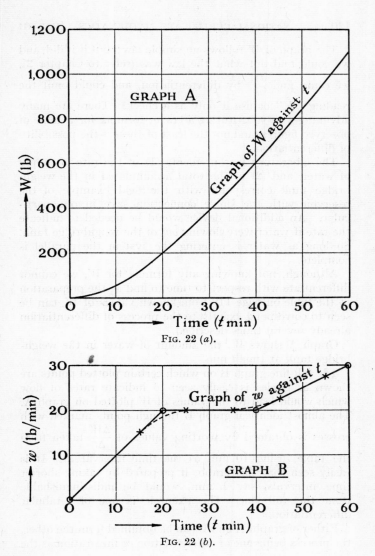

GRAPH A

Graph of W against t

W (lb)

Time (t min)

FIG. 22 (a).

Graph of w against t

GRAPH B

w (lb/min)

Time (t min)

FIG. 22 (b).

The graph of W follows no simple law; but if it did, and we could find out what the law was (refer to Chapter 2), we could find $\dfrac{dW}{dt}$ by differentiation, and could omit the reading " h " or use it only as a check.   There are many advantages in substituting a law or formula for a table of observed figures, and not the least of these is the possibility of differentiation.

The laboratory measurements (1) of the rate of supply of water, and (2) of the total accumulated in the weigh-bridge tank correspond with the field example of the reservoir with the single connection save in one particular.   An additional device would be needed to indicate the rate if water were flowing *out* of the weighbridge tank. So long as water is entering the system the parallel is complete.

Although, not knowing any formula for W, we cannot differentiate with respect to time to find w, the preparation of the table on page 118 from known values of W, can be seen to correspond exactly to the process of differentiation already several times described.

Graph A shows W, the amount of water in the weigh-bridge tank at time t min.

The full-line graph B on which certain plotted points are shown as circles is easily seen to indicate rates of flow which would lead to the values of W plotted on graph A. The almost identical graph B through points marked with crosses is obtained by plotting values of $\dfrac{\Delta W}{\Delta t}$ taken from the table, using 10 min as the time interval Δt.   It is easily seen that this graph, if prepared by taking shorter time intervals, say 1 min, would be indistinguishable from the full line.   The example is one of " tabular differentiation."

Either of graphs A and B can be obtained from the other, the process being one of differentiation or integration as the case may be.   Ordinates on graph A are seen to correspond to areas on graph B.

Having thus examined the processes of differentiation and integration without reference to algebraic expressions let us return to consideration of the important functional relations which *can* be expressed in symbols.

CHAPTER 6

DIFFERENTIATION REVERSED. INTEGRATION

1. In the previous chapter we were given certain functions of a variable, usually x, and we learned how to obtain the derivative or differential coefficient of the function.

In this chapter we learn how, in certain cases, to reverse the process.

We are given the derivative, and we try to find the original function.

2. If $\quad y = f(x)$

$$\frac{dy}{dx} = \underset{h \to 0}{\text{Lt}} \frac{f(x+h) - f(x)}{h} = \underset{\Delta x \to 0}{\text{Lt}} \frac{\Delta y}{\Delta x}.$$

Hence the relationship

$$\frac{dy}{dx} = \underset{\Delta x \to 0}{\text{Lt}} \frac{\Delta y}{\Delta x}$$

is always true, whilst the statement

$$\frac{dy}{dx} = \frac{\Delta y}{\Delta x}$$

becomes more nearly so (though not strictly true unless the graph of y is a straight line) the closer Δx tends to zero.

Hence $\Delta y = \dfrac{dy}{dx} \cdot \Delta x$ as $\Delta x \longrightarrow 0$, and in any case, when Δx is small, this expression gives a close approximation to the change in y corresponding to the small change Δx in x.

From the relationship

$$\Delta y = \frac{dy}{dx} \cdot \Delta x \quad . \quad . \quad . \quad . \quad (1)$$

which is widely used for the calculation of small corrections assuming that the ratio $\frac{\Delta y}{\Delta x}$ is actually equal to $\frac{dy}{dx}$ we see that $\frac{dy}{dx}$ is the coefficient of the " differential ", Δx, and it is for this reason that it is called a " differential coefficient ".

We may at this stage safely drop the Δ in (1) and write it:

$$dy = \frac{dy}{dx} \cdot dx \quad . \quad . \quad . \quad . \quad (2)$$

and may refer to dx and dy as the differentials of x and of y, respectively. In so doing we are treating them as distinct quantities, although the complete symbol $\frac{dy}{dx}$ is not itself divisible into a numerator and denominator, but is a limit.

If, for example, we now differentiate both sides of the equation

$$y = x^4$$

we get:

$$\frac{dy}{dx} = 4x^3 \quad . \quad . \quad . \quad . \quad (3)$$

Hence from (2):

$$dy = 4x^3 \cdot dx \quad . \quad . \quad . \quad (4)$$

Equation (3) tells us that $4x^3$ is the differential coefficient of x^4 with respect to x, whilst from (4) dy, the differential of x^4, is $4x^3 \cdot dx$.

3. Reversing the process of differentiation is called integration, and is indicated by using the symbol $\int$, an old-fashioned s, in front of a differential.*

Thus from

$$y = \frac{x^3}{3}$$

we get

$$dy = x^2 dx.$$

* The reason for the use of the term integration will become more and more apparent as we proceed. Already we can see that the **whole** expressed by any formula is made up of small elements such as we consider in differentiation.

Reversing the process:

$$\int x^2 dx = \frac{x^3}{3} . \quad . \quad . \quad . \quad . \quad . \quad (1)$$

Similarly, if
$$y = \frac{x^{n+1}}{n+1}$$
$$dy = x^n dx$$

and
$$\int x^n dx = \frac{x^{n+1}}{n+1}. \quad . \quad . \quad . \quad (2)$$

$\dfrac{x^{n+1}}{n+1}$ is called an integral of $x^n dx$.

From (1) and (2) of this paragraph the rule for integrating any power of x is seen to be

" Increase the index by one, and divide by the increased index."

4. The Constant of Integration or the Arbitrary Constant

Starting with
$$y = \frac{x^3}{3}$$

or with
$$y = \frac{x^3}{3} + C$$

where C is any constant we get $dy = x^2 dx$ in both cases.

Hence $\int x^2 dx = \dfrac{x^3}{3} + C$. This is the most general form of the integral. We do not know the value of the constant, and for this reason it is sometimes termed the Arbitrary Constant; it *must* be added each time we integrate. The need for the insertion of the constant of integration can be stated in this way: the differential coefficient expresses the rate at which some total is altering; it is determined by considering small additions to that total. Reversal of the process can give us the extent of the change over a substantive interval, but will not give us the value from which the change started.

Example 1

$$\int x^{\frac{1}{2}}dx = \tfrac{2}{3}x^{\frac{3}{2}} + \mathrm{C}.$$

Example 2

$$\int x^{-1 \cdot 02}dx = -\frac{x^{-0 \cdot 02}}{0 \cdot 02} + \mathrm{C}.$$

Example 3

$$\int \frac{1}{x^4} \cdot dx = \int x^{-4}dx = -\frac{x^{-3}}{3} + \mathrm{C}.$$
$$= -\frac{1}{3x^3} + \mathrm{C}.$$

Example 4

$$\int \frac{dx}{\sqrt[4]{x^3}} = \int \frac{dx}{x^{\frac{3}{4}}}$$
$$= \int x^{-\frac{3}{4}}dx$$
$$= 4x^{\frac{1}{4}} + \mathrm{C}.$$

Notice that we can always test the accuracy of our integration by differentiating the integral. Take the last example

$$\frac{d}{dx}(4x^{\frac{1}{4}} + \mathrm{C}) = x^{-\frac{3}{4}} = \frac{1}{\sqrt[4]{x^3}}.$$

Determination of the Constant of Integration

The constant can be determined if a corresponding pair of values of x and y are known. The following example indicates the method.

Example 5

If $dy = x^{-3}dx$, and $y = 3$ when $x = 2$, express y in terms of x.

We have
$$dy = x^{-3}dx$$
$$\therefore \quad y = \int x^{-3}dx$$
$$= \frac{x^{-2}}{-2} + C$$
$$= -\frac{1}{2x^2} + C.$$

Now put $x = 2$ and $y = 3$.
We get
$$C = 3 + \tfrac{1}{8} = \tfrac{25}{8}.$$
Hence
$$y = \tfrac{25}{8} - \frac{1}{2x^2}.$$

5. The Integration of a Sum

The differential coefficient of a sum of separate functions is the sum of their differential coefficients.   Hence, reversing the process, the integral of a sum of differentials will be the sum of their separate integrals.

Example 1

$$\int (x^3 + x^4)dx = \frac{x^4}{4} + \frac{x^5}{5} + C.$$

We need add only one constant.
There is no point in writing the integral as
$$\frac{x^4}{4} + C_1 + \frac{x^5}{5} + C_2$$

since the two constants combine into a single one.

Example 2

$$\int (x^2 - x^{-\frac{1}{2}} + x^{-3})dx = \frac{x^3}{3} - \frac{4}{3}x^{\frac{3}{4}} - \frac{x^{-2}}{2} + C.$$

6. A constant coefficient may be taken outside the integration sign.

Thus $\int 4x^3dx = 4\int x^3dx = 4 \cdot \dfrac{x^4}{4} + C$, *i.e.*, $= x^4 + C.$

Similarly, $\int ax^n dx = a \int x^n dx = \dfrac{ax^{n+1}}{n+1} + C.$

Example 1

$$\int (3x^2 - 4x + 2)dx = x^3 - 2x^2 + 2x + C.$$

Example 2

$$\int (1.3x^{2\cdot3} + 0.5x^{0\cdot3})dx = \frac{1\cdot3}{3\cdot3}x^{3\cdot3} + \frac{0\cdot5}{1\cdot3}x^{1\cdot3} + C$$
$$= 0.39x^{3\cdot3} + 0.38x^{1\cdot3} + C.$$

7. An Exception to the Rule for Integrating a Power of x

If we apply the rule for integrating a power of x to

$$\int \frac{dx}{x} = \int x^{-1}dx$$

we get $\dfrac{x^0}{0}$, *i.e.*, $\dfrac{1}{0}$, an expression that is meaningless.

The student must not infer that $\int \dfrac{dx}{x}$ is meaningless. We shall later show that

$$\int \frac{dx}{x} = \log_e x + C$$

a result that should be memorised.

EXERCISE 23

Integrate the following functions:

1. x^4.

2. $x^{\frac{1}{2}}$.

3. $x^{-\frac{3}{2}}$.

4. $\dfrac{1}{x^5}$.

5. $3x^5$.

6. $2x^{\frac{2}{3}}$.

7. $5x^{-\frac{1}{4}}$.

8. $\dfrac{4}{x^4}$.

9. $2x^{0\cdot6}$.

10. $3\cdot2x^{1\cdot3}$.

11. $\dfrac{2\cdot1}{x^{-3}}$.

12. $\dfrac{0\cdot1}{x^{1\cdot1}}$.

13. $(x^2 + 3x)$.   14. $\left(x^{1\cdot3} - x^{0\cdot4} + \dfrac{1}{2x^2}\right)$.

15. $\left(3x^2 + 2x^{-3} + \dfrac{1}{x^4}\right)$.   16. $(3x^{0\cdot2} + 2\cdot1x^{1\cdot3})$.

17. If $dy = 3x^4 dx$, express y in terms of x if $y = 4$ when $x = 1$.

18. If $ds = 3t^2 dt$, express s in terms of t, given that $s = 4$ when $t = 2$.

19. Given that $ds = (2t^2 + 5)dt$, and that $s = 2$ when $t = 3$, express as a function of t.

20. Integrate with respect to x:

$$(a)\ \frac{1}{2x^3}, \quad (b)\ \sqrt{2} - 4x^{0\cdot25}, \quad (c)\ \left(x - \frac{1}{x^3}\right)^2. \quad \text{(N.C.)}$$

21. Integrate (after simplifying where necessary) the following functions:

$(a)\ 6x^{\frac{3}{4}}$, $(b)\ 3 - 2x^{-0\cdot2}$, $(c)\ (x^3 - x^2)^2$, $(d)\ \dfrac{(x^2 - 1)(x^2 + 1)}{x^2}$

(U.L.C.I.)

22. Integrate (after simplifying where necessary):

$$(a)\ \frac{1}{2\sqrt{2x^3}}, \qquad (b)\ \pi - 5x^{-0\cdot5}, \qquad (c)\ 1 - \tfrac{1}{3}x^2 - \frac{1}{2\sqrt{x}},$$
$$(d)\ 8x(x^{\frac{1}{4}} + x^{-\frac{1}{4}})^2. \qquad \text{(N.C.)}$$

23. Integrate each of the following:

$$(a)\ \int \sqrt[3]{t^3}\,dt, \quad (b)\ \int\left(\frac{6}{\sqrt{x}} + 2\right)dx. \quad \text{(U.L.C.I.)}$$

See also Exercise 28A—Miscellaneous.

8. The " Formal " Aspect of Integration

We have previously drawn attention to the importance of **form** in differentiation.

It is equally important in integration. In fact the student must be warned at the beginning of his study of integration that his success in evaluating integrals will depend largely on his ability to recognise their **form**.

Consider $\qquad \int x^n dx = \dfrac{x^{n+1}}{n+1} + C.$

Under the sign of integration we notice a power, the nth, of x, followed by the differential of x. We could equally well say:

$$\int z^n dz = \frac{z^{n+1}}{n+1} + C,$$

where z may be a function of x, say $(x-3)$, in which case, substituting for z we have

$$\int (x-3)^n d(x-3) = \frac{(x-3)^{n+1}}{n+1} + C.$$

Now with experience we may write, or even just visualise

$$\int (\quad)^n d(\quad) = \frac{(\quad)^{n+1}}{n+1} + C \quad . \quad . \quad (1)$$

without needing to use the symbol z, or to write into the brackets any particular expression such as $(x-3)$. The incomplete statement (1) embodies the **form** of this particular process of integration. Of course when carrying out an actual integration the same function of x must be put into each bracket.

Example 1

$$I = \int (x-3)^2 dx \quad . \quad . \quad . \quad . \quad (1)$$

Notice dx is also $d(x-3)$, since the differential of the constant is zero.

$\therefore \quad I = \int (x-3)^2 d(x-3)$

$\qquad = \int z^2 dz$, making the " z " substitution for $(x-3)$.

$\qquad = \dfrac{z^3}{3} \quad$ or $\quad \dfrac{(x-3)^3}{3} + C.$

E

If the student will observe the **form** of (1), he can write down the value of the integral immediately.

Example 2

$$I = \int 2(x^2 + 5)^3 x dx.$$

We notice that $2xdx = d(x^2)$ or $d(x^2 + 5)$.

So, making the " z " substitution

$$I = \int \frac{z^3}{4} dz$$
$$= \frac{z^4}{4} + C,$$

which is $\dfrac{(x^2 + 5)^4}{4} + C.$

Alternatively we could omit the substitution and write

$$\therefore \quad I = \int (x^2 + 5)^3 d(x^2 + 5)$$

i.e., $\int (\quad)^3 d(\quad) = \dfrac{(x^2 + 5)^4}{4} + C.$

Example 3

$$I = \int (x^2 + a)^3 \cdot xdx$$

In this case $xdx = \tfrac{1}{2} d(x^2 + a)$

$$\therefore \quad I = \frac{1}{2} \int (x^2 + a)^3 d(x^2 + a)$$
$$= \frac{1}{2} \cdot \frac{(x^2 + a)^4}{4} + C.$$

It is always possible to evaluate integrals similar to the preceding in the following way:

Example 4

Put $I = \int (x^3 + 2)^3 x^2 dx$

Let
$$z = x^3 + 2$$
$$\therefore \quad dz = 3x^2 dx$$

i.e.,
$$x^2 dx = \frac{dz}{3}$$

$$\therefore \quad I = \int z^3 \cdot \frac{dz}{3} = \frac{1}{3} \int z^3 dz = \frac{z^4}{12} + C$$

i.e.,
$$I = \frac{(x^3 + 2)^4}{12} + C.$$

The student should, however, try to see the **form** of the integral at once, and should learn to recognise the differentials $x\,dx$, $x^2 dx$, $x^3 dx$, etc., as $\frac{1}{2}d(x^2 + \text{constant})$, $\frac{1}{3}d(x^3 + C)$, etc.

Example 5

$$I = \int \frac{x\,dx}{\sqrt{x^2 + a^2}}$$
$$= \frac{1}{2} \int (x^2 + a^2)^{-\frac{1}{2}} d(x^2 + a^2)$$
$$= \frac{1}{2} \cdot \frac{(x^2 + a^2)^{\frac{1}{2}}}{\frac{1}{2}} + C$$
$$= \sqrt{x^2 + a^2} + C.$$

EXERCISE 24

Evaluate

1. $\int (x + 3) dx$.   2. $\int (x + 4)^2 dx$.   3. $\int (5 + x)^{-4} dx$.

4. $\int \frac{dx}{(x + 3)^2}$.   5. $\int (x^2 + 3) \cdot 2x\,dx$.   6. $\int (x^2 + 3) x\,dx$.

7. $\int (x^2 - 1)^3 \cdot x\,dx$.   8. $\int (x^3 - 1) x^2 dx$.

9. $\int (x^3 + 3)^3 x^2 dx$.   10. $\int \frac{2x\,dx}{(x^2 + 5)^3}$.

11. $\int \frac{x\,dx}{(x^2 + 5)^4}$.   12. $\int \frac{3x^2 dx}{(x^3 - 2)^2}$.

13. $\int \dfrac{2x\,dx}{(\sqrt{x^2 + 3}\,)}$.

14. $\int \dfrac{x\,dx}{\sqrt[3]{x^2 + a^2}}$.

15. $\int \dfrac{(2x + 1)dx}{(x^2 + x + 3)^2}$.

16. $\int \dfrac{(3x^2 + 2x)dx}{(x^3 + x^2 + 1)^3}$.

See also Exercise 28A—Miscellaneous.

CHAPTER 7

SOME APPLICATIONS OF THE CALCULUS. MAXIMA AND MINIMA

1. Velocity and Acceleration

Suppose a body is moving in a straight line path; for example, a train moving on a level track, a stone falling vertically, or a weight vibrating at the end of a spring.

We can get expressions for the velocity and acceleration in the following way:

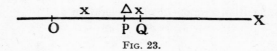

FIG. 23.

Suppose that O is a reference point in the line of motion OX. Let P be the position of the body at time t, and Q the position at time $t + \Delta t$. Then OP $= x$, PQ $= \Delta x$, and $\dfrac{\Delta x}{\Delta t}$ is the average velocity over the distance PQ.

Now, as $\Delta t \longrightarrow 0$, Q $\longrightarrow$ P; and the actual velocity at P is $\mathrm{Lt}\dfrac{\Delta x}{\Delta t}$ or $\dfrac{dx}{dt}$.

Hence $$\boldsymbol{v} = \frac{\boldsymbol{dx}}{\boldsymbol{dt}} \quad . \quad . \quad . \quad . \quad . \quad (1)$$

The relationship between acceleration and velocity is analogous to that between velocity and distance. We thus infer that:

Acceleration at P $$= \frac{\boldsymbol{dv}}{\boldsymbol{dt}} = \frac{\boldsymbol{d^2x}}{\boldsymbol{dt^2}} \quad . \quad . \quad . \quad (2)$$

133

Notice also that

$$\frac{dv}{dt} = \frac{dv}{dx} \cdot \frac{dx}{dt} = \frac{dv}{dx} \cdot c \text{ or } \frac{vdv}{dx} \quad . \quad . \quad . \quad (3)$$

All the expressions in (1), (2) and (3) are widely used.

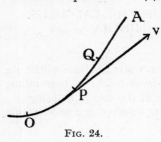

FIG. 24.

Should the body be moving in a curve, OA, let the length of the arc OP be s, where O is a reference point on the curve. If PQ $= \Delta s$, we get by reasoning similar to that in the last paragraph, that velocity at P

$$= v = \frac{ds}{dt}$$

and tangential component of acceleration at P

$$= \frac{dv}{dt} = \frac{d^2s}{dt^2} = \frac{vdv}{ds}.$$

There is also a component along the normal at P.

Example 1

Suppose a body is moving in a straight line, and its distance x from a fixed point O in the line, at any time t, is given by

$$x = 3t^2 - 2t + 1 \quad . \quad . \quad . \quad . \quad . \quad (1)$$

Then

$$v = \frac{dx}{dt} = 6t - 2 \quad . \quad . \quad . \quad . \quad (2)$$

and

$$\frac{dv}{dt} = \frac{d^2x}{dt^2} = 6 \quad . \quad . \quad . \quad . \quad . \quad (3)$$

From (3) we infer that the body has a constant acceleration of 6 ft/sec^2.

From (2) we deduce the velocity at any time.

Put $t = 3$, we get $\frac{dx}{dt} = 16$—*i.e.*, $v = 16$ ft/sec, after the body has moved for 3 secs.

Example 2

A body moving along a straight path passes a fixed point O of the path with a velocity of 12 ft/sec, and t sec later, when it is s ft from O, its acceleration is given by $\frac{d^2s}{dt^2} = 6t$.   Find the velocity of the body when $t = 4$, and its distance from O at that instant.   (U.L.C.I.)

We have
$$\frac{d^2s}{dt^2} = \frac{dv}{dt} = 6t$$

$$\therefore \quad dv = 6t\,dt$$

and
$$v = 3t^2 + C \quad . \quad . \quad . \quad . \quad (1)$$

When $v = 12$, $t = 0$ if we measure time from the instant the body was at the point O of the path.

$$\therefore \qquad C = 12.$$

Hence, from (1)
$$v = 3t^2 + 12 \quad . \quad . \quad . \quad . \quad (2)$$

i.e.,
$$\frac{ds}{dt} = 3t^2 + 12$$

$$\therefore \quad ds = (3t^2 + 12)dt$$

and
$$s = t^3 + 12t + C_1 \quad . \quad . \quad . \quad (3)$$

Now, when $t = 0$, the body was the point O.   Hence putting $s = 0$ and $t = 0$ in (3), we find $C_1 = 0$.

$$\therefore \quad s = t^3 + 12t \quad . \quad . \quad . \quad . \quad (4)$$

When
$$t = 4, \text{ we get}$$
$$v = 60 \text{ ft/sec [from (2)]}$$

and
$$s = 112 \text{ ft [from (4)]}$$

Example 3

If s is a function of t such that $\frac{d^2s}{dt^2}$ is inversely proportional to t^2, and the value of $\frac{ds}{dt}$ is 5 when $t = 1$, and 7 when $t = 3$, express $\frac{ds}{dt}$ as a function of t.   (N.C.T.E.C.)

We have $$\frac{d^2s}{dt^2} = \frac{dv}{dt} = \frac{k}{t^2}.$$

Integrating once,

$$v = \frac{ds}{dt} = \int \frac{k}{t^2} dt = -\frac{k}{t} + C \quad . \quad . \quad . \quad . \quad (1)$$

Now putting the given values in (1) we get

$$5 = -k + C$$

$$7 = -\frac{k}{3} + C.$$

These are two simultaneous equations for k and C. Solving, we find $k = 3$ and $C = 8$.

Substituting in (1) $\frac{ds}{dt} = -\frac{3}{t} + 8$.

EXERCISE 25

1. A body moves in a straight line, and its distance s ft from a fixed point O in the line is given by

$$s = 3t^2 - t + 2,$$

where t is the time in secs.

Find (1) How far the body was from O at zero time.

(2) Its velocity six seconds later.

(3) When its velocity vanishes.

(4) Its acceleration.

(5) Its average velocity from $t = 3$ to $t = 5$.

2. If s is a function of t such that $\frac{ds}{dt}$ is proportional to $\sqrt{t}$, and the value of s increases by 31 whilst the value of t increases from $+ 4$ to $+ 12\frac{1}{4}$, find the increase in the value of s whilst the value of t increases from $12\frac{1}{4}$ to 25. Find also the average rate of increase of s with respect to t for the interval $t = \frac{1}{4}$ to $t = 4$.   (N.C.T.E.C.)

3. If $s = 8 + 108t - t^3$, where s and t have the same meaning as in question (1), find (a) the velocity, (b) the

acceleration, (c) when and where the body stops and reverses the direction of motion.

4. If $s = t^3 + 2t^2 + 4t - 10$, plot a velocity time graph for the interval $t = 1$ to $t = 4$. From the graph, find the acceleration at time $t = 2\cdot5$. Compare the value you obtain with the value calculated from the given equation.

5. The distance covered s (ft) in time t sec is given by

$$s = 200t - 16t^2.$$

Find the velocity at $t = 1$, 2, 3, 4, 5 and 6 sec. Plot velocity vertically against time horizontally. From this velocity time curve find the acceleration by a graphic construction.   (U.E.I.)

See also Exercise 28A—Miscellaneous.

2. Further General Note on Integration

When we " integrate " a function, in general a summation is implied, as both the word and the sign of integration $\left(\int \right)$ suggest. The expression $\int y dx$ means in fact the sum (between limiting values of x) of all their strips of area $y\Delta x$. So we may regard integration as the summation of elementary areas on a graph, the height y of any particular element of area depending upon what function y is of x.

Often, however, not even a mental process of summation is needed in order to assign meaning to an integral or an expression containing integrals. Displacement, velocity and acceleration, are all familiar terms whose meaning need not be laboured. All three are concerned with distance and the second and third with time as well. Now since velocity is $\dfrac{ds}{dt}$, obtained by differentiation, the integration of an expression containing velocity (by reversing the process of differentiation) will lead to an expression containing a displacement term. Also, since acceleration is

$\frac{dv}{dt}$, obtained by differentiation, the integration of an expression containing acceleration will lead to an expression containing a velocity term. In this case the original function, and the first and second derived functions, all express familiar named conceptions, and convey their meanings to us directly.

We still need, however, to think of the constant of integration. Given some formula or equation for the acceleration of a body, before we can use it to find by integration the velocity at a particular time, we must know the actual velocity of the body at some earlier instant, since acceleration is concerned only with *changes* in velocity. In the same way velocity is concerned only with *changes* in position. Thus we need to introduce constants not supplied by the formula or equation with which we start.

A longer series of well-known expressions each of which can be obtained by differentiation or integration (as the case may be) of a neighbour in the series arises in the study of beams. Let x be distance measured along a horizontal beam from some fixed point. Let y be the sag or vertical deflection at the point x. Consider a beam which is so stiff or so lightly loaded that the deflections may be regarded as small. Then

$y = $ *deflection* at point x

$\frac{dy}{dx} = $ *gradient* of the beam centre-line at point x

$\frac{d^2y}{dx^2} = $ *curvature* of the beam centre-line at point x; and by alteration of the scale

$\frac{d^2y}{dx^2} = $ Bending Moment in the beam at point x. Let us call this moment M.

Now $\frac{dM}{dx} = $ Rate of change of Bending Moment with the distance x. This change is caused by and proportional to Shearing Force at point x. Thus working with suitable scale

$$\frac{d\text{M}}{dx} = \text{S}:$$ that is, the vertical or transverse force passed across the section at x.

$$\frac{d\text{S}}{dx} = \text{Value at } x \text{ of applied vertical load per unit run along the beam.}$$

Thus, if an expression embodying any of these functions of the loading and its distribution is integrated, the new expression will contain a named recognisable function of some practical importance. In these cases the constant of integration must be introduced using independent knowledge of the conditions for various values of x. For example, in a built-in cantilever when $x = 0$, $y = 0$; also $\frac{dy}{dx} = 0$; at the centre of a symmetrically loaded freely supported beam, again $\frac{dy}{dx} = 0$.

Leaving aside the case of the beam, whether or not $\int y \, dx$ prove to be a recognisable named function, it can be evaluated as an area on the graph given by plotting y against x. The area is taken between ordinates, and in deciding the position of these ordinates you are in fact assigning a value to the Constant of Integration.

3. Maxima and Minima

It is often important to know what the maximum or minimum value of a given function of x is, and where such a value occurs. For instance, we may wish to know where the maximum bending moment occurs in a loaded beam, and what is its value.

The determination of maximum and minimum values of a function of one variable is a simple exercise in differentiation.

The curve of Fig. 25 is one drawn merely for illustration.

Suppose its equation is $y = f(x)$. At the points marked, we observe that the curve turns. Hence, these points are called "turning points." At each of these points the tangent is parallel to the x-axis; therefore its gradient is zero; *i.e.*, at every turning point $\frac{dy}{dx} = 0$.

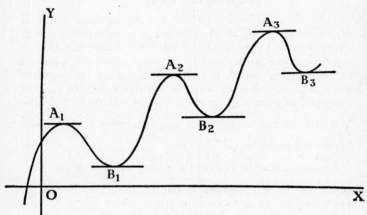

FIG. 25.

Example

Find the turning points on the curve

$$y = \frac{x^3}{3} - \frac{5x^2}{2} + 6x - 4 \quad . \quad . \quad . \quad (1)$$

We have

$$\frac{dy}{dx} = x^2 - 5x + 6$$
$$= (x - 3)(x - 2)$$

∴ for turning points

$$(x - 3)(x - 2) = 0$$

i.e., $x = 3 \text{ or } 2.$

Put $\qquad x = 3$ in (1) above.

We get $\qquad y = 9 - \frac{45}{2} + 18 - 4$

$\qquad\qquad = \frac{1}{2}.$

Now put $\qquad x = 2$ in (1)

$\qquad\qquad y = \frac{8}{3} - 10 + 12 - 4$

$\qquad\qquad = \frac{2}{3}.$

Hence $(3, \frac{1}{2})$ and $(2, \frac{2}{3})$ are the co-ordinates of the turning points.

4. Referring to Fig. 25, the ordinates at A_1, A_2, A_3 are maxima, those at B_1 and B_2 are minima.

Definition:

A maximum value of a given function of x is one that is greater than the values immediately before and immediately after it.

Similarly, a minimum value of a function is one less than the values immediately before and immediately after it.

It will be seen from the figure that the minimum at B_2 is greater than the maximum at A_1. The word " immediately " is therefore important in the above definitions.

Another inference may be made from the figure—viz., that maxima and minima occur alternately.

Hence, if we know that there are two turning points on a curve, and that one of them has a minimum ordinate, the other ordinate must be a maximum.

5. To Distinguish a Maximum from a Minimum

There are two very simple ways of distinguishing a maximum from a minimum.

First Method.

It will be recalled that $\frac{dy}{dx}$ is the gradient of the tangent to the curve $y = f(x)$, at the point (x, y).

i.e.,
$$\frac{dy}{dx} = \tan \psi$$

where A is any point (x, y) on the curve.

In Fig. 26 (1) $\frac{dy}{dx}$ is $+$ because ψ is acute.

In Fig. 26 (2) $\frac{dy}{dx}$ is $-$, because ψ is obtuse.

Notice that in Fig. 26 (1), as the value of x increases, that of y also increases, and the curve slopes upwards from left

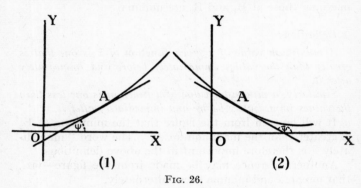

(1)   (2)

Fig. 26.

to right, whereas in Fig. 26 (2), as the abscissa increases—*i.e.,* moves from left to right—the ordinate y decreases, and the curve slopes downwards.

No matter how the curve be drawn, it will be found that when $\frac{dy}{dx}$ is positive, y increases as x increases, and when $\frac{dy}{dx}$ is negative, y decreases as x increases.

Consider the turning point A_1, illustrated in Fig. 27.

Notice that as we pass from the left to the right of a maximum, ψ changes from acute to obtuse—*i.e.,* $\frac{dy}{dx}$ changes from positive to negative.

This means that $\dfrac{dy}{dx}$ is itself decreasing as x increases, and that therefore *its* differential coefficient is negative—*i.e.*, at a maximum $\dfrac{d^2y}{dx^2}$ is negative.

Similarly, at a minimum, $\dfrac{d^2y}{dx^2}$ is positive.

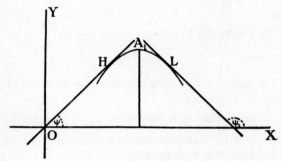

FIG. 27.

The results of this paragraph should be memorised. Taking the previous example:

$$y = \frac{x^3}{3} - \frac{5x^2}{2} + 6x - 4$$

$$\frac{dx}{dx} = x^2 - 5x + 6 = (x - 3)(x - 2)$$

$$\frac{d^2y}{dx^2} = 2x - 5.$$

The turning points occur where $x = 3$ and $x = 2$.   When $x = 3$

$$\frac{d^2y}{dx^2} = 6 - 5 = + 1, \text{ } i.e., \text{ is positive.}$$

$\therefore$ The ordinate at $x = 3$ is a minimum.

When $\qquad x = 2$

$$\frac{d^2y}{dx^2} = 4 - 5 = 1, \text{ } i.e., \text{ is negative.}$$

Hence the ordinate at $x = 2$ is a maximum.

We found the maximum value of the function was $\frac{2}{3}$, whilst the minimum value was $\frac{1}{2}$.

Summary:

(1) To find turning points on $y = f(x)$.

Solve $\qquad \dfrac{dy}{dx} = 0.$

The roots of this equation give the abscissæ of the turning points.

(2) Substitute each root in the expression for $\dfrac{d^2y}{dx^2}$.

A negative result indicates a maximum.   A positive result indicates a minimum.

(3) To find the maximum and minimum values of the ordinates, we must substitute the appropriate value of x in the original equation.

6. *A second method* which distinguishes maxima from minima can be employed which does not use any differential coefficient except the first.

It was seen that as we pass through a maximum from left to right, $\dfrac{dy}{dx}$ changes sign from positive to negative, whilst when we pass through a minimum, the change is from $-$ to $+$.

The change through the minimum is shown in Fig. 28, where as we pass through B from the immediate left to the immediate right, ψ_1 is obtuse, *i.e.*, $\dfrac{dy}{dx}$ is negative, whilst ψ_2 is acute, *i.e.*, $\dfrac{dy}{dx}$ is positive.

We take the example previously used to show how the above ideas are applied.

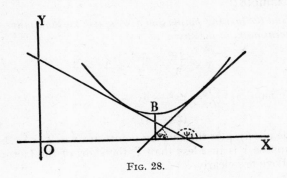

FIG. 28.

Example 1

$$y = \frac{x^3}{3} - \frac{5x^2}{2} + 6x - 4$$

$$\frac{dy}{dx} = x^2 - 5x + 6 = (x - 3)(x - 2) \quad . \quad . \quad (1)$$

The turning points are at $x = 3$ and $x = 2$.

The abscissa of a point immediately to the left of $x = 3$ is $x = 3 - h$, where h is very small.

Now, putting $(3 - h)$ for x in (1), the first factor becomes $(-h)$ and the second $(1 - h)$. Since h is very small, the signs of these two factors are $(-)(+)$, and the product is negative.

Similarly, taking the point immediately to the right of $x = 3$, i.e., putting $3 + h$ for x, we see that the signs of the two factors in (1) above are $(+)(+)$.

Hence when passing through $x = 3$, $\frac{dy}{dx}$ changes from $-$ to $+$; therefore $x = 3$, is the abscissa of a minimum point.

Similarly, the change in the sign of $\frac{dy}{dx}$ in passing through $x = 2$ will be from $+$ to $-$.

Example 2

Find the turning points and distinguish the maximum from the minimum on the curve

$$y = \frac{2x^3}{3} - \frac{5x^2}{2} + 2x - 3 \quad . \quad . \quad . \quad (1)$$

We have $\frac{dy}{dx} = 2x^2 - 5x + 2$

$$= (2x - 1)(x - 2) \quad . \quad . \quad . \quad . \quad (2)$$

The abscissæ of the turning points are $x = \frac{1}{2}$, $x = 2$.

Suppose x is just less than $\frac{1}{2}$, the signs of the factors in (2) above are clearly

$$(-)(-), \; i.e., \; \frac{dy}{dx} \text{ is } +.$$

If x is just greater than $\frac{1}{2}$ the signs are $(+)(-)$

$$\therefore \quad \frac{dy}{dx} \text{ is } (-).$$

Hence the change in $\frac{dy}{dx}$ is from $+$ to $-$.

We infer $x = \frac{1}{2}$ is the abscissa of a maximum.

Since maxima and minima occur alternately, $x = 2$ is the abscissa of a minimum.

The values of the maximum and minimum ordinates can be found by putting $x = \frac{1}{2}$, and $x = 2$ in (1) above, and will be found to be $- 2\frac{13}{24}$ and $- 3\frac{2}{3}$ respectively.

Example 3

Given the equation $y = x(12 - 2x)^2$, determine the values of x for which y is a maximum or minimum, and the value of y corresponding to each of the two values of x so determined.

(U.L.C.I.)

We have, $y = x(12 - 2x)^2$ . . . . (1)

$$\frac{dy}{dx} = 2x(12 - 2x)(-2) + (12 - 2x)^2$$

$$= (12 - 2x)(12 - 6x)$$
$$= 12(6 - x)(2 - x) \quad . \quad . \quad . \quad (2)$$

From (2) $\frac{dy}{dx} = 0$ when $x = 6$ and when $x = 2$

Putting $x = (6 - h)$ in (2), $\frac{dy}{dx}$ is $- ve$.

Putting $x = (6 + h)$ in (2), $\frac{dy}{dx}$ is $+ ve$

$\therefore$ $x = 6$ is the abscissa of a minimum
and $x = 2$ that of a maximum.

Substituting these values in (1)

      $y = 0$ is the minimum value
and $y = 128$ is the maximum value.

Example 4

The total surface area of a solid cylinder of diameter x in. is S sq in.   Obtain formulæ in terms of x and S for the height and volume of the cylinder.

If S is constant, prove that when the volume of this cylinder is a maximum, $x = \sqrt{\dfrac{2S}{3\pi}}$ and that the area of its curved surface is two-thirds of S.   (N.C.T.E.C.)

Let h = the height and V = the volume of the cylinder.
Then   S = the cylindrical surface + two ends

$$= \pi x h + 2 . \pi . \frac{x^2}{4} \quad . \quad . \quad . \quad . \quad (1)$$

$\therefore$ Solving (1) for h, we get:

$$h = \frac{1}{\pi x}\left(S - \frac{\pi x^2}{2}\right)$$

$$= \frac{S}{\pi x} - \frac{x}{2} \quad . \quad . \quad . \quad . \quad . \quad (2)$$

Similarly,

$$V = \frac{\pi x^2}{4} \cdot h$$

$$= \frac{\pi x^2}{4}\left(\frac{S}{\pi x} - \frac{x}{2}\right) \text{ using (2) above}$$

$$= \frac{xS}{4} - \frac{\pi x^3}{8} \quad \cdot \quad \cdot \quad \cdot \quad \cdot \quad \cdot \quad (3)$$

Differentiating (3) with respect to x, we get:

$$\frac{dV}{dx} = \frac{S}{4} = \frac{3\pi x^2}{8} \quad \cdot \quad \cdot \quad \cdot \quad \cdot \quad \cdot \quad (4)$$

Equating $\frac{dV}{dx}$ to zero gives:

$$\frac{S}{4} = \frac{3\pi x^2}{8}$$

i.e.,
$$x^2 = \frac{2S}{3\pi}.$$

i.e., $x = \sqrt{\dfrac{2S}{3\pi}}$, rejecting the negative value of the square root.

From (4) $\dfrac{d^2V}{dx^2} = -\dfrac{6\pi x}{8}$. Hence the value found for x gives a maximum value of V.

The area of the curved surface is $\pi x h$.

$$= \pi x\left(\frac{S}{\pi x} - \frac{x}{2}\right), \text{ using (2)}$$

$$= S - \frac{\pi x^2}{2}$$

$$= S - \frac{\pi}{2}\left(\sqrt{\frac{2S}{3\pi}}\right)^2, \text{ using the value found for } x$$

$$= S - \frac{S}{3}$$

$$= \frac{2S}{3}.$$

Example 5

Given that $\dfrac{ds}{dt} = 4\cdot8 - 3\cdot2t$, *and that* $s = 5$ *when* $t = 0\cdot5$,
express s as a function of t and find:

    (i) *the other value of t when* $s = 5$,
    (ii) *the maximum value of s*   (N.C.)

From $\dfrac{ds}{dt} = 4\cdot8 - 3\cdot2t$ . . . . (1)

we get, by integration, $s = 4\cdot8t - 1\cdot6t^2 + C$.

Put $s = 5$, $t = 0\cdot5$, and find $C = 3$.

    $\therefore$ $s = 4\cdot8t - 1\cdot6t^2 + 3$ . . . (2)

When $s = 5$, we have the quadratic equation

$$1\cdot6t^2 - 4\cdot8t + 2 = 0.$$

The sum of the roots of this equation is $\dfrac{4\cdot8}{1\cdot6}$, *i.e.,* 3.

Since one root is $0\cdot5$, the other is $2\cdot5$.

From (1) $\dfrac{ds}{dt} = 4\cdot8 - 3\cdot2t$

                      $= 0$ for a turning point.

$\therefore$ at this point $t = \dfrac{4\cdot8}{3\cdot2} = \dfrac{3}{2}.$

Since $\dfrac{d^2s}{dt^2} = -3\cdot2$ (by differentiating (1)) this value of t
gives a maximum value of s.

Substituting in (2), the maximum is given by

$$s = 4\cdot8 \times \tfrac{3}{2} - 1\cdot6 \times \tfrac{9}{4} + 3$$
$$= 7\cdot2 - 3\cdot6 + 3$$
$$= 6\cdot6.$$

EXERCISE 26

1. Find the maximum and minimum ordinates of the following curves:

$$\text{(i)} \quad y = \frac{x^3}{3} - \frac{x^2}{2} - 2x + 4,$$

(ii) $y = x^3 - 6x^2 + 12$,

(iii) $y = x^3 + x^2 - x + 4$.

2. A sphere has a radius of 1 ft. Find the volume of the greatest cylinder which can be cut from it.

3. What is the volume of the largest cone whose slant side is 8 in. long?

4. Explain how differentiation enables us to find the maximum or minimum value of a function.

The energy available in a certain water supply is given by the equation

$$E = 3(1732V - 0.602V^3).$$

Determine the value of V which makes E a maximum and calculate this value of E.   (U.L.C.I.)

5. A metal tank for a liquid motor starter has to be constructed on a square base to contain 8 cu ft of electrolyte. Calculate the dimensions of this tank so that the surface contact between the tank and liquid may be a minimum.   (U.L.C.I.)

6. A piece of wire is cut into two parts. One part is bent into the form of an equilateral triangle, and the other into that of a square. It is desired that the sum of the areas of these two figures should be a minimum. If the wire was originally 10 in. long, find the point at which it must be cut.   (U.L.C.I.)

7. Show how the sign of the gradient of the graph of the function $\left(\dfrac{x^2}{8} + \dfrac{2}{x}\right)$ changes as the graph passes through the point at which its gradient is zero.   (N.C.)

8. Draw the graph of $y = x^2 - 5x + 7$. Find graphically the slopes of the curve where $x = 1 \cdot 5$ and $x = -2$.

Show by the calculus that the values of the slopes found are correct.

Determine the minimum value of y and the value of x where it occurs.   (U.E.I.)

9. The curve $y = \dfrac{a}{x} + bx^2$ passes through the point given by $x = 3$, $y = 16 \cdot 5$, and the value of $\dfrac{dy}{dx}$ at this point is (-1). Find (i) the values of the constants a and b, (ii) the minimum ordinate of the given curve for positive values of x.   (U.L.C.I.)

10. A right triangular prism whose ends are equilateral triangles is to be made of aluminium. If the total surface area is to be 90 sq in., find the dimensions of the prism which will give the greatest volume.   (U.L.C.I.)

11. For what value or values of x is the value of the function $x^2(5x - 4)(x - 2)$, (i) a maximum, (ii) a minimum? Sketch the graph of the function for values of x from $-0 \cdot 2$ to 2.   (N.C.T.E.C.)

12. Prove that the turning values of the function $a(x^3 - 9x^2 + 15x) + b$, where a and b are constants occur when $x = 1$ and $x = 5$.

If this function has turning values of $+4$ and -2 when x has the values $+1$ and $+5$, respectively, find a and b and calculate the values of the function when x equals -1, $+3$, and $+7$.   (N.C.T.E.C.)

13. In estimating the cost of an electric cable the following equation was obtained:

$$y = (2x + 1) + \frac{1}{2x + 1}.$$

Determine the values of x which make y a maximum or minimum.   (U.L.C.I.)

14. The section of an open gutter is made of thin material, and is to be a rectangle of area 40 sq in. If the base is

x in. wide, express the perimeter of the section in terms of x. Hence find the dimensions of the section if its perimeter is to be a minimum.   (U.L.C.I.)

15. (a) Find the turning point on the curve

$$y = 2x^2 - 6x + 10.$$

State whether it is a maximum or a minimum.

(b) If $H = pV$ and $p = 3 - \frac{1}{2}V$, find the maximum value of H.   (U.L.C.I.)

16. A gas holder is a flat-topped cylinder without a bottom. Find the dimensions of a gas holder to hold 1 million cu ft of gas if the area of the metal plate used in its construction is a minimum.   (U.L.C.I.)

See also Exercise 28A—Miscellaneous.

7. Calculation of Small Corrections

Most of the following formulæ, and many others, will be familiar:

$$A = \tfrac{1}{2}bh \quad . \quad . \quad . \quad \text{Area of a triangle}$$
$$V = \tfrac{4}{3}\pi r^3 \quad . \quad . \quad . \quad \text{Vol. of sphere}$$
$$T = 2\pi\sqrt{\frac{l}{g}} \quad . \quad . \quad . \quad \text{Time of oscillation of a simple pendulum}$$
$$pv = C \quad . \quad . \quad . \quad . \quad \text{Boyle's law.}$$

The data employed in the formulæ are usually the results of measurements whose accuracy can only be vouched for between certain limits. It will thus be clear that results dependent on such data may be erroneous, and it is frequently necessary to calculate the relative error which is often stated as a percentage.

Example 1

Suppose the radius of a sphere is taken as 4 in. subject to an error of 0·01 in. What is the approximate error in the volume? Find also the relative and the percentage error.

$$V = \tfrac{4}{3}\pi r^3$$

$dV = 4\pi r^2 dr.$ Notice the use of differentials.

$$= 4\pi \, . \, 4^2 \, . \, (0{\cdot}01)$$

$$= 0{\cdot}64\pi \text{ cub in.}$$

The relative error $= \dfrac{\text{Calculated error}}{\text{Calculated volume}}$

$$= \dfrac{0{\cdot}64\pi}{\tfrac{4}{3} \, . \, \pi \, . \, 4^3}$$

$$= \dfrac{3 \times 0{\cdot}64}{4^4}$$

$$= 0{\cdot}0075.$$

The percentage error $=$ relative error $\times 100$

$$= 0{\cdot}75.$$

Example 2

A hollow cylindrical vessel was ordered whose height was to be 8 in. and diameter 10 in. It held the correct amount of liquid, but the radius of the base was $\tfrac{1}{10}$ in. too great. What was the height?

$$\text{Vol.} = \pi r^2 h = \pi \, . \, 25 \, . \, 8 = 200\pi \, . \text{ cu in.}$$

$$\therefore \quad h = \frac{200}{r^2}$$

$$\therefore \quad dh = -\frac{400}{r^3} \, . \, dr$$

i.e., $$dh = -\frac{400}{5^3} \times 0{\cdot}1$$

$$= -\tfrac{8}{25}.$$

Hence the decrease in height was $\tfrac{8}{25}$ in. and the approximate height was $7\tfrac{17}{25}$ in.

Notice in the above that if the radius was found to be

$\frac{1}{10}$ in. too small instead of too large, we should have taken $dr = -0.1$ in. and then

$$dh = -\frac{400}{5^3} \times (-0.1)$$

$$= +\tfrac{8}{25} \text{ in.}$$

Example 3

A standard type of question on the simple pendulum is the following.

Given the formula $t = 2\pi\sqrt{\dfrac{l}{g}}$, find the % change in t if the length is decreased by 1%.

Notice that 2π and g are constants, and we can write:

$$t = k \cdot l^{\frac{1}{2}} \left(\text{where } k = \frac{2\pi}{\sqrt{g}} \right) \quad . \quad . \quad . \quad (1)$$

Hence $dt = \tfrac{1}{2}kl^{-\frac{1}{2}}dl$.

Now $dl = -\dfrac{l}{100}$

$\therefore \quad dt = -\tfrac{1}{2} \cdot kl^{-\frac{1}{2}} \cdot \dfrac{l}{100} = -\dfrac{k}{200} \cdot l^{\frac{1}{2}} = -\dfrac{t}{200}$ from (1)

Hence the percentage change

$$= \frac{dt}{t} + 100 = -\tfrac{1}{2}.$$

Examples 1, 2 and 3 might be dealt with by means of a simple rule which can be deduced either directly from the Binomial Series for $\left(1 + \dfrac{h}{x}\right)^n$ or from the differential coefficient of x^n as in the working given.

If an error or alteration (h) is small in relation to the quantity (x) under consideration, if for example $\dfrac{h}{x}$ is of the order of 1% or 2%, then the corresponding alteration ratio in an expression of which x^2 is a factor will be $\dfrac{2h}{x}$, and in an

expression of which x^3 is a factor will be $\dfrac{3h}{x}$, and so on.
This rule can of course be used by calculators who would not be able to follow its derivation. Let us apply the rule calling its three applications Examples 1*a*, 2*a* and 3*a*.

Example 1*a*.   The error ratio in the radius is $\dfrac{0 \cdot 01}{4}$, that is $\frac{1}{400}$. The formula for volume embodies r^3 as a factor. Thus the error ratio is $\frac{3}{400}$, or 0·75% in any calculation of volume.

Example 2*a*.   The net error is nothing because there are compensating errors. The error in radius of the base is $\dfrac{0 \cdot 1}{5}$ or $\dfrac{1}{50}$. The formula for volume includes the factor r^2. So acting alone the given error would produce an error in volume of plus 2 parts in 50. The compensating error must therefore be minus 2 parts in 50. Since the height appears in the volume formula to the first power only the height must be below size by $\frac{2}{50}$ of 8 in. or 4% of 8 in., which is 0·032 in.

Example 3*a*.   The formula tells us that

$$t = kl^{\frac{1}{2}}.$$

We are given that there is a change in l of -1%.
Then the consequent change in t is $-\frac{1}{2}\%$.

Although the fact has not been emphasised in the above statements all of them are permissible because the error ratios involved have been small.

EXERCISE 27

1. If the side of an equilateral triangle can be measured accurately to 0·01 in., find the possible error in the area when its sides are 20 in.

2. Find the possible error in the area of a square whose side is 20 in., assuming the same accuracy of measurements as in Example 1.

3. The diameter of a circular disc can be measured accurately to $\frac{1}{50}$ in. Find the error in estimating the area of a disc of 8 in. diameter.

4. A cylindrical steel bar has to be made from a given volume of metal. Its diameter should be 8 in. and its length 30 in. If the diameter is found to be $\frac{1}{50}$ in. too small, find the difference in length.

5. Suppose that the pressure and volume of a gas are connected by the relation

$$pv = C \text{ (a constant).}$$

At a given instant $p = 14$ lb/sq in. and $v = 20$ cu ft. find v—   (1) when $p = 14 \cdot 1$ lb/sq in.
     (2) when $p = 13 \cdot 98$ lb/sq in.
Also   (3) find p when $v = 20 \cdot 2$ cu ft.

6. The formula $t = 2\pi \sqrt{\dfrac{l}{g}}$ gives the time of oscillation of a simple pendulum of length l. Find the change in the time of oscillation when the length l is increased by 2%.

7. The area of a triangle ABC is Δ, where $\Delta = \frac{1}{2}bc \sin A$.

If A and c are measured correctly, but there is an error of 2% in the measurement of b, find the relative error in the calculated area.

8. If x and y are the sides of a rectangle of constant area A, we get $xy = A$. If the side x is slightly altered to $x + dx$, show that the correction to be applied to y is

$$= y\,\frac{dx}{x}.$$

9. If h is the hypotenuse of a right-angled triangle and x and y the other two sides we have $h^2 = x^2 + y^2$, and get by differentiation

$$2h \cdot dh = 2x \cdot dx + 2y \cdot dy \quad . \quad . \quad . \quad (1)$$

If when $x = 8$ in. and $y = 6$ in., both sides receive an increment of 0·02 in., find from (1) above the increase in the hypotenuse.

10. Derive the simple rule for small corrections stated on p. 80 and embodied in examples 1a, 2a and 3a.

See also Exercise 28A—Miscellaneous.

8. Rates

A velocity and an acceleration are examples previously met with of " **rates** ". The underlying idea in most rates is that of "change per unit time," but there are also railway rates (cost per mile or per ton or per ton mile), prices and many others. In general we may apply the term to a fractional expression in which the numerator and denominator are of different " dimensions " so that the units of both must be given. If the units have the same dimension they can be cancelled, and the expression becomes a ratio or pure number.

Example 1

Suppose the radius of a circular ripple on a pond is increasing at $\frac{1}{10}$ ft/sec. At what rate is the area increasing when the radius of the circle is 10 ft?

Let A be the area, and r the radius at any time. Then

$$A = \pi r^2 \quad . \quad . \quad . \quad . \quad . \quad (1)$$

and

$$\frac{dr}{dt} = \frac{1}{10} \text{ (given)} \quad . \quad . \quad . \quad . \quad (2)$$

We require $\dfrac{dA}{dt}$

$$\frac{dA}{dt} = \frac{dA}{dr} \cdot \frac{dr}{dt}$$

From (1) $$\frac{dA}{dr} = 2\pi r$$

and $$\frac{dr}{dt} = \frac{1}{10}$$

$$\therefore \quad \frac{dA}{dt} = 2\pi r \cdot \frac{1}{10} = \frac{\pi r}{5}.$$

This result gives the rate of growth for any radius, r. To answer the question put $r = 10$.

We get $$\frac{dA}{dt} = \frac{\pi \cdot 10}{5} = 2\pi \text{ sq ft per sec.}$$

Example 2

The adiabatic law for the expansion of air is $pv^{1\cdot4} = k$. At a given time, $p = 100$ lb per sq in. and $v = 20$ cu ft. Find at what rate the pressure is changing, if, at the given time, the volume is decreasing at 2 cu ft per sec.

$$pv^{1\cdot4} = k$$

$$\therefore \quad p = \frac{k}{v^{1\cdot4}} \quad . \quad . \quad . \quad . \quad . \quad (1)$$

We are given

$$\frac{dv}{dt} = -2 \text{ cu ft/sec} \quad . \quad . \quad . \quad (2)$$

Now $$\frac{dp}{dt} = \frac{dp}{dv} \cdot \frac{dv}{dt}$$

and from (1) $$\frac{dp}{dv} = -\frac{k \times 1\cdot4}{v^{2\cdot4}}$$

Hence

$$\frac{dp}{dt} = -\frac{k \times 1\cdot4}{v^{2\cdot4}} \times (-2)$$

$$= \frac{k \times 2\cdot8 \times p}{pv^{1\cdot4} \times v}.$$

(Notice the multiplication of numerator and denominator by p.)

$$= \frac{2 \cdot 8 \times p}{v}.$$

Now put $p = 100$ and $v = 20$. This gives

$$\frac{dp}{dt} = \frac{2 \cdot 8 \times 100}{20} = 14 \text{ lb/sq in. per sec.}$$

EXERCISE 28

1. The radius of a sphere is increasing at the rate of $\frac{1}{10}$ in. per sec. At what rate is the volume increasing when the radius is 6 in.?

2. If $y = 3x + x^2$, and $\frac{dx}{dt} = 2$, find $\frac{dy}{dt}$ when $x = 4$.

3. Find the rate at which the volume of a cone is increasing when the radius of its base is 4 in., given that its height is constant and equal to 6 in., whilst the radius of the base increases at the rate of 0·3 in. per sec.

4. An inverted conical vessel with its axis vertical has water running into it at a constant rate. Show that the height H at which the water stands after a time t is

$$H = c \sqrt[3]{t},$$

where c is a constant. Prove that the rate of increase of H at any particular height is inversely proportional to the square of the height.   (U.L.C.I.)

5. A rod AB, 15 ft long, slides in slots along two bars OX, OY, at right angles and fixed. A moves along OX at the rate of 0·2 ft per sec. At what rate is B moving along OY when OA = 6 ft?

6. Coal is pouring steadily into a symmetrical bunker of wedge shape whose inverted apex angle is 40° and whose length is 5 ft at the rate of 10 cu ft per sec. Find by

calculus the rate at which the depth of the coal in the bunker increases.   (U.E.I.)

7. A weight is being lifted by means of a rope passing over a pulley 25 ft above the ground. The rope is 50 ft long. A man holds the other end of the rope at a height of 5 ft and walks away at 10 ft/sec. How rapidly does the weight start to ascend?

8. A water cistern has the form of an inverted cone, radius 3 ft and height 10 ft. At what rate is the water pouring into the cistern when its height in the cistern is 4 ft and rising at the rate of 2 in./sec?

EXERCISE 28A—MISCELLANEOUS

Each of the Exercises 9 to 28 inclusive has comprised examples related to the matter of immediately preceding paragraphs. It is desirable that the reader should have some practice without the assistance given by so direct a lead. Accordingly, the varied questions reproduced below are taken by permission from numerous recent papers approved for final-year examinations of National Certificate Courses. These papers range over complete final-year syllabuses; also many individual questions deal with more than one section. It is therefore necessary for the reader to pick out questions or parts of questions which he is in a position to attempt at his present stage. He will find that the task of deciding what procedures are necessary, and whether he is familiar with them, will in itself constitute useful practice.

1. Using the binomial series, obtain the expansion of

$$\text{(i)} \ (1 + 10x)^{\frac{1}{2}} \qquad \text{(ii)} \ \frac{1 + 6x}{1 + 4x}$$

in positive powers of x as far as the terms in x^3 inclusive. Hence, by giving x a suitable value, find a simple fraction which is approximately equal to $\sqrt[5]{1\cdot5}$. Is the approximation likely to be greater or less than the true value?

(Worcester)

2. (i) Find from first principles the differential coefficient of x^3.

(ii) Determine the following differential coefficients

(1) $\dfrac{d\sqrt[7]{x^2}}{dx}$;

(3) $\dfrac{d\sin\theta\cos\theta}{d\theta}$;

(2) $\dfrac{d4\cos\frac{1}{2}x}{dx}$;

(4) $\dfrac{d5\cos^3(3x+2)}{dx}$.

(iii) By writing $\tan x$ as a quotient, determine its differential coefficient.   (West Riding.)

3. (a) Find $\dfrac{dy}{dx}$ if (i) $y = \dfrac{x^2 - x}{(2x - 1)^2}$; (ii) $y = \sqrt{1 - 3x^2}$.

(b) If $y = e^{2x}\sin 2x\sqrt{3}$, find the least positive value of x for which the curve has a turning point and determine whether the value of y at this point is a maximum or minimum.   (Burton-upon-Trent.)

4. (a) Show with the aid of sketches, that $\dfrac{d^2y}{dx^2}$ is negative for values of x for which $f(x)$ is a maximum.

(b) An open rectangular tank is to contain 300 cu ft and its length and breadth are to be in the ratio 3 : 1. What is its depth, if the area of plate used is to be a minimum?   (E.M.E.U.)

5. (a) Write down the first four terms in the expansion of $(1 + x)^{\frac{1}{2}}$. Find the greatest value which x can have in order that the fourth term shall not exceed 0·001.

(b) Given that

$$\frac{(1 - x)^{\frac{2}{3}}}{(8 + x)^{\frac{2}{3}}} = A + Bx + Cx^2 + \ldots \quad (|x| < 1)$$

express in fractional form the values of the three constants A, B and C.

F

(c) If l/d is small enough for terms in $(l/d)^2$ to be neglected in comparison with unity, prove that

$$\frac{M}{(d-l)^2} - \frac{M}{(d+l)^2} \text{ is approximately equal to } \frac{4Ml}{d^3}.$$

(N.C.T.E.C.)

6. (i) Differentiate $\dfrac{1}{x^2}$ with respect to x, from first principles.

(ii) Find the differential coefficients of (a) $x^2 \sin (3x + 1)$; (b) $\dfrac{x^7 - 1}{x^7 + 1}$; (c) $(7x^4 - 1)^5$.   (N.C.T.E.C.)

7. If the focal length of a lens is f in., the distance of the object from the lens is u in. and the distance of the image from the lens is v in., then $\dfrac{1}{f} = \dfrac{1}{u} + \dfrac{1}{v}$.

(a) Express v as a function of f and u. (b) If $f = 7$ in., find the change in v when u is increased from 40 to 40·3 in. (c) Also if u is decreasing steadily at the rate of 1 in. every 5 sec, find the rate of change of v when $u = 25$ in.

(S.W. Essex.)

8. (a) The shaded area of Fig. 29 is part of the cross-section of a hollow shaft. Determine the internal radius of the shaft, and hence calculate the weight per foot run of the shaft in terms of w the weight per cubic inch of material.

(b) The equations $S = \pi r l$, $l^2 = r^2 + h^2$, $V = \frac{1}{3}\pi r^2 h$ all relate to a right circular cone. If $\dfrac{r}{4} = \dfrac{h}{3}$, evaluate $\dfrac{S^3}{V^2}$ leaving your answer in terms of π. Hence find $\dfrac{dS}{dV}$ and determine its value when $V = 2$.

(Handsworth.)

9. (a) A ladder 50 ft long rests with its upper end against a vertical wall and its lower end on the ground 14 ft from the wall. If the lower end is pulled a further 3 in. from the wall, find by a method employing the calculus how far the upper end will descend.

(b) A point moves so that its displacement in feet after t sec. is $a + b \sin pt + a \cos pt$, where p is in radians per second. Find its initial velocity and its acceleration $\dfrac{2\pi}{p}$ seconds after starting.

(Cannock.)

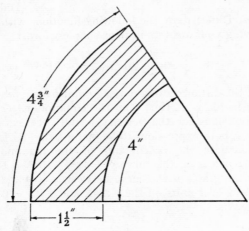

$4\frac{3}{4}''$

$4''$

$1\frac{1}{2}''$

Fig. 29.

10. (i) Find the maximum and minimum values of the function $2x^3 - 3x^2 - 12x + 5$, and sketch sufficient of the graph of this function to show its essential features.

(ii) A closed metal container is in the form of a circular cylinder, surmounted by a hemisphere of the same radius as the cylinder. If the total area of metal used in its construction is 110 sq ft, find the dimensions of the container in order that it may have a maximum capacity.

(Cheltenham.)

11. (a) (i) Write out the complete expansion of $(1 - 3x)^5$, expressing coefficients in simple numerical form.

(ii) Calculate, using binomial expansions, the values of $(0.997)^5$ and $(1003)^{\frac{1}{3}}$ correct to 5 decimal places in each case.

(b) Use the tables provided to find A from

$$\tan \tfrac{1}{2}A = \sqrt{\frac{(S - b)(S - c)}{S(S - a)}}.$$

Where $a = 8\!\cdot\!45$, $b = 10\!\cdot\!3$, $c = 11\!\cdot\!45$, $S = \tfrac{1}{2}(a + b + c)$.

(Halifax.)

12. (a) Differentiate the following functions with respect to x, giving your answers in their simplest form:

(i) $\dfrac{2x^2 + 3}{x - 1}$ (ii) $\sqrt{x^2 - 3x + 4}$

(b) If the distance x of a moving point from a fixed point is given in terms of time t by the equation $x = e^{-3t} \sin t$, find expressions for the velocity v and acceleration f in terms of t, both expressions to be factorised.   (U.L.C.I.)

13. Calculate the coordinates of the maximum and minimum points on the curve $y = 4x^3 - 15x^2 + 12x + 2$.

Draw the graph of the curve between $x = 0$ and $x = 3$, taking 1 in. = 2 units on the y-axis, and 1 in. = 0·4 units on the x-axis.   (U.L.C:I.)

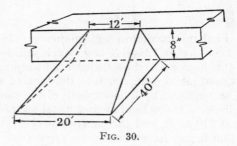

FIG. 30.

14. A concrete ramp is to be constructed, the width decreasing regularly from 20 ft at ground level to 12 ft at the upper end. The base is a rectangle 20 ft × 40 ft and the total rise 8 ft. See Fig. 30.

(a) Calculate (i) the volume of the ramp in cubic yards; (ii) the angle at which the sides are inclined to the horizontal.

(b) If a model of the ramp is made $\frac{1}{12}$ full-size, apply the principle of similar figures to find its volume in cubic feet.

(Coventry.)

15. (i) Differentiate with respect to x and express in their simplest forms:

$$(1) \quad (x - 3)\sqrt{(2x + 1)}; \quad (2) \quad \frac{x^3 + 2}{x - 1};$$

$$(3) \quad x \sin x + \cos x.$$

(ii) Two straight roads intersect at right angles. A cyclist travelling at 15 ft per sec along one road passes the crossing at noon, and at this instant another cyclist is approaching the crossing at 12 ft per sec but is still 30 yds away. Assuming that both cyclists continue with uniform velocity, show that t sec, after noon their distance apart, S ft, is given by:

$$S^2 = 369t^2 - 2160t + 8100.$$

Calculate the time when the distance between the cyclists is least, and show mathematically that your result does give a minimum.

(West Riding.)

16. (a) Solve the equation

$$2^x \cdot 5^{x+1} = 8^{2x-1}.$$

(b) The curve $y = a + bx + cx^2$ passes through the points $(-1, -1)$, $(2, 1)$, $(3, 0)$. Make a sketch of the curve, and determine its law. Determine also the equation to the tangent at the point $(2, 1)$.

(Handsworth.)

17. Differentiate

$$\frac{x^2}{\cos^2 x}; \quad e^x \log \frac{x}{2}.$$

Obtain $\displaystyle\int_0^{\pi/2} (1 - \sin x)^2 dx; \quad \int (x + 2)(x - 3)dx.$

(Sunderland.)

18. The curve $y = a + bc^x$ passes through the points $x = 0$, $y = 26 \cdot 62$; $x = 1$, $y = 35 \cdot 70$; $x = 2$, $y = 49 \cdot 81$. Find a, b and c.

Calculate (i) the gradient of the curve at the point where $x = 0$; (ii) the area under the curve from the ordinate $x = 0$ to ordinate $x = 2$, using Simpson's Rule with the three given ordinates. (Worcester.)

19. (a) Evaluate the following integrals:

$$\text{(i)} \int_2^4 \frac{dx}{\sqrt{17 - 4x}};$$

$$\text{(ii)} \int_1^2 \frac{6 + 2x}{x^2} \, dx;$$

$$\text{(iii)} \int_0^1 e^x(1 + e^x) \, dx.$$

(b) If $\dfrac{d^2y}{dx^2} = 6 - 2x$, find the value of y when $x = 3$, given that $y = 6$ when $x = 0$, and that $y = \frac{2}{3}$ when $x = 1$. (Surrey.)

20. A long, thin bar is heated at one end. If $t°$ be the excess of its temperature above that of the surrounding air at a distance x cm. from the heated end it can be proved that $t = Ae^{-bx}$, where A and b are constants and $e = 2 \cdot 718$.

Given that $t = 65$ when $x = 0$ and that $t = 60$ when $x = 30$, find the values of A and b.

Hence differentiate t with respect to x and find the value of $\dfrac{dt}{dx}$ when $x = 30$.

Explain briefly the meaning of your result. (Coventry.)

21. (a) Find by putting $x = 2 + h$ an approximation to the root of the equation $x^5 + 2x = 35$ which is near to $x = 2$.

(b) The formula $\dfrac{g^1}{g} = \dfrac{r^2}{(r + h)^2}$ gives the value of the acceleration due to gravity g^1, at a height h above the earth's surface, where g is its value at the surface, and r is the radius of the earth.

Find an approximate formula for g^1 if $\dfrac{h}{r}$ is so small that powers of $\dfrac{h}{r}$ above the first may be neglected. If h is 5 miles and r is 4000 miles, find the percentage decrease in g.

(Stafford.)

22. (a) Expand fully $\left(x + \dfrac{1}{x} \right)^4$.

(b) Write down the first four terms of $\dfrac{1}{1 - 2x}$ expressed as a series in ascending powers of x. State the values of x for which the expansion is valid.

(c) When x is very small compared to 1, state approximate values of (i) $\sqrt{1 + x}$; (ii) $\sqrt{1 - x}$, and hence find approximately $\sqrt{1 \cdot 01}$ and $\sqrt{0 \cdot 98}$.

(d) If $W = \dfrac{E^2 t^2}{2L}$, find approximately the percentage change in the value of W if E is increased 3% and t and L are each decreased 5%. (Nuneaton.)

23. (a) Evaluate (i) $\displaystyle\int_{\frac{1}{4}}^{\frac{1}{2}} \dfrac{x^2 - 1}{x^3} \, dx$; (ii) $\displaystyle\int_{-\frac{1}{4}}^{0} (e^{4x} + e^{-4x}) \, dx$.

(b) Find the area between the curves $y = x^2 + 5x + 12$ and $y = 6 + 13x - x^2$. (Burton-upon-Trent.)

24. (a) The normal probability curve has the equation

$$y = \dfrac{k}{\sqrt{\pi}} e^{-k^2 x^2}$$

Transpose this equation to obtain one giving x in terms of y and k.

(b) In the formula $R = a + bT + cT^2$ a, b and c are

constants. Find the values of these constants, given the following values R and T.

R =	6·6	7·0	12·0
T =	6	10	15

(c) Given that $x = 5$ is one root of the equation

$$x^3 - 6x^2 + 25 = 0$$

calculate the other values of x which satisfy the equation.

(Coventry.)

25. Sketch that portion of the curve $y^2 = 1 + \cos 2x$ between $x = 0$ and $x = \dfrac{\pi}{2}$ which lies in the first quadrant, taking values of x at intervals of $\dfrac{\pi}{12}$. Using Simpson's Rule find the approximate value of $\displaystyle\int_0^{\frac{\pi}{2}} \sqrt{1 + \cos 2x}\, dx$ and also find the value of the integral directly.

(Burton-upon-Trent.)

26. (i) Write down the first four terms of the expansion of $(1 + x)^n$.

(ii) Using this expansion find as accurately as three terms permit:

(1) $(0·997)^{\frac{1}{2}}$; (2) $\dfrac{1}{\sqrt{(1·04)}}$.

(iii) The formula $h = \dfrac{2fv^2l}{gd}$ is used in hydraulics.

In a particular experiment f was made 1% too large; v, 0·5% too small, and l, 0·25% too small. What percentage error was obtained for the value of h? (West Riding.)

27. In a crank and connecting rod mechanism the displacement x of the piston is given by

$$x = l + r - l \cos \phi - r \cos \theta,$$

where

$$\cos \phi = \left(1 - \frac{r^2}{l^2} \sin^2 \theta \right)^{\frac{1}{2}}.$$

Expand $\left(1 - \frac{r^2}{l^2} \sin^2 \theta \right)^{\frac{1}{2}}$ by the binomial theorem and find approximate expressions for x when (i) the first two terms, (ii) the first three terms of the expansion are used.   Evaluate these expressions for x when $\theta = 90°$ and $l = 4r$, and show that the effect of using the third term is to increase x by approximately 0·174%.   (Sunderland.)

28. By means of the substitution $z = x - 1$ show that the equation

$$3z^3 + 9z^2 + 8z + 3 = 0 \quad . \quad . \quad . \quad (A)$$

reduces to the equation

$$3x^3 - x + 1 = 0 \quad . \quad . \quad . \quad . \quad (B)$$

Find the turning points on the graph whose equation is

$$y = 3x^3 - x + 1.$$

Sketch the graph roughly and deduce that equation (B) has only one real root; indicate the approximate value of this root, that is, to the first place of decimals.   Using common axes, plot accurately the graphs of

$$y = 3x^3 \text{ and } y = x - 1$$

from $x = -1·2$ to $x = -0·6$ (use 1 in. to $\frac{1}{10}$ of a unit on the x axis) and read off the value of this root correct to two decimal places.   Hence find the real root of equation (A) to the same accuracy.   (Halifax.)

29. (a) Evaluate the integrals (i) $\int \sin \left(3x - \frac{\pi}{2} \right) dx$;

(ii) $\int x\sqrt{x^2 + 25} \cdot dx$; (iii) $\int \left(1 + \frac{1}{x} \right)^2 dx.$

(b) Find the value of a if

$$\int_2^a \frac{1000}{x^3} dx = \frac{2}{3} \int_2^{10} \frac{1000}{x^3} dx. \quad \text{(Coventry.)}$$

30. (a) The efficiency of a compressor is given by

$$\frac{k \log_e r}{r^k - 1} \quad \text{where} \quad k = \frac{n - 1}{2n}.$$

Calculate the efficiency when $r = 6.4$ and $n = 1.4$.

(b) The cutting speed of a tool, V ft per min, and the life of a tool t minutes are related by the formula $Vt^{\frac{1}{4}} = c$, where c is a constant. If for a certain tool $t = 32$ when $V = 118$, find the speed at which the tool will last for 128 minutes.   (Stafford.)

31. (a) Differentiate with respect to x

(i) $\dfrac{5x^3 + 6x^2 + 3 \cdot \sqrt{x}}{\sqrt{x^3}}$;

(ii) $x^3 \tan^2 4x$;

(iii) $\log_e \dfrac{1 + x}{1 - x}$.

(b) Show that the point $(2, 1)$ lies on the circle $x^2 + y^2 + 4x + 2y = 15$ and find the slope of the tangent to the curve at this point.   (Shrewsbury.)

32. (a) Find the differential coefficients of the following:

(i) $\log_e (2x - 3)^2$;

(ii) $6x^3 - \dfrac{3}{x^2} + \dfrac{1}{2\sqrt{x}}$;

(iii) $e^{2x} \sin 6x$.

(b) If $y = Ae^{3x} + Be^{-\frac{1}{2}x}$, where A and B are constants, show that

$$2 \frac{d^2y}{dx^2} - 5 \frac{dy}{dx} = 3y. \qquad \text{(Worcester.)}$$

33. (a) Find the value of a if

$$\int_2^a (3x + 5)dx = \tfrac{2}{3} \int_2^8 (3x + 5) \, dx.$$

(b) Find the centre of area of that portion of the parabola $y = x^2 - 4x$ which lies below the axis of x.

(S. W. Essex.)

34. (i) Find the maximum and minimum values of the function $x^3 - 5x^2 + 8x - 6$ and sketch sufficient of the graph to show its essential features.

(ii) The base of a right circular cone is a section of a sphere, centre O, and of unit radius. The vertex of the cone is on the sphere and the centre of the sphere is within the cone. If the distance of O from the base of the cone is x, prove that the volume of the cone is $\frac{\pi}{3} (1 + x - x^2 - x^3)$.

Hence find the value of x which makes the volume of the cone a maximum. (Cheltenham.)

35. (a) In a network analysis three currents, a, b, c are connected by the equations:

$$a + b + c = 10$$
$$2a - 3b = 0\!\cdot\!5$$
$$5a + 2c = 27\!\cdot\!5$$

Find the values of a, b and c.

(b) If in the diagram AD = 20 ft, AB = 6 ft and BP = x ft, find the value of x if AP + PC = 25 ft.

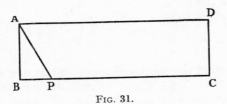

Fig. 31.

(c) Using the same diagram, let BC represent a road, the distance BC being 80 ft. A is a point such that AB is 20 ft and is perpendicular to BC. It is required to lay a cable from A to C. The cost is £3 per foot along the line BC and £5 per foot elsewhere. Find the position of the point P so that the cost of laying the cable from A to C via P shall be a minimum. (S.W. Essex.)

36. (a) Integrate the following:

$$\text{(i)} \int_0^1 \frac{1 + x + x^2}{\sqrt{x}} \, dx;$$

$$\text{(ii)} \int (\sec^2 4x - e^{2x}) dx;$$

$$\text{(iii)} \int \frac{x - 1}{4x^2 - 8x + 3} \, dx.$$

(b) The displacement S ft of a body measured from a fixed point is given in terms of the time t sec. such that the velocity $\frac{ds}{dt}$ is given by $\frac{ds}{dt} = 6t^2 - 3t + A$, where A is a constant.

When $t = 1$ sec, S $= 3$ ft; and when $t = \frac{1}{2}$ sec, S $= 1\frac{3}{8}$ ft. Find the displacement of the body when $t = 1\frac{1}{2}$ sec. (Stafford.)

37. (a) Evaluate the integrals: (i) $\int (3x - 7)^5 \, dx$; (ii) $\int \sin (5x - 7) \cdot dx$.

(b) Find the value of a for which

$$\int_0^a \frac{100}{(x + 3)^2} \cdot dx = \frac{1}{3} \int_0^7 \frac{100}{(x + 3)^2} \, dx.$$

(S.W. Essex.)

38. (a) Find the maximum and minimum values of the function $2x^3 - 3x^2 - 12x + 18$ and distinguish between them. Use the information gained to sketch the curve $y = 2x^3 - 3x^2 - 12x + 18$.

(b) A beam of length l, uniformly loaded, has a bending moment M at a distance x from its fixed end given by

$$M = \frac{Wl}{2} \cdot x - \frac{W}{2} x^2.$$

Find the value of x which makes M a maximum and find M at that point. (Shrewsbury.)

39. ABC is a triangle of base BC = 12 in. and height (from A) = 10 in. A line parallel to BC at a distance x in. *from* A meets AB and AC at P and Q. The triangle is now folded about PQ so that the portion APQ is at right angles to BPQC.

Show that the volume of the pyramid with vertex A and base BPQC is $\dfrac{x}{5}(100 - x^2)$ cu in. and determine the value of x for which the volume is a maximum.   (Worcester.)

40. (*a*) Expand $\dfrac{1}{1 - x}$ as far as the term containing x^4. By integrating the expression term by term obtain a series for $\log_e(1 - x)$ and hence obtain the value of $\log_e 0.9$ to five decimal places.

(*b*) If $x = 2 + h$ and powers of h above the first may be neglected, find the approximate value of $x^3 + 3x^2 + 2x$ in terms of h. Use this result to find, correct to three significant figures, the value of x given by $x^3 + 3x^2 + 2x = 22$, the value of x differing from 2 by a small amount.

(Burton-upon-Trent.)

41. (*a*) Differentiate $\dfrac{x^2}{1 + x^3}$ with respect to x. At what values of x does $\dfrac{x^2}{1 + x^3}$ have stationary values?

(*b*) Show that $y = kte^{-3t}$ satisfies the equation

$$\frac{d^2y}{dt^2} + 6\,\frac{dy}{dt} + 9y = 0.$$

(*c*) If $x = t^2 + 3t$ and $y = 4t^3 + 9t^2$, find and simplify $\dfrac{dy}{dx}$ in terms of t.   (Handsworth.)

42. (*a*) Find $\dfrac{dy}{dx}$ when

(i) $y = \sqrt{2x^3 - 4x}$;

(ii) $y = \dfrac{x^2}{1 + x}$;

(iii) $y = e^{4x+1}$.

(b) If $y = \log_e \tan\left\{\dfrac{\pi}{4} + \dfrac{x}{2}\right\}$, show that $\dfrac{dy}{dx} = \sec x$.

(c) If $y = \dfrac{1 + \sin x}{\cos x}$ show that $\dfrac{dy}{dx} = \dfrac{1}{1 - \sin x}$.

(Burton-upon-Trent.)

43. (a) Differentiate, with respect to x,

$$4 \cdot \sqrt{x} + \frac{12}{\sqrt[3]{x^2}} - 2 + 3 \cdot \sqrt[3]{x^4},$$

giving the answer in root form.

(b) If $y = 3 \sin 2\theta + 4 \cos \tfrac{1}{2}\theta - \log \cos \theta$, find $\dfrac{dy}{dx}$.

(c) Find $\dfrac{d}{dx} \dfrac{(7 - 3x)}{(2 + 5x)}$, expressing the answer in its simplest form.

(d) The equations to a curve is $y = Kx^{\frac{1}{3}}$. It passes through the point $x = 8$, $y = 3$. Find K. Hence find the gradient of the curve at the point (8, 3).

(e) If $f(t) = \dfrac{3t^3 - 5t^2 + 2t - 3}{t^2}$, find $f''(t)$.

(Shrewsbury.)

44. (a) In a circuit there are two resistances, one constant of 10 ohms, and one variable, r ohms. The total resistance, R ohms, is given by:

$$R = \frac{10r}{10 + r}.$$

Without finding its actual value, find the change in the value of R when r is increased from 16 to 16·04 ohms.

(S.W. Essex.)

45. (i) If the expansion of $(1 + x)^x$ can be deduced from the expansion of $(1 + x)^n$ by replacing n by x, show that the first four terms in the expansion of $(1 + x)^x$ are

$$1 + x^2 - \tfrac{1}{2}x^3 + \tfrac{5}{6}x^4.$$

(ii) The deflection at the centre of a bar loaded transversely is proportional to $\dfrac{Wl^3}{d^4}$. What is the percentage change in the deflection if W is increased 2%, l is decreased $1\frac{1}{2}$% and d is increased 1%?   (Sunderland.)

46. A rectangular box, open at the top, is to be made from sheet metal. The width (w) is to be twice the height (h) and the box is to be made from 20 sq ft of metal. Find: (a) the length (l) of the box in terms of the height (h); (b) the maximum capacity of the box; (c) the maximum capacity of a geometrically similar box made from 25 sq ft of metal.   (N.C.T.E.C.)

47. (a) If $y = x^2 - 3$, find $\frac{dy}{dx}$ from first principles.

(b) Differentiate each of the following expressions with respect to x:

$\quad$ (i) $x^2 e^{2x}$ $\quad$ (ii) $\log_e \dfrac{2}{\sqrt{x}}$ $\quad$ (iii) $\sqrt{4 - x^4}$.

(c) If $E = L\dfrac{di}{dt} + Ri$ for all values of t and if

$$i = 10 \sin 100\pi t,$$

$R = 0.5$, $L = 0.0004$ and $100\pi t$ is an angle of radians, calculate the value of E when $t = 0.003$.

$\hfill$ (E.M.E.U.)

48. A closed storage tank consists of a cylinder with hemispherical ends. If the volume of the tank is 600 cu ft show that the surface area A sq ft of the tank is given by $A = \dfrac{4\pi r^2}{3} + \dfrac{1200}{r}$, where r ft is the radius of the tank. Hence, find this radius when the surface area is a minimum and show clearly that this is a minimum.   (Surrey.)

49. (i) What conditions must be satisfied if the function $y = f(x)$ is to have a maximum at $x = a$?

(ii) A body moves s ft in t sec given by

$$s = t^4 - 6t^3 - 24t^2 + 16t - 7.$$

Find the time at which the acceleration is zero. Also find the time at which the velocity is a minimum and find the minimum velocity.   (West Riding.)

CHAPTER 8

TRIGONOMETRY

1. Measurement of Angles

The figure below, to which we shall refer as the "angle generator," consists of the usual axes XOX_1, YOY_1 at right angles to each other, and a movable radius OP.

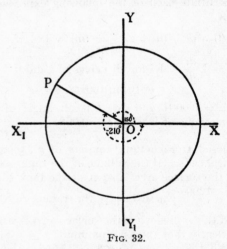

FIG. 32.

The amount of turning which OP undergoes in passing from the position OX to its present position is called the angle POX.

If OP turns anti-clockwise, the angle POX is regarded as positive; if clockwise, negative.

Thus OP will occupy the same position on the generator if POX $= 150°$ or $- 210°$.

We observe, further, that we can generate positive or negative angles of any size, though the greatest angle we can picture on the generator is one of 360° or four right angles.

In generating an angle of 390°, OP would occupy the same position as in generating an angle of 30°.

Angles will be measured in degrees or in radians, a radian being the angle subtended at the centre of a circle by an arc equal in length to the radius. Observe in this definition that the radius must be bent to coincide with the arc.

The value of 1 radian in degrees, minutes and seconds is 57° 17′ 44″, approx.

We assume that the student can convert degrees to radians, or radians to degrees. (See Volumes I and II.)

An angle can be measured in terms of a unit angle, that is as so many degrees, or so many radians, but the fundamental measure of an angle is by the ratio $\dfrac{arc}{radius}$. This is a ratio of two lengths; and if both are stated in terms of the same unit the unit length can be cancelled, leaving the radian as a unit not tied to any system of length measurement.

Example

A thin rod whose length is 25 in. is bent into the form of an arc of a circle. The distance between the ends of the rod is 20 in. If ϕ is the angle in degrees subtended by the rod at the centre of the circle of which it forms part show that

$$\sin \frac{\phi}{2} = \frac{\pi\phi}{450} \qquad \text{(U.L.C.I.)}$$

Suppose that O is the centre of the circle.

OA is the radius $= r$, say.

ODB bisects the arc, the chord AC, and the angle AOC $(= \phi)$.

Then arc AB = $12\frac{1}{2}$ in. and AD = 10 in.

(1) Express $\dfrac{\phi}{2}$ in radian measure, thus: let $\dfrac{\phi^\circ}{2} = \alpha$ radians.

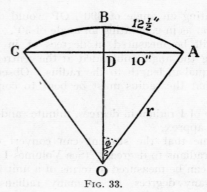

FIG. 33.

Then

$$\frac{\phi}{360} = \frac{\alpha}{\pi}$$

i.e.,

$$\alpha = \frac{\pi\phi}{360} = \frac{12\frac{1}{2}}{r}$$

i.e.,

$$\frac{25}{2r} = \frac{\pi\phi}{360} \qquad \cdots \cdots \quad (1)$$

From the figure $r \sin \dfrac{\phi}{2} = 10 \qquad \cdots \cdots \quad (2)$

Substitute for r in (1) and get the result.

2. The Trigonometrical Ratios of Angles of Any Magnitude

Let XOP be any angle.   The radius OP is shown (Fig. 34) in each of the four quadrants.

Drop PM perpendicular to the x-axis.

The triangle MOP will be referred to always as the " defining triangle," since its sides are used to define the trigonometrical ratios of the angle XOP.

Each side of this triangle will be named thus: OP is the hypotenuse—denoted by " *h* " the initial letter.

PM is the ordinate (or opposite), denoted by " *o*."

OM is the abscissa (or adjacent) denoted by " *a*."

The terms ordinate and abscissa will be quite familiar from the student's graphic work.

For the ordinate and abscissa the rule of signs, as in graphs, holds; whilst OP or *h* is always positive.

The appropriate signs are placed on each figure.

In every case let XOP = θ.

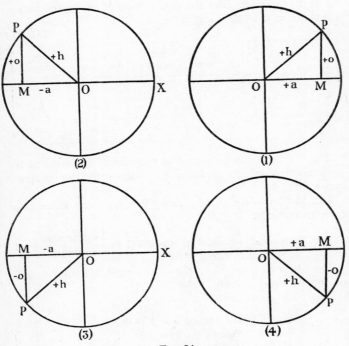

FIG. 34.

The equations of definition are:

$$\sin \theta = \frac{\text{ordinate}}{\text{hypotenuse}} = \frac{o}{h}$$

$$\cos \theta = \frac{\text{abscissa}}{\text{hypotenuse}} = \frac{a}{h}$$

$$\tan \theta = \frac{\text{ordinate}}{\text{abscissa}} = \frac{o}{a}.$$

The signs of these ratios vary with the quadrant in which OP stops. Anyone familiar with graphs will have no difficulty in seeing that the signs to be given to the ratios are those in the following table.

	1st Quadrant.	2nd Quadrant.	3rd Quadrant.	4th Quadrant.
sin . . .	+	+	−	−
cos . . .	+	−	−	+
tan . . .	+	−	+	−
positive . .	All	sin	tan	cos

The words in the bottom row may assist the student in remembering which ratios are positive in the various quadrants.

In addition to the three ratios given, we must know also their **reciprocals.**

The reciprocal of $\sin \theta$ is *cosec* θ $\left(= \dfrac{\text{hypotenuse}}{\text{ordinate}} \right)$, of $\cos \theta$ is *sec* θ, and of $\tan \theta$ is *cot* θ.

The abbreviations are those of cosecant θ, secant θ and cotangent θ respectively.

Hence for all angles

$$\left. \begin{array}{l} \sin \theta \, . \, \text{cosec} \, \theta = 1 \\ \cos \theta \, . \, \sec \theta = 1 \\ \tan \theta \, . \, \cot \theta = 1 \end{array} \right\} \quad . \quad . \quad . \quad . \quad (1)$$

Notice also that $\tan \theta = \dfrac{o}{a} = \dfrac{\dfrac{o}{h}}{\dfrac{a}{h}} = \dfrac{\sin \theta}{\cos \theta}$ . . . (2)

And $\therefore$ $\cot \theta = \dfrac{\cos \theta}{\sin \theta}$ . . . . . . (3)

Further, in each of the four figures—*i.e.*, for all values of θ

$$o^2 + a^2 = h^2 \quad . \quad . \quad . \quad . \quad (4)$$

Dividing both sides of (4) by h^2, we get:

$$\dfrac{o^2}{h^2} + \dfrac{a^2}{h^2} = 1$$

i.e., $\sin^2 \theta + \cos^2 \theta = 1$ . . . . (5)

Similarly, dividing (4) by o^2 and a^2 in succession

we get $1 + \cot^2 \theta = \operatorname{cosec}^2 \theta$ . . . . (6)

and $\tan^2 \theta + 1 = \sec^2 \theta$ . . . . (7)

The values of the trigonometrical ratios of certain angles are given below.

	0°	30°	45°	60°	90°
sin . . .	0	$\frac{1}{2}$	$\frac{1}{\sqrt{2}}$	$\frac{\sqrt{3}}{2}$	1
cos . . .	1	$\frac{\sqrt{3}}{2}$	$\frac{1}{\sqrt{2}}$	$\frac{1}{2}$	0
tan . . .	0	$\frac{1}{\sqrt{3}}$	1	$\sqrt{3}$	∞
cosec . .	∞	3	$\sqrt{2}$	$\frac{2}{\sqrt{3}}$	1
sec . . .	1	$\frac{2}{\sqrt{3}}$	$\sqrt{2}$	2	∞
cot . . .	∞	$\sqrt{3}$	1	$\frac{1}{\sqrt{3}}$	0

3. Graphs of the Trigonometrical Functions

The following facts assist us in drawing the graphs of the trigonometrical functions:

1. $\sin \theta$ and $\cos \theta$ are never numerically greater than unity. Both have values between $+ 1$ and $- 1$.

2. Their reciprocals $\operatorname{cosec} \theta$ and $\sec \theta$ are never numerically less than unity.

3. $\tan \theta$ and $\cot \theta$ have values ranging from $- \infty$ to $+ \infty$.

4. We need to know the values of any of the functions only in the range from $\theta = 0$ to $\theta = 90°$ $\left(\text{or } \dfrac{\pi}{2}\right)$, in order to ascertain the values for any angle.

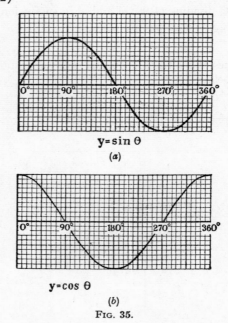

y = sin θ

(a)

y = cos θ

(b)

Fig. 35.

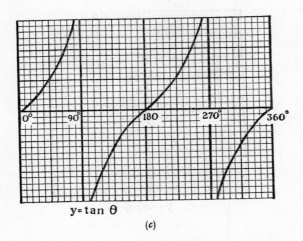

y= tan θ

(c)

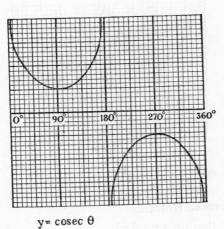

y= cosec θ

(d)

FIG. 35.

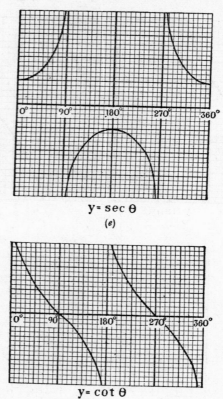

y = sec θ

(e)

y = cot θ

(f)

FIG. 35.

4. The Inverse Notation

Suppose that we are asked: "Given that $\sin \theta = \frac{2}{3}$, find $\tan \theta$, $\cos \theta$ and $\cot \theta$."

We remember that $\sin \theta$ is the ratio of two sides of a right-angled triangle in which we know the acute angle θ

as well as the right angle. Since the three angles of this triangle are equal to two right angles we also know that the third angle is

$$(90 - \theta) \text{ degrees}$$

or
$$(\pi - \theta)$$

if the angles are measured in radians. This third angle is also acute.

Thus, starting with any line as base we can draw lines from its two ends at angles θ and 90° respectively to it. The two lines will intersect and give us a triangle.

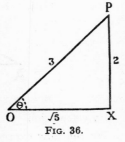

FIG. 36.

The actual size of this triangle depends upon the length of base line taken. All triangles drawn thus will, however, be of the same shape, corresponding angles being equal. By deciding the length of any one side the others are determined and can be measured; or we can use the figure as a reference diagram only, and calculate the lengths of the two outstanding sides. Suppose that we proceed in this way taking the side PX as two units of length, and PO as three units. Clearly by Pythagoras' theorem the base OX must be $\sqrt{5}$ units of length. Then we can write down from the figure any ratio of the angle θ.

Thus

$$\tan \theta = \frac{2}{\sqrt{5}} = \frac{2\sqrt{5}}{5}$$

$$\cos \theta = \frac{\sqrt{5}}{3} \text{ and } \cot \theta = \frac{\sqrt{5}}{2}.$$

Similarly, if we are asked to express every trigonometrical ratio of θ in terms of $\tan \theta$, we proceed in exactly the same way.

Putting $\tan \theta = a$

i.e., $\tan \theta = \dfrac{a}{1}$

we construct a triangle embodying the angle θ, and two lengths whose ratio is the tangent of θ.

The triangle is sketched.   Since the value of $\tan \theta$ is a, we let BC = a, and AB = 1.

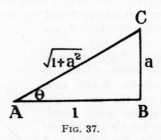

FIG. 37.

By calculation $AC = \sqrt{1 + a^2}$.

We can now express every trigonometrical ratio of θ in terms of a—*i.e.*, in terms of $\tan \theta$.

Thus $\sin \theta = \dfrac{a}{\sqrt{1 + a^2}} = \dfrac{\tan \theta}{\sqrt{1 + \tan^2 \theta}}$

We now come to the " Inverse of Notation."

If $\cos \theta = a$,

it is common to write: $\theta = \cos^{-1} a$.

Any equation such as this must be read by the student thus: " θ is the angle whose cosine is a."

For example, $\cos^{-1} \frac{1}{2}$ means the angle whose cosine is $\frac{1}{2}$ —*i.e.*, $60°$ or $\dfrac{\pi}{3}$.

Similarly, $\tan^{-1} 1$ is the angle whose tangent is 1—*i.e.*, $45°$ or $\dfrac{\pi}{4}$.

Further,

$$\sin^{-1}\frac{\sqrt{3}}{2} + \cos^{-1}\frac{1}{\sqrt{2}} = 60° + 45°$$
$$= 105°$$

and is thus the sum of two angles.

It is convenient to have a notation which expresses by an easy symbol: " The angle whose sine is . . ."

Once the inverse notation is adopted it is clear that $\sin^{-1} x$ and $(\sin x)^{-1}$ must be carefully differentiated.

Sin$^{-1} x$ is the angle whose sine is x; but

$$(\sin x)^{-1} = \frac{1}{\sin x} = \operatorname{cosec} x,$$

and means the reciprocal of $\sin x$, just as $x^{-1} = \frac{1}{x}$, the reciprocal of x.

The inverse notation very well expresses the fact that, unless sample angles are available in form suitable for comparison,* an angle must in practice be measured by forming the ratio of two lengths—these lengths to be taken from a standard figure whose shape is determined by the angle. If we speak of an angle as so many radians, the reference figure is a sector of a circle having the given angle between the two bounding radii. When we say that an angle is $\sin^{-1} a$ our figure of reference is a *right-angled* triangle which incorporates the given angle. Just as when we measure an angle in radians, the length unit cancels.

For most practical purposes $\sin^{-1} a$ or $\tan^{-1} a$ is the best way of stating the size of an angle, because in forming the ratio we need only measure *straight* lines.

The sine-bar method of producing the angle $\sin^{-1} x$ in the workshop was introduced in Volume I, p. 232. Further examples of its use occur in the miscellaneous examples of Volumes 2 and 3.

---

* Such specimen angles are marketed by firms that produce precision measuring equipment for use in engineering.

EXERCISE 29

1. State the values of the following, using tables where necessary:

(i) $\sin 124°$,   (ii) $\cos 130°$,   (iii) $\tan(-320°)$,

(iv) $\operatorname{cosec} 348°$,   (v) $\sec(-290°)$,   (vi) $\cos \frac{\pi}{6}$,

(vii) $\sin \frac{3\pi}{7}$,   (viii) $\tan \frac{7\pi}{8}$.

2. Given that $\sec \theta = \frac{3}{2}$, find $\cot \theta$ and $\sin \theta$.

3. If $\tan A = 3$, find all the other trigonometrical ratios of A.

4. If $\theta = \cos^{-1} \frac{1}{3}$, find $\sin \theta$ and $\tan \theta$.

5. Show that $\sin^{-1} \frac{\sqrt{3}}{2} + \cos^{-1} \frac{\sqrt{3}}{2} = 90°$.

6. Express the following angles in circular measure:

(i) $30°$,   (ii) $45°$,   (iii) $60°$,   (iv) $120°$,   (v) $228°$.

7. Express the following angles in degrees:

(i) $\frac{\pi}{5}$,   (ii) $\frac{3\pi}{8}$,   (iii) $\frac{\pi}{7}$,   (iv) $\frac{\theta}{3}$,   (v) $\frac{2}{3}$ radians.

8. Show that $\cos^{-1} \frac{1}{\sqrt{2}} + \sin^{-1} \frac{1}{2} = 75°$.

9. Show that $\sin^{-1} 1 + \cos^{-1} 1 = \frac{\pi}{2}$.

10. The following formula is developed in connection with a high-pressure transmission line

$$E_S^2 = (E_R \cos \phi + RI)^2 + (E_R \sin \phi + X . I)^2$$

where E_S is the sending end voltage and E_R the receiving end voltage. Find E_R given that $E_S = 8000$, $\cos \phi\ 0.8$, $R = 8.5$, $X = 6.5$ and $I = 200$.   (U.E.I.)

11. By drawing to scale set off the angles $\sin^{-1} 0.75$ and $\tan^{-1} 1.5$. By drawing circular arcs, and stepping off their lengths with dividers set to a short length, determine these angles in radians, and hence in degrees. Check your work

by reference to the tables of natural sines and natural tangents.

5. Periodic Functions

It will have been noticed that as θ completes the range from $0°$ to $360°$, or from 0 to 2π, $\sin \theta$ takes every possible value. If OP continues to revolve, $\sin \theta$ repeats the previous values.

Now $\sin \theta$ satisfies our definition of a function of θ, since when θ is given a value, $\sin \theta$ takes a value.

It is called a *periodic* function of θ whose period is **360°** or 2π radians, because each time θ is increased by 2π, $\sin \theta$ has the same value as before.

Thus $\sin \theta = \sin (\theta + 2\pi)$.
Similarly, $\cos \theta = \cos (\theta + 2\pi)$.

But note $\tan \theta = (\theta + \pi)$, showing that the period of $\tan \theta$ is π.

Now let OP start from OX, and turn in the positive sense at the rate of 3 radians per sec. In t sec, $\text{XOP} = 3t$ radians and $\sin \text{XOP} = \sin 3t$.

No matter what value t may have

$$\sin 3t = \sin (3t + 2\pi)$$
$$= \sin \left[3\left(t + \frac{2\pi}{3} \right) \right].$$

Notice that the sine has the same value at times " t " and " $t + \dfrac{2\pi}{3}$." In this case $\sin 3t$ is a periodic function of t, and its period is $\dfrac{2\pi}{3}$.

Generally, since

$$\sin nx = \sin (nx + 2\pi)$$
$$= \sin n\left(x + \frac{2\pi}{n} \right)$$

the period of $\sin nx$ is $\dfrac{2\pi}{n}$.

Similarly, we find that the period of $\cos k\theta$ is $\dfrac{2\pi}{k}$,

since $$\mathbf{cos}\ \mathit{k}\theta = \mathbf{cos}\ (\mathit{k}\theta + 2\pi)$$
$$= \mathbf{cos}\ \mathit{k}\left(\theta + \frac{2\pi}{k}\right)$$

showing that $\cos k\theta$ has the same value for angles θ and $\left(\theta + \dfrac{2\pi}{k}\right)$.

The addition of a constant to the angle does not affect the period.

Thus $$\sin(3x + 4) = \sin(3x + 4 + 2\pi)$$
$$= \sin\left\{3\left(x + \frac{2\pi}{3}\right) + 4\right\}$$

showing that the period is $\dfrac{2\pi}{3}$.

Now consider $3\sin 2x + 4\cos 4x$. The period of $\sin 2x$ is $\dfrac{2\pi}{2}$—*i.e.*, π—that of $\cos 4x$ is $\dfrac{2\pi}{4}$—*i.e.*, $\dfrac{\pi}{2}$.

Hence the expression $3\sin 2x + 4\cos 4x$ will have the same value for angles x, $x + \pi$, $x + 2\pi$, etc.—*i.e.*, its period is π.

Trigonometric ratios are by their nature *periodic* functions. Hence if there is need to define some periodic function, this will be done by an expression involving trigonometrical ratios even though no angle is directly concerned. An example is the law of the vibration of a mass suspended from a spring.

6. The Solution of Trigonometrical Equations

Fig. 38 (1) shows two angles XOP, XOP_1 whose sines are equal.

If $$\text{XOP} = \theta \quad \text{XOP}_1 = \pi - \theta$$
and $$\sin\theta = \frac{\text{MP}}{\text{OP}} = \frac{\text{M}_1\text{P}_1}{\text{OP}_1} = \sin(\pi - \theta).$$

Hence between 0 and 2π there are two angles whose sines have the same value.

We know that $\sin 60° = \dfrac{\sqrt{3}}{2} = 0\cdot866$. If we try to solve $\sin x° = \dfrac{\sqrt{3}}{2}$, we infer at once that *one* value of x is 60°. There is, however, another value—viz., the supplement of 60°. Hence there are two solutions giving angles between 0° and 360°—viz., 60° and 120°.

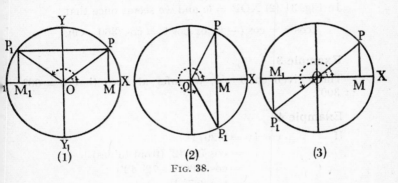

Fig. 38.

The number of solutions is infinite, since we can increase either of the above angles by any integral multiple of 360°.

Usually we are interested only in those values of x between 0° and 360°.

Example 1

Solve $\sin 3x° = \tfrac{1}{2}$.
                           $\sin 3x° = \sin 30° = \sin 150°$
                    $\therefore \quad 3x = 30°$ or $150°$
i.e., $x = 10°$ or $50°$.

Example 2

Solve $\sin 5x = 0\cdot3971$.

We have, $\sin 5x = \sin 23° 24'$ (from the tables)
$$= \sin 156° 36' \text{ (using the supplement)}$$

$\therefore \quad 5x = 23° 24' \text{ or } 156° 36' \quad . \quad . \quad . \quad . \quad (1)$

$\therefore \quad x = 4° 41' \text{ or } 31° 19' \quad . \quad . \quad . \quad . \quad (2)$

correct to the nearest minute.

If we require any more values, we can get them by adding multiples of 360° to the angles (1), or what is the same thing multiples of 72° to the angles (2).

In Fig. 31 (2) XOP = θ, and we see at once that

$$\cos \theta = \cos (-\theta) \text{ or } \cos \theta = \cos (360 - \theta).$$

Example 3

Thus, given $\cos \theta = \frac{1}{2}$, we infer at once that $\theta = 60°$ or 300°.

Example 4

If $\qquad \cos 4x = 0.2974$
$$= \cos 72° 42' \text{ (from tables)}$$
$$= \cos (360° - 72° 42')$$
$$= \cos 287° 18'$$

$\therefore \quad 4x = 72° 42' \text{ or } 287° 18'$

i.e., $\qquad x = 18° 10.5' \text{ or } 71° 49.5'.$

In Fig. 38 (3) if   XOP = θ and XOP$_1$ = $\pi + \theta$,
$$\tan \theta = \tan (\pi + \theta).$$

Example 5

$$\text{Solve } \tan x° = \frac{1}{\sqrt{3}}.$$

$$\tan x° = \frac{1}{\sqrt{3}} = \tan 30°$$
$$x = 30° \text{ or } (180 + 30)°$$
$$= 30° \text{ or } 210°.$$

7. To Express the Trigonometrical Ratios of Negative Angles in Terms of those of the Corresponding Positive Angle

Suppose $XOP = \theta$ and $XOP_1 = -\theta$.

Notice that the defining triangles for each angle are congruent. They have a common side OM. The signs to be placed on abscissæ and ordinates are shown. We get:

$$\sin \theta = \frac{MP}{OP} = -\frac{MP_1}{OP_1} = -\sin(-\theta)$$

$$\cos \theta = \frac{OM}{OP} = \frac{OM}{OP_1} = \cos(-\theta)$$

$$\tan \theta = \frac{MP}{OM} = -\frac{MP_1}{OM} = -\tan(-\theta)$$

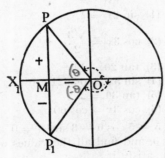

Fig. 39.

Hence
$$\left.\begin{array}{l}
\sin(-\theta) = -\sin \theta \\
\cos(-\theta) = \cos \theta \\
\tan(-\theta) = -\tan \theta
\end{array}\right\}$$

Taking the reciprocals of these, we have:

$$\left.\begin{array}{l}
\operatorname{cosec}(-\theta) = -\operatorname{cosec} \theta \\
\sec(-\theta) = \sec \theta \\
\tan(-\theta) = -\tan \theta
\end{array}\right\}$$

EXERCISE 30

1. Explain what is meant by saying that $\sin \theta$, $\cos \theta$ and $\tan \theta$ are periodic functions of θ. State their periods.

2. If t represents time in seconds measured from some fixed instant, find the number of seconds that has elapsed before $\sin 2t$ again reaches the value it had at time t.

3. Find the periods of (i) $\sin 3t$, (ii) $\cos 4t$, (iii) $\tan 3t$, (iv) $\cos (5x + 4)$, (v) $\sin (ax + \alpha)$, (vi) $3 \sin 5x + 4 \cos 2x$, (vii) $2 \cos 3x - \sin 4x$.

4. Write down the values of the trigonometrical ratios of $(90 + A)$ in terms of those of A.

5. Solve the following trigonometrical equations, giving in each case two values of the angle between $0°$ and $360°$ which satisfies it:

$\quad$ (1) $\sin 2x = \frac{1}{2}$.

$\quad$ (2) $\cos 3x = \dfrac{\sqrt{3}}{2}$.

$\quad$ (3) $\tan 2\theta = 1$.

$\quad$ (4) $\sin 5x = 0\cdot3621$.

$\quad$ (5) $\tan 3\theta = 2$.

$\quad$ (6) $\cos 3x = \cos 60°$.

6. Express $5 - 5 \cos \theta - 3 \sin^2 \theta = 0$ as a quadratic equation in $\cos \theta$, and find all the values of θ between $0°$ and $360°$ which satisfy it.

7. Use the relation $\sec^2 \theta = 1 + \tan^2 \theta$ to find all the values of θ between $0°$ and $360°$ which satisfy the equation

$$\tan^2 \theta - \sec \theta - 5 = 0.$$

8. Solve $14 - 11 \sin \theta - 12 \cos^2 \theta = 0$, for values of θ between $0°$ and $360°$.

9. Find the periods of

$\quad$ (1) $\sin (3t + 2)$.

$\quad$ (2) $\cos (5t + 3)$.

$\quad$ (3) $\sin (2t + \alpha)$.

    (4) $\tan (4t + \beta)$.

    (5) $\sin (ax + \alpha) + \cos (3ax + \beta)$.

10. Express the following in terms of the trigonometrical ratios of the corresponding positive angle:

    (1) $\sin (- 20°)$.

    (2) $\cos (- 60°)$.

    (3) $\tan (- 42°)$.

    (4) $\sec (- 130°)$.

CHAPTER 9

COMPOUND ANGLES

1. Projections

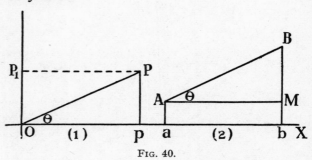

Fig. 40.

AB is any segment of a straight line. It may be considered to have two senses—viz., AB and BA, which leads to the statement AB = − BA.

If Aa, Bb are perpendicular to any line OX, then ab is the orthogonal projection of AB on OX.

If OP is equal and parallel to AB, and Pp is drawn perpendicular to OX, then Op = ab. This may be expressed "equal and parallel straight lines have equal projections on any other straight line."

If AM is parallel to OX, we have AM = ab = AB cos θ.

Further, notice that Op_1 = pP = MB = AB sin θ.

Hence, the projections of any line AB which makes an angle θ with OX are

$$\left.\begin{array}{l}\text{AB cos θ on the } x\text{-axis}\\ \text{AB sin θ on the } y\text{-axis}\end{array}\right\} \quad \cdots \cdots \quad (1)$$

and

also   AB^2 = AM^2 + BM^2.

196

Hence if we know the lengths, AM and BM, of the projections of AB on two straight lines at right angles, we can find the length of AB.

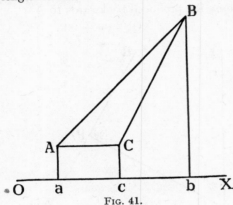

FIG. 41.

2. The Sum of Projections

Let ABC be any triangle; drop the perpendiculars Aa, Bb, Cc on OX.

Now notice from the above figure that

$$ab = ac + cb,$$

i.e., the projection of AB = the sum of the projections of the two straight lines joining A to B.

By drawing any figure, the student will see that the projection of AB = sum of the projections of all the straight lines joining A to B in any way. It is not even necessary to keep to the plane of the paper.

The above property of projections is often stated thus:

The sum of the projections of the sides of any closed polygon, on any straight line is zero.

In the case of the triangle above, we have

$$ac + cb + ba = 0,$$

since
$$ba = -ab.$$

3. Let OP make θ with OX, and let PR be perpendicular to OP.

Then PR makes 90° + θ with OX, as can readily be seen by imagining RP produced backwards to Q

$$\angle XQP = θ + 90°.$$

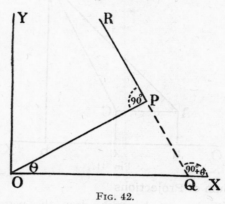

FIG. 42.

Hence the projection of PR on OX is, by using a previous result,

$$PR \cos (90 + θ).$$

But $\qquad \cos (θ + 90) = - \sin θ.$

∴ the projection of PR on OX = − PR sin θ.

The projection of OP on the X-axis = OP cos θ⎫
and the projection of OP on the Y-axis = OP sin θ⎭

Similarly, the projection of PR on the Y-axis is

$$PR \sin (90 + θ) = PR \cos θ.$$

Example

Suppose AB = 3 in. and BC = 2 in., and that AB is inclined at 14° to OX, whilst BC makes 30° with AB, as shown in Fig. 43.

We require the length of the projection of AC on OX.

The projection could be readily found by a drawing to scale, but we are interested in calculating it from the diagram.

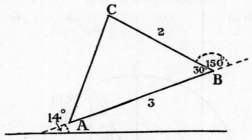

FIG. 43.

The projection of AC = proj. of AB + proj. of BC
$$= 3 \cos 14° + 2 \cos 164° \quad . \quad (1)$$

{Notice that BC makes 150° with AB, and hence 164° with OX.}

(1) becomes
$$3 \cos 14° - 2 \cos 16°$$
$$= 3 \times 0\cdot9703 - 2 \times 0\cdot9613$$
$$= 2\cdot9109 - 1\cdot9226$$
$$= 0\cdot9883 \text{ in.}$$

4. To find cos (A + B) and sin (A + B)

In Fig. 44 suppose $\angle XOQ = A$ and $\angle QOP = B$.
Let PR be $\perp$ to OQ.
Then the projection of OP on OX = the projection of OR on OX + the projection of RP on OX.

i.e., OP cos (A + B) = OR cos A + RP cos (A + 90°)
$$= OR \cos A - RP \sin A \quad . \quad . \quad (1)$$

Now OR = OP cos B and RP = OP sin B.
Substituting for OR and RP in (1), we get:

OP cos (A + B) = OP cos A cos B - OP sin A sin B.

Hence, cancelling OP,

$$\cos (A + B) = \cos A \cos B - \sin A \sin B \qquad (2)$$

For sin (A + B), project OP on OY. We get:

$$OP \sin (A + B) = OR \sin A + RP \sin (A + 90°)$$
$$= OR \sin A + RP \cos A.$$

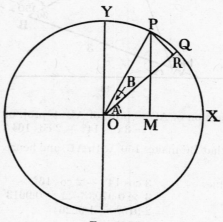

Fig. 44.

Substitute for OR and RP as before, and get:

$$OP \sin (A + B) = OP \sin A \cos B + OP \cos A \sin B.$$

Now divide throughout by OP, and

$$\sin (A + B) = \sin A \cos B + \cos A \sin B \qquad (3)$$

The figure in the preceding proof has been drawn for two positive angles whose sum falls in the first quadrant, but the proof is quite general for all angles.

Now take cos (A + B) = cos A cos B — sin A sin B and write (— B) for + B.

We get:

$$\cos (A - B) = \cos A \cos (- B) - \sin A \sin (- B)$$

i.e., $\qquad \mathbf{cos\ (A - B) = cos\ A\ cos\ B + sin\ A\ sin\ B}$. (4)

since $\qquad\qquad\qquad \cos (- B) = \cos B$

and $\qquad\qquad\qquad \sin (- B) = - \sin B.$

Similarly, writing $- B$ for $+ B$ in (3) we get:

$$\sin (A - B) = \sin A \cos (- B) + \cos A \sin (- B)$$

i.e., $\qquad \mathbf{sin\ (A - B) = sin\ A\ cos\ B - cos\ A\ sin\ B}$ . . (5)

The four formulæ (2), (3), (4), (5) are collected here for reference, and should be memorised.

$$\left.\begin{array}{l} \mathbf{sin\ (A + B) = sin\ A\ cos\ B + cos\ A\ sin\ B} \\ \mathbf{sin\ (A - B) = sin\ A\ cos\ B - cos\ A\ sin\ B} \end{array}\right\}$$

$$\left.\begin{array}{l} \mathbf{cos\ (A + B) = cos\ A\ cos\ B - sin\ A\ sin\ B} \\ \mathbf{cos\ (A - B) = cos\ A\ cos\ B + sin\ A\ sin\ B} \end{array}\right\}.$$

Example

Find, without using tables, sin 75°.

$$\sin 75° = \sin (45 + 30)° = \sin 45° \cos 30° + \cos 45° \sin 30°$$

$$= \frac{1}{\sqrt{2}} \cdot \frac{\sqrt{3}}{2} + \frac{1}{\sqrt{2}} \cdot \frac{1}{2}$$

$$= \frac{\sqrt{3} + 1}{2\sqrt{2}}.$$

5. Consider the two equations

$$r \sin \alpha = 2 \quad . \quad . \quad . \quad . \quad . \quad (1)$$

$$r \cos \alpha = 3 \quad . \quad . \quad . \quad . \quad . \quad (2)$$

they are a pair of simultaneous equations in which one unknown is a number, the other an angle.

Squaring both sides, then adding, we get:

$$r^2 (\sin^2 \alpha + \cos^2 \alpha) = 13$$

i.e., $\qquad r^2 = 13$, since $\sin^2 \alpha + \cos^2 \alpha = 1.$

Taking the positive square root for r, this gives:

$$r = \sqrt{13} = 3 \cdot 61.$$

Now divide (1) by (2) we get:

$$\tan \alpha = \tfrac{2}{3} = 0 \cdot 6666 \ldots$$

$$\therefore \quad \alpha = 33° \ 41' \text{ from the tables.}$$

This method of finding r and α by squaring and adding, as illustrated above, is important. It depends of course on the fact that the trigonometrical ratios are formed from the sides of a right-angled triangle, to which Pythagoras' Theorem applies.

Example 1

Express $3 \sin x + 2 \cos x$ *in the form* $r \sin (x + \alpha)$, *where r and α are determinate.*

Let $3 \sin x + 2 \cos x \equiv r \sin (x + \alpha)$; then expanding $\sin (x + \alpha)$ we get:

$$3 \sin x + 2 \cos x \equiv r \sin x \cos \alpha + r \cos x \sin \alpha$$
$$\equiv r \cos \alpha \,.\, \sin x + r \sin a \,.\, \cos x.$$

This will be true if $r \cos \alpha = 3$ and $r \sin \alpha = 2$.
We have found values for r and α above.
Hence:

$$3 \sin x + 2 \cos x = \sqrt{13} \sin (x + 33° \ 41').$$

Example 2

Express $3 \sin nx + 4 \cos nx$ *in the form* $R \sin (nx + \alpha)$ *where R and α are independent of x.*
Find the values of x between $0°$ and $360°$ for which

$$3 \sin \frac{x}{2} + 4 \cos \frac{x}{2} = 2. \qquad \text{(N.C.T.E.C.)}$$

We must have

$$3 \sin nx + 4 \cos nx \equiv R \sin (nx + \alpha)$$
$$\equiv R (\sin nx \cos \alpha + \cos nx \sin \alpha)$$
$$\equiv R \cos \alpha \,.\, \sin nx + R \sin \alpha \cos nx.$$

Hence we put:

$$R \cos \alpha = 3 \quad . \quad . \quad . \quad . \quad . \quad (1)$$

and

$$R \sin \alpha = 4 \quad . \quad . \quad . \quad . \quad (2)$$

Solving (1) and (2) in the way shown, it follows that:

$R^2 = 25$, $\therefore$ R = 5 (taking the + square root) and dividing (2) by (1)

$$\tan \alpha = \tfrac{4}{3} = 1 \cdot 3333$$
$$\therefore \quad \alpha = 53° \, 8' \text{ (from the tables)}.$$

So that:

$$3 \sin nx + 4 \cos nx = 5 \sin (nx + 53° \, 8') \quad . \quad (3)$$

To solve

$$3 \sin \frac{x}{2} + 4 \cos \frac{x}{2} = 2 \quad . \quad . \quad . \quad (4)$$

notice that the left-hand side of (4) is the same as that of (3) if we put $n = \tfrac{1}{2}$.

$$\therefore \quad 5 \sin \left(\frac{x}{2} + 53° \, 8' \right) = 2$$

or

$$\sin \left(\frac{x}{2} + 53° \, 8' \right) = \frac{2}{5} = 0 \cdot 4.$$

From the tables, $\sin 23° \, 35' = 0 \cdot 4.$
Hence, also, $\sin (180 - 23° \, 35') = 0 \cdot 4.$

$$\therefore \quad \frac{x}{2} + 53° \, 8' = 23° \, 35' \text{ or } 156° \, 25' \text{ or } 383° \, 35' \text{ or } \ldots$$

$$\therefore \quad \frac{x}{2} = -29° \, 33' \text{ or } 103° \, 17' \text{ or } 330° \, 27' \text{ or } \ldots$$

$$\therefore \quad x = -59° \, 6' \text{ or } 206° \, 34' \text{ or } 660° \, 54' \text{ or } \ldots$$

$\therefore$ For the values of x between 0° and 360°, $x = 206° \, 34'$

EXERCISE 31

1. A man walks for 3·2 miles in a direction 13° N. of E., and then 5·4 miles in a direction 27° N. of E. How far due E. has he travelled; and how far due N.?

2. ABC is a triangle whose side AB is inclined at 13°
to the horizontal OX.

If AB = 7 in., BC = 5 in., and the angle ABC = 63°,
find

> (1) the projection of AC on OX.
> (2) its projection on a perpendicular to OX.

Hence deduce the length of AC.

3. Solve for r and α

$$(1) \quad \left.\begin{array}{l} r\cos\alpha = 2 \\ r\sin\alpha = 1 \end{array}\right\}$$

$$(2) \quad \left.\begin{array}{l} r\sin\alpha = 3 \\ r\cos\alpha = 5 \end{array}\right\}.$$

Then put $2\sin x + \cos x$ in the form $r\sin(x + \alpha)$ and
$5\cos x - 3\sin x$ in the form $r\cos(x + \alpha)$.

4. Find all the values of x between 0° and 360° for which

$$4{\cdot}37\cos 3x + 3{\cdot}84\sin 3x = 5{\cdot}73.$$

(U.L.C.I.)

5. (*a*) Write out the formulæ for sin (A + B), sin (A − B),
cos (A + B), and cos (A − B).   Prove any one of them.

(*b*) Use the formulæ to find the value of sin 75° and of
tan 15°.   (U.L.C.I.)

6. Show $\sin\theta + \sin(\theta + 120) + \sin(\theta + 240) = 0$.

(U.L.C.I.)

7. By expanding $\sin(\theta + 90)$ and $\cos(\theta + 90)$ or
otherwise, show

$$\sin(\theta + 90) = \cos\theta \text{ and } \cos(\theta + 90) = -\sin\theta.$$

(U.L.C.I.)

8. Find, without using the calculus, the maximum value
of $2\cos x + 3\sin x$.

9. Two straight rods OA, OB of lengths 3 ft and 2 ft
respectively, are rigidly joined at O so that ∠AOB = 30°.
Initially OA lies along a horizontal line OX, and B is above
OX.   If the rods rotate about O in a vertical plane, with a
uniform angular velocity of 4 radians/sec, find an expression

for the length of the projection on OX of the join BA at time t sec.   Deduce the maximum value of this projection and the smallest value of t which gives it.   (U.L.C.I.)

10. Show that
$$\cos (A + B) . \cos (A - B) = \cos^2 A - \sin^2 B = \cos^2 B - \sin^2 A.$$

11. Find A and α so that $20 \sin \theta + 41 \cos \theta$ may equal $A \sin (\theta + \alpha)$ for all values of θ.

Deduce the values of θ between $0°$ and $360°$ for which the given expression has (1) a maximum value, (2) a minimum value, (3) zero value, (4) the value $43\cdot4$.   (U.L.C.I.)

12. Put the expression $3 \sin x + \sqrt{2} \cos (x + 45)$ in the form $A \sin (x + \alpha)$, where A and α are known.

6.
$$\tan (A + B) = \frac{\sin (A + B)}{\cos (A + B)}$$

$$= \frac{\sin A \cos B + \cos A \sin B}{\cos A \cos B - \sin A \sin B}$$

$$= \frac{\cos A \cos B \left[\dfrac{\sin A}{\cos A} + \dfrac{\sin B}{\cos B} \right]}{\cos A \cos B \left[1 - \dfrac{\sin A}{\cos A} \cdot \dfrac{\sin B}{\cos B} \right]}$$

i.e., $$\tan (A + B) = \frac{\tan A + \tan B}{1 - \tan A \tan B}.$$

Changing the sign of B, we get:

$$\tan (A - B) = \frac{\tan A - \tan B}{1 + \tan A \tan B}.$$

Example

An object which is 6 ft high stands on the top of a tower. At a place on the same horizontal plane as the foot of the tower and 40 ft away from it, the object subtends an angle of 5°. Find the height of the tower.   (U.L.C.I.)

AB is the tower, BC the object, O the point at which BC subtends an angle of 5°.

OA = 40 ft.   BC = 6 ft.

Let $AB = x$ ft and $\angle BOA = \theta°$.

Then $\dfrac{x}{40} = \tan \theta$

and $\dfrac{x + 6}{40} = \tan (\theta + 5)° = \dfrac{\tan \theta + \tan 5°}{1 - \tan \theta \,.\, \tan 5°}$

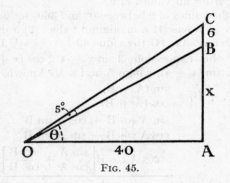

Fig. 45.

$\therefore$ $\dfrac{x + 6}{40} = \dfrac{\dfrac{x}{40} + a}{1 - \dfrac{ax}{40}}$ $\left(\begin{array}{l} a \text{ is put for } \tan 5°\text{—}i.e., \\ a = 0\cdot0875 \end{array}\right)$

i.e., $\dfrac{x + 6}{40} = \dfrac{x + 40a}{40 - ax}.$

$\therefore$ $(x + 6)(40 - ax) = 40(x + 40a)$

i.e., $40x + 240 - ax^2 - 6ax = 40x + 1600a$

giving $ax^2 + 6ax + 1600a - 240 = 0$

i.e., $x^2 + 6x + 1600 - \dfrac{240}{a} = 0$ . . . (1)

$\dfrac{240}{a} = \dfrac{240}{0\cdot0875} = \dfrac{2400}{\frac{7}{8}} = 2743$ (nearly).

Hence (1) becomes

$$x^2 + 6x - 1143 = 0$$

$$x = \frac{-6 \pm \sqrt{36 + 4 \times 1143}}{2}$$

The value of x required is

$$\frac{-6 + \sqrt{36 + 4572}}{2}$$

$$= \frac{-6 + 68}{2} \text{ to the nearest ft.}$$

$$= 31 \, ft.$$

Although mathematically this method is correct, in practice a surveyor would prefer if possible to measure the larger angle θ rather than the small angle $5°$.

7. Double Angle Formulæ

Writing A for B in $\sin (A + B)$, we get:

$$\sin (A + A) = \sin A \cos A + \cos A \sin A$$

i.e., $\sin 2A = 2 \sin A \cos A$.   .   .   .   (1)

or $\sin$ (angle) $= 2 \sin (\tfrac{1}{2}$ angle$) \cos (\tfrac{1}{2}$ angle$)$.

Similarly,

$$\cos (A + A) = \cos A \,.\, \cos A - \sin A \sin A$$

i.e., $\cos 2A = \cos^2 A - \sin^2 A$.   .   .   (2)

This gives the form

$$\cos \text{(angle)} = \cos^2 (\tfrac{1}{2} \text{ angle}) - \sin^2 (\tfrac{1}{2} \text{ angle}).$$

In (2), put $1 - \cos^2 A$ for $\sin^2 A$; then:

$$\cos 2A = \cos^2 A - (1 - \cos^2 A)$$

i.e., $\cos 2A = 2 \cos^2 A - 1$.   .   .   .   (3)

Similarly, putting $(1 - \sin^2 A)$ for $\cos^2 A$ in (2) we get:

$$\cos 2A = 1 - 2 \sin^2 A$$.   .   .   .   (4)

(1), (2), (3) and (4) are important formulæ, frequently very useful in making the substitutions needed in order to solve trigonometrical equations.

Example 1

Given $\cos 30° = \dfrac{\sqrt{3}}{2}$, *find* $\cos 15°$.

$$\cos 30° = 2 \cos^2 15° - 1$$

i.e., $\qquad 2 \cos^2 15° = 1 + \dfrac{\sqrt{3}}{2} = 1\cdot866$

$$\therefore \quad \cos^2 15° = 0\cdot933$$

and taking the square root, we get:

$$\cos 15° = 0\cdot966.$$

Example 2

Given $\sin A = \frac{1}{5}$, *find by calculation*, $\sin 2A$ *and* $\cos 2A$.

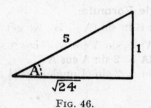

Fig. 46.

We are given $\sin A = \frac{1}{5}$. Sketching the usual triangle containing the angle A, we find the third side is $\sqrt{24}$.

Now $\qquad \sin 2A = 2 \sin A \cdot \cos A$

$$= 2 \times \tfrac{1}{5} \times \dfrac{\sqrt{24}}{5}$$

$$= \dfrac{2\sqrt{24}}{25}.$$

$$\cos 2A = 1 - 2 \sin^2 A$$
$$= 1 - 2 \times \tfrac{1}{25}$$
$$= \tfrac{23}{25}.$$

8. The Tangent of the Double Angle

Since $\tan (A + B) = \dfrac{\tan A + \tan B}{1 - \tan A \tan B}$

putting A for B, we get:

$$\tan 2A = \frac{2 \tan A}{1 - \tan^2 A}$$

Example 1

Given cos A = $\frac{1}{3}$, find tan 2A.

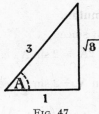

Fig. 47.

Since $\cos A = \frac{1}{3}$, the third side of the triangle is $\sqrt{8}$.

$$\tan 2A = \frac{2 \tan A}{1 - \tan^2 A} = \frac{2\sqrt{8}}{1 - 8} = -\frac{2\sqrt{8}}{7} = -\frac{4\sqrt{2}}{7}.$$

Similarly, if we are given any trigonometrical ratio of the angle A, we can calculate from the double angle formulæ all the trigonometrical ratios of the angle 2A.

Example 2

The values of the crank angle θ for which the velocity of the piston of a certain engine is a maximum are obtained from the equation $\cos \theta + \frac{2}{15} \cos 2\theta = 0$. *Find the two solutions of this equation between* $0°$ *and* $360°$. (U.L.C.I.)

We have $\cos \theta + \frac{2}{15} (2 \cos^2 \theta - 1) = 0$ by substituting for $\cos 2\theta$.

Rewriting the equation, we get:

$$4 \cos^2 \theta + 15 \cos \theta - 2 = 0$$

$$\therefore \quad \cos \theta = \frac{-15 \pm \sqrt{15^2 + 32}}{8}$$

$$= \frac{-15 \pm 16 \cdot 03}{8}$$

$$= 0 \cdot 1288 \text{ (other value rejected as it} > \text{unity).}$$

$\therefore$ From the tables $\theta = 82° \, 36'$ or $360° - 82° \, 36'$, i.e., $277° \, 24'$.

9. Half-Angle Formulæ

It will now be clear since

$$\sin 2A = 2 \sin A \cdot \cos A$$

that

$$\sin A = 2 \sin \frac{A}{2} \cdot \cos \frac{A}{2}$$

for

$$\sin A = \sin \left(2 \cdot \frac{A}{2} \right).$$

Similarly, we get the other " half-angle formulæ "

viz.,

$$\left. \begin{array}{l} \cos A = \cos^2 \dfrac{A}{2} - \sin^2 \dfrac{A}{2} \\[2mm] \qquad = 1 - 2 \sin^2 \dfrac{A}{2} \\[2mm] \qquad = 2 \cos^2 \dfrac{A}{2} - 1 \end{array} \right\}$$

and

$$\tan A = \frac{2 \tan \dfrac{A}{2}}{1 - \tan^2 \dfrac{A}{2}}$$

It will be observed that the formulæ above have the same form as those of pars. 7 and 8.

10. The following very important formulæ will now be proved:

$$\sin S + \sin T = 2 \sin \frac{S + T}{2} . \cos \frac{S - T}{2} \quad . \quad . \quad (1)$$

$$\sin S - \sin T = 2 \cos \frac{S + T}{2} . \sin \frac{S - T}{2} \quad . \quad . \quad (2)$$

$$\cos S + \cos T = 2 \cos \frac{S + T}{2} . \cos \frac{S - T}{2} \quad . \quad . \quad (3)$$

$$\cos T - \cos S = 2 \sin \frac{S + T}{2} . \sin \frac{S - T}{2} \quad . \quad . \quad (4)$$

In the above T is the smaller angle.

$\therefore \cos T > \cos S.$　In (4) we change the order to keep the left-hand side positive.

The above formulæ should be remembered in words. Thus (2) is "*The difference between two sines is equal to twice cos (semi-sum) . sin (semi-difference)*."

(1), (3) and (4) can be translated into similar forms.

11. Proofs of the Formulæ of 10 above

$$\sin (A + B) = \sin A \cos B + \cos A \sin B$$
$$\sin (A - B) = \sin A \cos B - \cos A \sin B.$$

Now add and subtract these: we get

$$\sin (A + B) + \sin (A - B) = 2 \sin A \cos B \quad . \quad . \quad (5)$$

$$\sin (A + B) - \sin (A - B) = 2 \cos A \sin B \quad . \quad . \quad (6)$$

Put 　　　　　　　$A + B = S$

and 　　　　　　　$A - B = T$

adding, 　　　$2A = S + T \qquad \therefore A = \frac{S + T}{2}$

Subtracting 　$2B = S - T \qquad \therefore B = \frac{S - T}{2}.$

Hence (5) becomes:

$$\sin S + \sin T = 2 \sin \frac{S+T}{2} . \cos \frac{S-T}{2}$$

and (6)

$$\sin S - \sin T = 2 \cos \frac{S+T}{2} . \sin \frac{S-T}{2}$$

These are the formulæ (1) and (2).

To prove (3) and (4) we have:

$$\cos (A + B) = \cos A \cos B - \sin A \sin B$$
$$\cos (A - B) = \cos A \cos B + \sin A \sin B$$

adding

$$\cos (A + B) + \cos (A - B) = 2 \cos A \cos B \quad . \quad (7)$$

i.e., $\cos S + \cos T = 2 \cos \dfrac{S+T}{2} \cos \dfrac{S-T}{2}.$ This is (3).

Subtracting, we get

$$\cos (A - B) - \cos (A + B) = 2 \sin A \sin B \quad . \quad (8)$$

i.e., $\cos T - \cos S = 2 \sin \dfrac{S+T}{2} \sin \dfrac{S-T}{2}.$ This is (4).

12. Formulæ (5) to (8) of the last paragraph should be noted. Remember the " form " of these results.

Take (5):

$$2 \sin A \cos B = \sin (A + B) + \sin (A - B).$$

It enables us to express the product $2 \sin A \cos B$ as the sum of two trigonometrical ratios.

This transformation is useful when we come to deal with the integration of trigonometrical functions.

Example

$$2 \sin 3x \cos 2x = \sin 5x + \sin x$$
$$2 \sin 33° \cos 12° = \sin 45° + \sin 21°$$

Similarly, from (7) we get:

$$2 \cos A \cos B = \cos (A + B) + \cos (A - B)$$

Thus $\cos 4x \cos 3x = \frac{1}{2}\{\cos 7x + \cos x\}$

and $\cos 51° \cos 31° = \frac{1}{2}\{\cos 82° + \cos 20°\}.$

From (8) we have:

$$2 \sin A \sin B = \cos (A - B) - \cos (A + B)$$

Hence $2 \sin 3\theta \sin \theta = \cos 2\theta - \cos 4\theta.$

Similarly, from (6)

$$2 \cos 5\alpha \,.\, \sin 2\alpha = \sin 7\alpha - \sin 3\alpha$$

EXERCISE 32

1. (*a*) Write out the formulæ for $\sin 2\theta$ and $\cos 2\theta$ in terms of $\sin \theta$ and $\cos \theta$. Use these formulæ to show that

$$\tan 2\theta = \frac{2 \tan \theta}{1 - \tan^2 \theta}.$$

If $\tan 2\theta = 2$ find without the use of tables the values of $\tan \theta.$ (U.L.C.I.)

2. If $\tan 2A = \dfrac{2\cdot5}{1\cdot375 - b}$ and $\tan A = 2b.$

Calculate:

    (i) the value of b,

    (ii) the least positive value of the angle A to the nearest degree.   (U.E.I.)

3. Write out the value of $\cos 2\theta$ in terms of $\cos \theta$.

Hence solve $5 \cos 2\theta - 13 \cos \theta + 9 = 0$, giving all the solutions between $0°$ and $360°$.   (U.L.C.I.)

4. Assuming the formulæ for the sine of the sum and of the difference of two angles, show that:

$$\sin A + \sin B = 2 \sin \frac{A + B}{2} \cos \frac{A - B}{2}.$$

Express in factors $\sin 3A + \sin A$. Find the value of $\sin 75° + \sin 15°$ using the above formula.   (U.L.C.I.)

5. Find, without using tables, tan B if

$$\tan (A + B) = 3\cdot81 \text{ and } \tan A = 2.$$

6. Express as sums or differences of two trigonometrical ratios:

(1) $\sin 32° \cos 18°$. (2) $\cos 53° \sin 37°$.

(3) $2 \cos 44° \cos 38°$. (4) $2 \sin 38° \sin 42°$.

(5) $2 \sin (2\theta + \alpha) \sin (2\theta - \alpha)$.

7. Express as products:

(1) $\sin 3x + \sin 2x$. (2) $\sin 48° + \sin 36°$.

(3) $\cos 51° + \cos 29°$. (4) $\cos (x + h) - \cos x$.

8. If $y = mx + c$ and $y = m_1x + b$ are the equations of two straight lines, and θ is the angle between them, show that:

$$\tan \theta = \frac{m_1 - m}{1 + m_1m}.$$

9. Find $\cos 3\theta$ in terms of $\cos \theta$ and $\sin 3\theta$ in terms of $\sin \theta$ Hence deduce the values of $\cos^3 \theta$ and $\sin^3 \theta$.

10. Solve $4 \cos \theta + \cos 2\theta = 0$.

CHAPTER 10

THE SOLUTION OF TRIANGLES

1. Formulæ Connected with any Triangle. Problems which call for the Solution of Triangles

1. In dealing with any triangle the capital letters A, B, C stand for the measures of the angles, while the small letters a, b, c denote the measures of the sides opposite these angles.

2. The Sine Rule

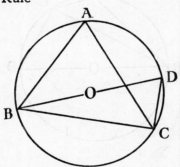

Fig. 48.

Let O be the centre of the circumscribed circle of the triangle ABC; let R = radius of this circle.

Draw the diameter BOD, and join CD.

Then $\angle BDC = \angle BAC$ (angles in the same segment).

Also $\angle BCD = 90°$ (angle in a semi-circle).

$$\therefore \frac{BC}{BD} = \sin D = \sin A$$

215

i.e., $$\frac{a}{2R} = \sin A$$

or $$\frac{a}{\sin A} = 2R.$$

Similarly, we can prove $\frac{b}{\sin B} = 2R = \frac{c}{\sin C}$.

Hence:

$$\frac{a}{\sin A} = \frac{b}{\sin B} = \frac{c}{\sin C} = 2R.$$

This statement is often known as the **sine rule,** and shows that the sides of any triangle are respectively proportional to the sines of the opposite angles.

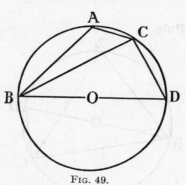

Fig. 49.

If the angle A is obtuse, perform the same construction as in Fig. 48.

ABCD is a cyclic quadrilateral, and $\angle A + \angle D = 180°$, *i.e.,* A and D are supplementary.

$$\therefore \quad \sin A = \sin D$$

as before $$\frac{BC}{BD} = \sin D = \sin A$$

i.e., $$\frac{a}{2R} = \sin A$$

giving $$\frac{a}{\sin A} = 2R.$$

If we know two angles and one side of a triangle, we can now find by calculation the other two sides and the third angle.

Example 1

Given $a = 26.2$ in., $B = 38° 41'$, $C = 53°$, find b and c.

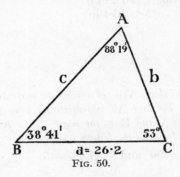

FIG. 50.

The angle $A = 180° - (53° 41') = 88° 19'$.

Put in the angles, and letter the sketch as shown. Using the sine rule we get:

$$\frac{c}{\sin 53°} = \frac{26.2}{\sin 88° 19'}$$

i.e., $$c = \frac{\sin 53° \times 26.2}{\sin 88° 19'}$$

$\log c = \log \sin 53° + \log 26.2 - \log \sin 88° 19'$
$\qquad = 1.3208$
$\therefore \quad c = 20.9$ in.

sin 53	$\overline{1}$·9023
26·2	1·4183
	1·3206
sin 88° 19′	$\overline{1}$·9998
	1·3208

Similarly,

$$\frac{b}{\sin 38° 41'} = \frac{26·2}{\sin 88° 19'}$$

$$\therefore \quad b = \frac{\sin 38° 41' \times 26·2}{\sin 88° 19'}$$

	log
sin 38° 41'	$\bar{1}$·7959
26·2	1·4183
	1·2142
sin 88° 19'	$\bar{1}$·9998
	1·2144

$$\therefore \quad \log b = 1·2143$$

and $$b = 16·4 \text{ in.}$$

Example 2

In the sketch below, ABC *is a wireless mast and* EDC *is the ground level. To find* AC *observations were taken from* D *and* E *to points* A *and* B *on the mast. The point* C *was not accessible. Determine the length* AC.   (U.L.C.I.)

Since $\angle C = 90°$ and $\angle AEC = 45°$ $\therefore$ $\angle A = 45°$
and $AC = EC.$

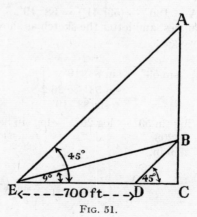

Fig. 51.

If BC = x ft then DC is x ft.

∴ EC = AC = $(700 + x)$ ft.

Now $\dfrac{BC}{EC} = \dfrac{x}{700 + x} = \tan 9° = 0.1584$

$x = 0.1584 \, (700 + x)$

$= 110.88 + 0.1584x$

$x(1 - 0.1584) = 110.88$

$x = \dfrac{110.88}{0.8416} = 132$ ft (nearly)

∴ AC = 832 ft.

Examples (2) and (3) below are standard and illustrate useful methods of solving problems.

Example 3

Suppose the height AB has to be determined from observations taken from the bottom and top of a tower CD whose height is known. In the above case CD = 200 ft.

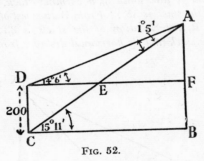

Fig. 52.

Draw DF parallel to CB, and let the angles of elevation of A from C and D be 15° 11′, and 14° 6′, respectively.

By parallels ∠AEF = ∠ACB = 15° 11′.

Hence ∠DAE = 1° 5′.

Start the solution by comparing the unknown height AB with the known one CD.

$$\frac{AB}{CD} = \frac{AB}{AC} \cdot \frac{AC}{CD} \quad \cdots \cdots \cdots \quad (1)$$

$$\frac{AB}{AC} = \sin 15° \ 11'$$

and

$$\frac{AC}{CD} = \frac{\sin (90° + 14° \ 6')}{\sin 1° \ 5'} = \frac{\cos 14° \ 6'}{\sin 1° \ 5'}.$$

Substituting in (1) we get:

$$\frac{AB}{CD} = \frac{\sin 15° \ 11' \ . \ \times \cos 14° \ 6'}{\sin 1° \ 5'}$$

$$\therefore \quad AB = \frac{200 \times \sin 15° \ 11' \times \cos 14° \ 6'}{\sin 1° \ 5'}$$

$$\log AB = 3·4270$$

and $\therefore$ AB = 2673 ft.

Number	log
200	2·3010
sin 15° 11'	$\bar{1}$·4181
cos 14° 6'	$\bar{1}$·9867
	1·7058
sin 1° 5'	$\bar{2}$·2788
	3·4270

Example 4

At a point A due south of a chimney-stack, the angle of elevation of the stack is 55°. From B due west of A, such that AB = 300 ft, the elevation of the stack is 33°. Find the height of the stack and its horizontal distance from A.

(U.E.I.)

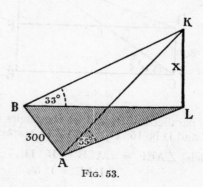

FIG. 53.

KL is the stack, and the points B, L, A are on the ground. Since A is south of L, $\angle LAB = 90°$.

Let $KL = x$ ft.
Then $LA = x \cot 55°$.
and $LB = x \cot 33°$.

By Pythagoras' Theorem,

$$LB^2 = LA^2 + BA^2$$

i.e., $LB^2 - LA^2 = BA^2$

giving $x^2(\cot^2 33° - \cot^2 55°) = 300^2$.

$$\therefore \quad x^2 = \frac{300^2}{\cot^2 33° - \cot^2 55°}$$

$$\therefore \quad x = \frac{300}{\sqrt{(\cot 33° + \cot 55°)(\cot 33° - \cot 55°)}}$$

i.e., $x = \dfrac{300}{\sqrt{2 \cdot 2401 \times 0 \cdot 8397}}$

$$= 219 \text{ ft.}$$

Also $LA = LK \cot 55°$
$$= 219 \times 0 \cdot 7002$$
$$= 153 \text{ ft.}$$

Example 5

A hillside, which may be considered a plane inclined at $13\frac{1}{2}°$ to the horizontal, is traversed by a straight path which makes 54° with a line of greatest slope. Find the distance between two points on the path whose levels differ by 100 ft.

(N.C.T.E.C.)

OD is a line of greatest slope, OBA the path on the hillside, EOK is the horizontal plane through the base of the hill. A and B are the points whose levels differ by 100 ft.

CG is parallel to OE, and OD is at right angles to OK.

Then   DG = 100

∴   CD = 100 cosec $13\frac{1}{2}°$

          = BM, where BM is parallel to CD.

∴   BA = BM sec 54°

          = 100 cosec $13\frac{1}{2}°$ sec 54°

          = 729 ft.

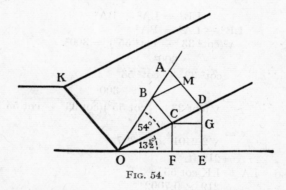

Fig. 54.

Problems demanding the solution of triangles occur just as frequently in engineering drawing offices and shops as in connection with surveying. Problems in surveying generally start with a measured line on the ground, and the measurement of the angles made with this base line by other lines in the vertical or horizontal plane. Naturally, the tangent is much used in these problems. But in the part of a workshop assigned for technical measurement complete components can be laid on a flat table, or sometimes held between centres. Angles can be directly determined, though not quite so simply as by the sighting of distant objects: lengths, however, can be easily and precisely measured by means of micrometer and Vernier gauges. These are well-known instruments commonly found in Physics laboratories.

Example 6

The length of the crank of a vertical reciprocating engine is 6 in., and the length of the connecting rod is 24 in.

(i) *How far has the piston moved from its top dead-centre position when the crank and connecting rod are at right angles?*

(ii) *How far does the piston move from its top dead-centre position as the crank turns through 45°?*

(i) Draw the figure: it is better to build it up from the information in the question than to copy it from the figure printed on this page.

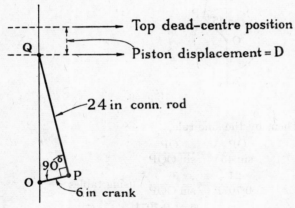

Fig. 55.

Then
$$OQ = \sqrt{OP^2 + PQ^2}$$
$$= 6\sqrt{1 + 16}$$
$$= 6\sqrt{17}$$
$$= 6 \times 4\cdot123$$
$$= 24\cdot75 \text{ approx.}$$
$$D = (30 - 24\cdot75) = 5\tfrac{1}{4} \text{ in.}$$

or   Displacement of piston = $5\tfrac{1}{4}$ in. approx.

(ii) As before, draw the figure.

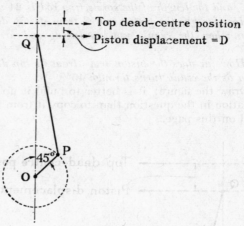

FIG. 56.

Then, by the sine rule,

$$\frac{QP}{\sin 45^\circ} = \frac{OP}{\sin OQP}$$

$$\frac{24}{0.7071} = \frac{6}{\sin OQP} \quad \text{using tables}$$

$$\sin OQP = \frac{6 \times 0.7071}{24}$$

$$= 0.1768$$

$$= \sin 10^\circ 11' \quad \text{using tables}$$

Angle OPQ $= 180^\circ - (45^\circ + 10^\circ 11')$

$$= 124^\circ 49'.$$

Then

$$\frac{OQ}{\sin 124^\circ 49'} = \frac{24}{0.7071} \quad \text{from above}$$

$$OQ = \frac{24 \times \sin 55^\circ 11'}{0 \cdot 7071} \quad \begin{array}{l} \text{by rule for sine of} \\ \text{supplementary angle} \end{array}$$

$$OQ = \frac{24 \times 0 \cdot 8209}{0 \cdot 7071}.$$

Using logarithms

$$\begin{array}{l}
1 \cdot 3802 \\
\overline{1} \cdot 9143 \\
\hline
1 \cdot 2945 \quad \text{by addition} \\
\overline{1} \cdot 8495 \\
\hline
1 \cdot 4450 \quad \text{by subtraction}
\end{array}$$

$$OQ = 27 \cdot 86$$
$$D = 30 - 27 \cdot 86 = 2 \cdot 14$$

or   Displacement of piston is 2·14 in. approx.

Example 7

The included angle of a wedge-shaped metal part has to be measured (the two faces of the wedge having been tested and found to be truly flat).

The wedge piece is laid upon a sine bar, as in the figure, the sine bar supported on a true horizontal table. The parallel packing P is adjusted until the upper face of the wedge piece is shown by a spirit level to be horizontal, and therefore parallel with the table. The parallel packing consists of a pile of engineers' slip gauges, and the height of the pile can be raised in steps as little as 0·00001 in.

The included angle of the wedge is intended to be 5°. If the piece has been made correctly, what will be the value of P?

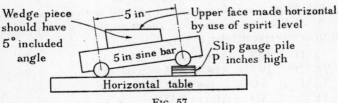

FIG. 57.

It can easily be seen from the figure that the included angle of the wedge piece is the same as the angle between the horizontal table and the upper face of the sine bar. Further, this second angle is

$$\sin^{-1} \frac{P}{5}.$$

It is therefore specified that $\sin^{-1} \frac{P}{5}$ must have the value 5°.

Now from the 4-figure tables at the end of this book,

$$\sin 5° = 0·0872$$

∴ P should be 5 × 0·0872 in., *i.e.*,

$$P = 0·4360 \text{ in.}$$

Thus, as nearly as we can learn from the 4-figure tables, the roller of the sine bar needs to be packed up from the table by 0·4360 in.

From the table of natural sines we can read that, for an angle of 5° or nearly, a difference of 1 minute alters the sine by 0·0003. If the angle to be measured were 5° 1′, P would need to be increased by 0·0015 in. to 4·375 in. If a standard set of slip blocks were available the alteration would present no difficulty. It is thus apparent that the combination of an accurate sine bar and a set of engineers' slip blocks affords a most precise means of measuring *or originating* angles.

3. The Cosine Formulæ

Fig. 58 (1) is an acute-angled triangle.

Fig. 58 (2) is an obtuse-angled triangle, with ∠A obtuse.

By well-known geometrical theorems, we have: if BD is drawn perpendicular to CA,

In (1) $BC^2 = AB^2 + AC^2 - 2AC \cdot AD$.   .   (1)

In (2) $BC^2 = AB^2 + AC^2 + 2AC \cdot AD$.   .   (2)

In (1) $AD = c \cdot \cos A$

In (2) $AD = AB \cos BAD = -c \cos A$

$\therefore$ From (1) $a^2 = b^2 + c^2 - 2bc \cos A$ $\left.\right\}$ . . (3)
and from (2) $a^2 = b^2 + c^2 - 2bc \cos A$

Hence whether the triangle is acute or obtuse angled we get the same formula.

Similarly, $b^2 = c^2 + a^2 - 2ca \cos B$ . . (4)

and $c^2 = a^2 + b^2 - 2ab \cos C$ . . (5)

Notice the cyclic order of the letters.

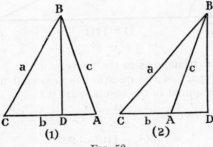

(1)   (2)

FIG. 58.

From these formulæ, if we know two sides and the included angle of any triangle, we can find the third side.

From (3) we get $\cos A = \dfrac{b^2 + c^2 - a^2}{2bc}$ . . . (6)

From (4) $\cos B = \dfrac{c^2 + a^2 - b^2}{2ca}$ . . . (7)

and from (5) $\cos C = \dfrac{a^2 + b^2 - c^2}{2ab}$ . . . (8)

These are sometimes called the cosine formulæ.

If we are given all the sides of a triangle, we can use (6) and (7) to get $\angle A$ and $\angle B$; knowing these we find C at once; $C = 180 - A - B$.

Example 1

Show that in any triangle $a^2 = b^2 + c^2 - 2bc \cos A$. In a triangle ABC find the angle ACB when AB = 92 *ft*, BC = 50 *ft, and* CA = 110 *ft.*   (U.L.C.I.)

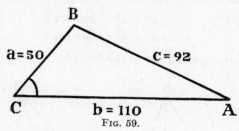

Fig. 59.

Letter the triangle as in the figure.

The first part of the question is answered in the text. The angle required in the second part is C.

$$\cos C = \frac{a^2 + b^2 - c^2}{2ab}$$

$$= \frac{50^2 + 110^2 - 92^2}{2 \times 50 \times 110}$$

$$= \frac{2500 + 12100 - 8464}{100 \times 110}$$

$$= \frac{6 \cdot 136}{11}$$

$$= 0 \cdot 5578.$$

Hence C = 56° 6′ from the tables.

Example 2

P *and* Q *are points on a straight coast line,* Q *being 5·3 miles E. of* P. *A ship starting from* P *steams 4 miles in a direction* $65\frac{1}{2}°$ *north of east.*

Calculate:

(i) *the distance the ship is now from the coast line,*

(ii) *the ship's bearing from* Q.   (N.C.T.E.C.)

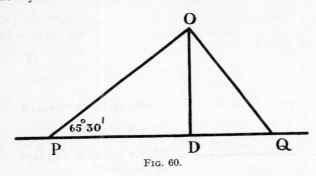

Fig. 60.

Let O be the present position of the ship, and OD the perpendicular from O on the coast line PQ.

Then $\qquad$ OP $= 4$, $\quad$ PQ $= 5\cdot3$.

$$\text{OD} = \text{OP} \sin 65\tfrac{1}{2}° = 4 \times 0\cdot91 = 3\cdot64 \text{ ml.}$$

Also PD $=$ OP cos $65\tfrac{1}{4} = 4 \times 0\cdot4147$
$\qquad\qquad\qquad\quad = 1\cdot66$ ml (correct to two places).

$$\therefore \quad \text{DQ} = \text{PQ} - \text{PD}$$
$$= 5\cdot3 - 1\cdot66$$
$$= 3\cdot64 \text{ ml.}$$

Hence $\qquad \tan \text{OQD} = \dfrac{\text{OD}}{\text{DQ}} = \dfrac{3\cdot64}{3\cdot64} = 1$

$$\therefore \quad \angle\text{OQD} = 45°$$

and the ship's bearing from Q is 45° west of north, *i.e.*, N. 45° W.

Notice that if we required the distance QO, we could find it at once since $\text{OQ}^2 = \text{PQ}^2 + \text{PO}^2 - 2\text{PQ} \cdot \text{PO} \cos 65\tfrac{1}{2}°$.

Section 1 of Chapter 9 dealt with **Projections,** and showed that the projection of a line AB upon a line (or plane) with which AB made an angle θ was AB cos θ. It is often useful to remember this property of the cosine. If AB represents a vector or directed quantity, for example a displacement or velocity, then the component of that quantity along any chosen axis at an angle θ is AB cos θ. Similarly, the projection of an area (*a*) upon a plane at an angle θ with the given area is *a* cos θ.

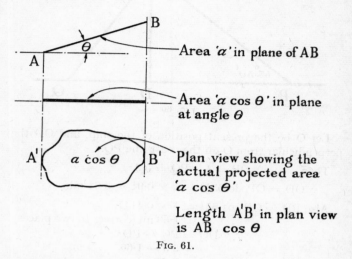

B

Area '*a*' in plane of AB

Area '*a* cos θ' in plane at angle θ

Plan view showing the actual projected area '*a* cos θ'

Length A'B' in plan view is AB cos θ

Fig. 61.

Example 3

British Standard 427 defines a method of testing hardness (in general the hardness of a metal specimen) by forcing a small diamond pyramid into the flat surface of the specimen and dividing the applied load by the *pyramidal area* of the impression to obtain the " diamond pyramid hardness number."

The business end of the diamond indenter is formed to a square pyramid having an included angle of 136° between opposite faces. The applied load varies between 5 kg for soft materials and 30 or more kg for hard ones. The test clearly rests upon the assumption that the diamond indenter is indefinitely harder than any specimen to be tested.

The area of the impression in sq mm is found by

measuring the two diagonals of the square impression by means of a measuring microscope, and averaging them.

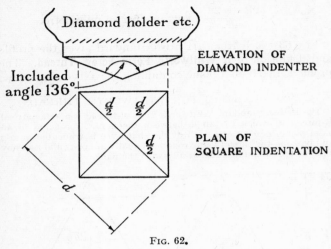

FIG. 62.

Construct a formula for the diamond pyramid hardness number in terms of the diagonal d mm and the load P *kgm.*

The square impression whose diagonal is d has an area $\dfrac{d^2}{2}$. (You should check this, adding any necessary construction lines to your figure.) But this square is the total area projected from the four facets of the diamond each of which is inclined at 22° to the face of the specimen, the angle of inclination being $\dfrac{180° - 136°}{2}$.

Then, if A is the " pyramidal area " of the impression, that is, the sum of the four inclined faces,

$$\frac{d^2}{2} \div A = \cos 22°$$

$$A = \frac{d^2}{2 \cos 22°}.$$

And the hardness number $= \dfrac{P}{A}$

$$= \dfrac{2P \cos 22^\circ}{d^2} \text{ kilograms per sq millimetre.}$$

Fig. 63 taken from a British Standard gives the profile and definition of a **Whitworth Form Screw Thread.** The profile is taken on a plane containing the axis of the screw.

STANDARD FORM FOR WHITWORTH THREADS

The British Standard Whitworth form of thread is a symmetrical V-thread in which the angle between the flanks, measured in an axial plane, is 55°; one-sixth of the sharp vee is truncated at top and bottom, the thread being rounded equally at crests and roots by circular arcs blending tangentially with the flanks.

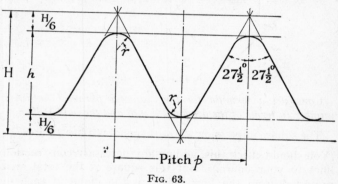

FIG. 63.

The thread form can be produced (or at least given a finishing cut) by a chasing tool, set as shown in Fig. 64, and traversed parallel to the axis of the blank by a distance p per revolution. The chasing tool will show the standard form on the end U of its upper face UF, but the front of the tool has to fall away, as shown, by a clearance angle marked θ, in order that the tool may penetrate the work instead of merely rubbing upon it.

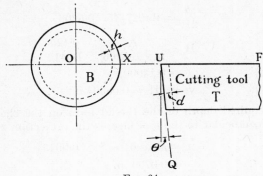

FIG. 64.

Example 4

A one-inch diameter Whitworth bolt has 8 threads to the inch. From the particulars already given as to the Whitworth form determine the perpendicular depth of a chasing tool (clearance angle 6°) for finishing such a thread.

We first determine the actual depth of the Whitworth thread. Using the nomenclature of Fig. 63 and of Fig. 65 below

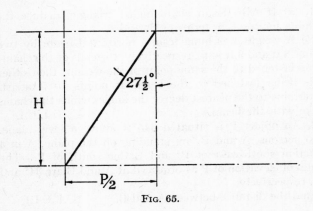

FIG. 65.

we have $$\frac{p}{2H} = \tan 27\frac{1}{2}° = 0\cdot5206$$

$$H = \frac{p}{2 \times 0\cdot5206} = \frac{0\cdot125}{1\cdot0412}$$

$$= 0\cdot12000$$

$$h = \tfrac{2}{3}H = 0\cdot08004 \text{ in.}$$

The required depth of the thread form on the chasing tool, perpendicular to the tool face, is the projection of h.

$$d = h \cos 6° = h \times 0\cdot9945$$

$$= 0\cdot0796 \text{ in.}$$

The figures of the working show that the last figure is very nearly exact. Since this figure stands for $\frac{6}{10,000}$ in. it should be clear that it is only if the screw in question is being produced by extremely accurate methods (for use as a standard) that any account can be taken of it.

EXERCISE 33

1. (a) If ABC is an acute-angled triangle, deduce the formula for cos A in terms of the sides.

(b) A weight was hung from a horizontal beam by two chains 8 ft and 9 ft long, respectively, the ends of the chains being fastened to the same point of the weight, their other ends being fastened to the beam at points 10 ft apart. Determine to the nearest degree the angles which the chains make with the beam.   (U.L.C.I.)

2. An object P is situated 345 ft above a level plane. Two persons, A and B, are standing on the plane, A in a direction south-west of P, and B due south of P. The angles of elevation of P as observed at A and B are 34° and 26°, respectively.

Find the distance between A and B.   (U.L.C.I.)

3. Prove that in any triangle ABC

$$\frac{a}{\sin A} = \frac{b}{\sin B} = \frac{c}{\sin C} = D,$$

where D is the diameter of the circle through A, B and C.

A rod whose cross-section is a triangle having sides 1 in., 1·93 in. and 1·93 in., respectively, can just be driven lengthwise into a cyclindrical tube. Find the internal diameter of the tube.   (U.L.C.I.)

4. One panel of a girder consists of four bars forming a parallelogram of sides 3 ft and 4 ft, respectively, and a fifth bar 3 ft 6 in. long is a diagonal. Find the length of the remaining diagonal and find the angles between adjacent sides of the parallelogram.   (U.L.C.I.)

5. The lengths of the sides of a triangle are 5·6 in., 5 in., and 3·4 in. Find the angles.   (N.C.)

6. OB and OC are two straight lines at right angles in a horizontal plane. OB = 50 in. and OC = 120 in., whilst A is 73·86 in. vertically above O. Calculate the angle between the planes ABC and OBC.   (N.C.)

7. Two angles of a triangle are 53° 18' and 70° 13'. The greatest side of the triangle is 22·3 ft long. Find the other two sides and the third angle.

8. The angles of elevation of a chimney are 11° 20' from A and 14° 35' from B where AB = 55 yd. Find the height of the chimney, if the line AB passes through its base.

9. A weight hangs from the junction of two ropes 2·4 ft and 2·8 ft long, respectively, the other ends being attached one to each of two small hooks fixed 3 ft apart on the underside of a horizontal beam. Find the angle between the ropes and the depth of the junction of the ropes below the beam.   (U.L.C.I.)

10. Four rods, AB = 18 in., BC = 21 in., CD = 20 in. and DA = 24 in., are jointed to form a plane quadrilateral ABCD. A fifth rod joining A to C keeps the frame rigid

with the angle BCD = 90°.   Find by calculation the length
of this fifth rod.   (U.L.C.I.)

11. The angle of elevation of the top of a hill is 10° 13′,
and on walking 2000 ft up an incline of 6° 50′, it is found
to be 14° 12′.   Find the height of the hill.

12. X and Y are two points on a straight shore 1200 ft
apart, Y lying due E. of X.   The bearings of a buoy are
28° N. of E. from X and 51° N. of W. from Y.   How far is
the buoy from the shore?

13. Observations are taken from the bottom and from
the top of a tower 200 ft high, to find the height of a hill.

From the bottom of the tower the angle of elevation of
the summit is 14° 30′, and from the top it is 13° 25′.   Find
the height of the hill.

14. A Whitworth form screw is cut on a bolt 2 in. dia.
There are 4½ threads per inch.

Draw out the thread form to a large scale, taking all the
additional information you need from Fig. 63.   *Determine
H, the height of the sharp vee containing the thread, h the
actual depth of the thread, and r the radius of the circle giving
the rounding at crest and root.*

What is the " effective diameter " of the thread?   (The
effective diameter is the length of a line drawn from a
point on the flank of the thread perpendicularly through
the axis of the bolt to meet an opposite flank.)

*In the data for the next question there is incorporated
engineering information which should however be readily
appreciated by National Certificate students.*

*Fig. 64, p. 233, indicated a " form " tool (actually for
screw-cutting) which would show on its " breast " or front top
face the profile of a screw thread.   Such a tool, to retain its
form, must frequently be sharpened as shown in Fig. 66 (i),
p. 237.   Since wear takes place at the front the amount to be
removed at each grinding is considerable.*

In order that the form, which is expensive to produce,

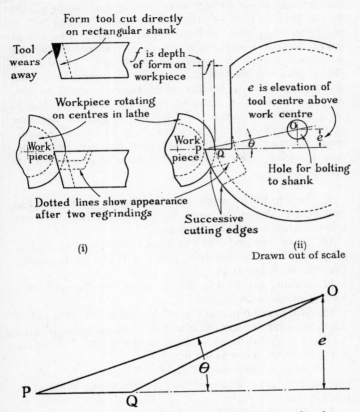

OP = R.   OQ = r.   PQ is true depth of form to be produced.
(R − r) = d, the radial depth of form on the circular form tool.
THE TRIANGLE OPQ, drawn very much out of scale, is to be SOLVED
FOR OQ.

(iii)

FIG. 66.

may be maintained through more grindings, it can be worked on the periphery of a " circular form tool " which can be sharpened as shown in Fig. 66 (ii), p. 237. The tool is bolted on to a shank which can be carried in a lathe tool post, just as can a simple one-piece tool. Although a thread chaser is in fact a form tool, the name more often indicates a tool to produce short tapers, curved profiles, etc., by means of a plunging cut without traverse lengthways of the workpiece. In Fig. 66 the greatest diameter of the circular form tool is taken to be $2\frac{1}{2}$ in. The minimum clearance angle to ensure that the tool will penetrate the work rather than polish it is to be taken as 6° as before.

15. In Fig. 66 (ii) what must be the elevation e of the tool centre above the work centre to give the specified front clearance angle at the point P ?

16. Show how and why the front clearance at Q, and at all parts of the cutting edge between P and Q, is greater than the 6° value at P.

17. Making use of Fig. 66 (iii) solve the triangle OPQ for OQ which is the radius " r ".

18. Still in reference to Fig. 66 determine " d " the radial depth of form on the circular tool, and compare it with " f " the required depth of form on the work. " f ", that is PQ, may be taken as 0·2 in.

Note that the difference between " d " and " f " will in general be slight. One good reason for working it out is to confirm this.

Any student who is taking an interest in this calculation in its practical application should note that SIDE clearance is not obtainable on a tool which is to retain its form when sharpened as in Fig. 66.

19. " $\theta = \sin^{-1} x$ " is a precise way of defining small angles, but can give only a vague indication of the measure of angles near 90°. Explain this, and show how the

combination of a sine bar and a true square can be used to deal with these larger angles.

4. Cosine Formulæ Adapted to Logarithms

An objection to the cosine formulæ is that they are not suitable for logarithmic calculation.

They can, however, be adapted in the following way:

$$\cos A = 1 - 2 \sin^2 \frac{A}{2} = \frac{b^2 + c^2 - a^2}{2bc}$$

$$\therefore \ 2 \sin^2 \frac{A}{2} = 1 - \left(\frac{b^2 + c^2 - a^2}{2bc} \right)$$

$$= \frac{2bc - (b^2 + c^2 - a^2)}{2bc}$$

$$= \frac{a^2 - (b - c)^2}{2bc}$$

$$\therefore \ \sin^2 \frac{A}{2} = \frac{a^2 - (b - c)^2}{4bc}$$

$$= \frac{(a - b + c)(a + b - c)}{4bc}$$

$$= \frac{(a + b + c - 2b)(a + b + c - 2c)}{4bc}.$$

The sum of the sides of a triangle is usually denoted by $2s$, so that s is the semi-sum

$$i.e., \quad a + b + c = 2s.$$

Hence $$\sin^2 \frac{A}{2} = \frac{(2s - 2b)(2s - 2c)}{4bc}$$

Giving $$\sin \frac{A}{2} = \sqrt{\frac{(s - b)(s - c)}{bc}} \ . \ . \ . \ (1)$$

Similarly,

$$\cos A = 2 \cos^2 \frac{A}{2} - 1 = \frac{b^2 + c^2 - a^2}{2bc} \ .$$

$$\therefore \quad 2\cos^2\frac{A}{2} = 1 + \left(\frac{b^2 + c^2 - a^2}{2bc}\right)$$

$$= \frac{(b + c)^2 - a^2}{2bc}$$

$$= \frac{(b + c - a)(b + c + a)}{2bc}$$

$$\therefore \quad \cos^2\frac{A}{2} = \frac{2s(2s - 2a)}{4bc}$$

and $$\cos\frac{A}{2} = \sqrt{\frac{s(s - a)}{bc}} \quad \cdot \quad \cdot \quad \cdot \quad (2)$$

Now divide (1) by (2) and get

$$\tan\frac{A}{2} = \sqrt{\frac{(s - b)(s - c)}{s(s - a)}} \quad \cdot \quad \cdot \quad \cdot \quad (3)$$

In a similar way we may prove that:

$$\tan\frac{B}{2} = \sqrt{\frac{(s - c)(s - a)}{s(s - b)}} \quad \cdot \quad \cdot \quad \cdot \quad (4)$$

and $$\tan\frac{C}{2} = \sqrt{\frac{(s - a)(s - b)}{s(s - c)}} \quad \cdot \quad \cdot \quad \cdot \quad (5)$$

These formulæ are readily remembered if the cyclic order of the letters a, b and c is observed.

Further, when we have found the necessary logarithms for calculating $\tan\frac{A}{2}$, we use them for finding $\tan\frac{B}{2}$.

Area of a Triangle

We can now find an important formula for the area of a triangle.

$$\text{Area} = \tfrac{1}{2}bc\sin A$$

$$= \tfrac{1}{2}bc \cdot 2\sin\frac{A}{2} \cdot \cos\frac{A}{2}$$

$$= bc\sqrt{\frac{(s - b)(s - c)}{bc}} \cdot \sqrt{\frac{s(s - a)}{bc}}$$

i.e.,   **Area** $= \sqrt{s(s-a)(s-b)(s-c)}$

where a, b and c are the sides and s is their semi-sum.

Example

Let the lengths of the sides be 48·3 ft, 31·6 ft and 62·4 ft.

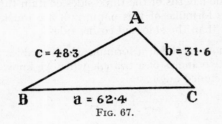

$$C = 48·3 \qquad b = 31·6$$

$$B \qquad a = 62·4 \qquad C$$

Fig. 67.

$a =$	62·4	$\therefore \quad s =$	71·15
$b =$	31·6	$s - a =$	8·75
$c =$	48·3	$s - b =$	39·55
		$s - c =$	22·85
$2s =$	142·3		

$$\tan \frac{A}{2} = \sqrt{\frac{39·55 \times 22·85}{71·15 \times 8·75}}$$

This expression is such as to emphasise the necessity for logarithms when dealing with the numbers arising in surveying or navigation.

We find $\log \tan \dfrac{A}{2} = 0·0809$

$$\therefore \quad \frac{A}{2} = 50° \ 18' \ 20''$$

$$A = 100° \ 37' \text{ to the nearest minute}$$

Similarly, $\tan \dfrac{B}{2} = \sqrt{\dfrac{22·85 \times 8·75}{71·15 \times 39·55}}$

Giving $\dfrac{B}{2} = 14° \ 56'.$

Hence $\qquad$ B $= 29°\ 52'$

$\qquad\qquad\qquad$ C $= 49°\ 31'$, and

the area of the triangle $= \sqrt{(71\cdot15 \times 8\cdot75 \times 39\cdot55 \times 22\cdot85)}$

$\qquad\qquad\qquad\qquad = 750$ sq ft to three figures.

When the lengths of the three sides contain three or four figures the formulæ of this paragraph are much easier to work with than the sine and cosine rules.

5. We now establish a formula which enables us to find the other two angles of a triangle when we know two sides and the included angle.

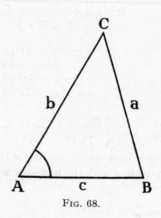

Fig. 68.

Suppose that we are given A, b, and c, we could find a, as we have done previously from the formula

$$a^2 = b^2 + c^2 - 2bc \cos A.$$

This gives us a tiresome calculation when the lengths of the sides contain three or four figures.

Since $\angle A$ is known, B + C is known. We now find a formula which gives us (B − C).

Knowing $(B + C)$ and $(B - C)$, we readily find B and C.
a can then be found by using the sine rule.

To prove

$$\tan \frac{B - C}{2} = \frac{b - c}{b + c} \cdot \cot \frac{A}{2} \quad . \quad . \quad . \quad (1)$$

Put $\quad \dfrac{a}{\sin A} = \dfrac{b}{\sin B} = \dfrac{c}{\sin C} = k$

then $a = k \sin A$, $b = k \sin B$ and $c = k \sin C$.

Hence $\quad \dfrac{b - c}{b + c} = \dfrac{k(\sin B - \sin C)}{k(\sin B + \sin C)}$

$$= \frac{2 \cos \dfrac{B + C}{2} \sin \dfrac{B - C}{2}}{2 \sin \dfrac{B + C}{2} \cos \dfrac{B - C}{2}}$$

$$= \cot \frac{B + C}{2} \cdot \tan \frac{B - C}{2}$$

$$= \tan \frac{A}{2} \cdot \tan \frac{B - C}{2} \quad . \quad . \quad . \quad (2)$$

since $\dfrac{A}{2}$ and $\dfrac{B + C}{2}$ are complementary angles

and $\qquad \therefore \quad \tan \dfrac{A}{2} = \cot \dfrac{B + C}{2}$

Hence from (2), dividing both sides by $\tan \dfrac{A}{2}$

$$\tan \frac{B - C}{2} = \frac{b - c}{b + c} \cot \frac{A}{2}$$

Similarly, $\quad \tan \dfrac{C - A}{2} = \dfrac{c - a}{c + a} \cot \dfrac{B}{2} \quad . \quad . \quad . \quad (3)$

and $\qquad \tan \dfrac{B - A}{2} = \dfrac{b - a}{b + a} \cot \dfrac{C}{2} \quad . \quad . \quad . \quad (4)$

Example

Given A = 71° 9′, *b* = 43·2 *ft and c* = 31·7 *ft, find the other three parts of the triangle.*

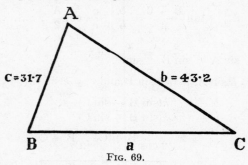

FIG. 69.

Sketch a figure.   Notice that since $b > c$, $\angle B > \angle C$.

$$\tan \frac{B - C}{2} = \frac{43·2 - 31·7}{43·2 + 31·7} \cot \frac{71° 9′}{2}$$

$$= \frac{11·5}{74·9} \cot 35° 34\tfrac{1}{2}′$$

	Number	log
$\log \tan \frac{B-C}{2} = \bar{1}·3315$	11·5	1·0607
	cot 35° 34½′	0·1453
$\therefore \quad \frac{B-C}{2} = 12° 6\tfrac{1}{2}′$		1·2060
$\therefore \quad B - C = 24° 13′$	74·9	1·8745
also $\quad\quad\;\; B + C = 108° 51′$		$\bar{1}·3315$

from which   2B = 133° 5′,   and $\therefore$ B = 66° 32½′
and   2C = 84° 38′,   and $\therefore$ C = 42° 19′

To get *a*, we have

		log
$\dfrac{a}{\sin 71° 9′} = \dfrac{43·2}{\sin 66° 32\tfrac{1}{2}′}$	43·2	1·6355
	sin 71° 9′	$\bar{1}·9760$
$\therefore \quad a = \dfrac{43·2 \sin 71° 9′}{\sin 66° 32\tfrac{1}{2}′}$		1·6115
		$\bar{1}·9625$
$a = 44·6$ ft.	sin 66° 32½′	1·6490

EXERCISE 34

1. In a triangle $b = 39 \cdot 6$, $c = 43 \cdot 2$ and $A = 58° 24'$.
   Use the formula

$$\tan \frac{C - B}{2} = \frac{c - b}{c + b} \cot \frac{A}{2} \text{ to find } (C - B).$$

Hence find C and B.

2. Find the area of a triangular plot of ground whose sides are 48·3 ft, 62·7 ft and 79·3 ft.

3. AB subtends an angle of 38° 4' at a point O, where OA = 37·3 ft and OB = 49·3 ft.   Find the length of AB, and the angles at A and B.

4. Find the greatest angle of the triangle in question 2.

5. Find the angles of a parallelogram two of whose sides are 5·93 in. and 6·45 in. long, whilst a diagonal has a length 7·32 in.
   Find the area of the parallelogram.

CHAPTER 11

Differentiation and Integration of Trigonometrical Functions, with Some Applications

1. The differentiation of both sin θ and cos θ depends on the following limit, viz.

$$\underset{\theta \to 0}{\text{Lt}} \frac{\sin \theta}{\theta} = 1.$$

From many worked examples and exercises the student will already be familiar with the fact that as an angle θ becomes smaller and smaller the sine, the measure of the angle in radians, and the tangent, become indistinguishable and the individual fractions approach the value zero; while the ratio of any one to another approaches the value one.

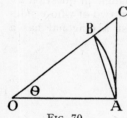

Fig. 70.

A more formal method of arriving at the limit is as follows.

O is the centre of a circle, radius r.

Let $\angle AOB = \theta$ (radians).

AC is the tangent to the circle at A, cutting OB produced at C.

Then area of $\triangle AOB = \frac{1}{2}r^2 \sin \theta$, and of $\triangle AOC = \frac{1}{2}OA \cdot AC = \frac{1}{2}r^2 \tan \theta$.

Also $\triangle AOB <$ sector $AOB < \triangle AOC$.

i.e., $\frac{1}{2}r^2 \sin \theta < \frac{1}{2}r^2 \theta < \frac{1}{2}r^2 \tan \theta$.

$$\therefore \quad \sin \theta < \theta < \tan \theta$$

or dividing by sin θ,

$$1 < \frac{\theta}{\sin \theta} < \sec \theta.$$

Hence $\dfrac{\theta}{\sin \theta}$ always lies between 1 and sec θ.

As $\theta \longrightarrow 0$, sec $\theta \longrightarrow 1$, ∴ $\dfrac{\theta}{\sin \theta} \longrightarrow 1$

or inverting $\underset{\theta \to 0}{Lt} \dfrac{\sin \theta}{\theta} = 1.$

It should be observed that θ is in radians, and that the angle must be the same in both numerator and denominator. It is not sufficient that both be small.

Thus $\underset{\theta \to 0}{Lt} \dfrac{\sin 2\theta}{\theta} = \underset{\theta \to 0}{Lt} 2 . \dfrac{\sin 2\theta}{2\theta}$

$= 2.$

2. To Find the Derivative of sin θ, with respect to θ

The student should recall two results:

(1) that if $y = f(x)$,

$$\frac{dy}{dx} = \underset{h \to 0}{Lt} \frac{f(x + h) - f(x)}{h}$$

and (2) $\sin S - \sin T = 2 \cos \dfrac{S + T}{2} . \sin \dfrac{S - T}{2}$ (see page 211).

Put $y = \sin \theta$

then $\dfrac{dy}{d\theta} = \underset{h \to 0}{Lt} \dfrac{\sin (\theta + h) - \sin \theta}{h}$

$$= Lt \frac{2 \cos \left(\theta + \dfrac{h}{2} \right) \sin \left(\dfrac{h}{2} \right)}{h}$$

$$= Lt \cos \left(\theta + \frac{h}{2} \right) . \frac{\sin \dfrac{h}{2}}{\dfrac{h}{2}} \quad . \quad . \quad . \quad (1)$$

Now let $h \longrightarrow 0$; $\cos\left(\theta + \dfrac{h}{2}\right) \longrightarrow \cos\theta$, and $\dfrac{\sin\dfrac{h}{2}}{\dfrac{h}{2}} \longrightarrow 1$

$$\therefore \quad \frac{dy}{d\theta} = \cos\theta \quad . \quad . \quad . \quad . \quad . \quad (2)$$

Hence if
$$y = \sin\theta$$
$$\frac{dy}{d\theta} = \cos\theta$$

i.e.,
$$\frac{d(\sin\theta)}{d\theta} = \cos\theta.$$

The " form " of this result is important

$$y = \sin(\quad)$$
$$\frac{dy}{d(\quad)} = \cos(\quad) \quad \binom{\text{any expression may be put}}{\text{in the bracket.}}$$

Thus, suppose $y = \sin 3\theta$.   (Put 3θ in the bracket.)

then
$$\frac{dy}{d(3\theta)} = \cos 3\theta.$$

But
$$\frac{dy}{d\theta} = \frac{dy}{d(3\theta)} \cdot \frac{d(3\theta)}{d\theta} = \cos 3\theta \cdot 3 = 3\cos 3\theta.$$

Similarly, if $y = \sin a\theta$

$$\frac{dy}{d\theta} = \frac{dy}{d(a\theta)} \cdot \frac{d(a\theta)}{d\theta} = a\cos a\theta.$$

Example 1

$$z = \sin\frac{t}{2}. \quad (\text{Here, } a = \tfrac{1}{2})$$
$$\frac{dz}{dt} = \frac{1}{2}\cos\frac{t}{2}.$$

Example 2

$$y = 5\sin 4x$$
$$\frac{dy}{dx} = 20\cos 4x$$

Example 3

$$y = \tfrac{1}{4} \sin \tfrac{1}{3}t$$
$$\frac{dy}{dt} = \frac{1}{12} \cos \frac{1}{3}t.$$

Example 4

$$y = \sin\left(t + \frac{\pi}{6}\right)$$
$$\frac{dy}{dt} = \cos\left(t + \frac{\pi}{6}\right).$$

Example 5

$$y = \sin(2ft + \alpha) \text{ where } \alpha \text{ is constant}$$
$$\frac{dy}{dt} = 2f \cos(2ft + \alpha).$$

3. To Find the Differential Coefficient of $\cos \theta$, with respect to θ

Let $\qquad y = \cos \theta$

then $\qquad \dfrac{dy}{d\theta} = \underset{h \to 0}{\mathrm{L}t} \dfrac{\cos(\theta + h) - \cos \theta}{h}$

$$= - \underset{h \to 0}{\mathrm{L}t}\, 2 \sin\left(\theta + \frac{h}{2}\right)\frac{\sin \dfrac{h}{2}}{h}$$

$$= - \underset{h \to 0}{\mathrm{L}t}\, \sin\left(\theta + \frac{h}{2}\right)\frac{\sin \dfrac{h}{2}}{\dfrac{h}{2}}$$

$$= - \sin \theta.$$

Thus if $\qquad y = \cos \theta$

$$\frac{dy}{d\theta} = - \sin \theta$$

i.e., $\qquad \dfrac{d(\cos \theta)}{d\theta} = - \sin \theta$

or in form
$$y = \cos \text{ (any angle)}$$
$$\frac{dy}{d \text{ (angle)}} = - \sin \text{ (angle)}.$$

If
$$y = \cos 3\theta$$
$$\frac{dy}{d\theta} = \frac{dy}{d(3\theta)} \cdot \frac{d(3\theta)}{d\theta} = - 3 \sin 3\theta$$

And generally, as with sin θ,

If
$$y = a \cos (b\theta + c)$$
$$\frac{dy}{d\theta} = - ab \sin (b\theta + c).$$

Example 1

$$y = \frac{1}{2} \cos \frac{t}{3}$$
$$\frac{dy}{dt} = - \frac{1}{6} \sin \frac{t}{3}.$$

Example 2

$$y = 5 \cos \left(3t + \frac{\pi}{6} \right).$$
$$\frac{dy}{dt} = - 15 \sin \left(3t + \frac{\pi}{6} \right).$$

EXERCISE 35

Differentiate with respect to the appropriate variable:

1. $\sin t$.

2. $\sin 4t$.

3. $\sin \dfrac{t}{3}$.

4. $\sin \pi t$.

5. $\sin nt$.

6. $3 \sin 2t$.

7. $\dfrac{1}{2} \sin \dfrac{t}{3}$.

8. $\dfrac{2}{\pi} \sin \pi t$.

9. $a \sin bt$.

10. $5 \sin (\theta + \alpha)$.   11. $3 \sin (\theta + \pi)$.   12. $a \sin \left(\theta - \dfrac{\pi}{3}\right)$.

13. $5 \sin \left(3\theta - \dfrac{\pi}{5}\right)$.   14. $\dfrac{1}{2} \sin \left(\dfrac{1}{2}\theta + \dfrac{\pi}{3}\right)$.

15. $a \sin (2ft + n\pi)$.   16. $\cos 3x$.   17. $\cos \dfrac{x}{5}$.

18. $\cos \pi x$.   19. $5 \cos 3\theta$.

20. $3 \cos (5\theta + \alpha)$.   21. $4 \cos \left(3\theta + \dfrac{\pi}{4}\right)$.

22. $\dfrac{1}{2} \cos (k\theta + \alpha)$.   23. $a \cos (2nx + k\pi)$.

4. The differential coefficients of $\tan \theta$, $\operatorname{cosec} \theta$, $\sec \theta$ and $\cot \theta$ are all easily obtained from those for $\sin \theta$ and $\cos \theta$ if we use the formula for differentiating a quotient.

Thus if $\qquad y = \tan \theta$

i.e., $\qquad y = \dfrac{\sin \theta}{\cos \theta}$

$$\therefore \quad \frac{dy}{d\theta} = \frac{\cos \theta . \cos \theta - \sin \theta . (-\sin \theta)}{\cos^2 \theta}$$

$$= \frac{\cos^2 \theta + \sin^2 \theta}{\cos^2 \theta}$$

$$= \frac{1}{\cos^2 \theta}$$

$$= \sec^2 \theta.$$

Hence $\dfrac{\boldsymbol{d}}{d\theta}(\boldsymbol{\tan} \theta) = \boldsymbol{\sec^2} \theta$

If $\qquad y = \tan 5\theta$

$$\frac{dy}{d\theta} = 5 \sec^2 5\theta.$$

5. If
$$y = \operatorname{cosec} \theta$$
$$y = \frac{1}{\sin \theta}$$
$$\frac{dy}{d\theta} = \frac{-\cos \theta}{\sin^2 \theta}$$
$$= -\frac{1}{\sin \theta} \cdot \frac{\cos \theta}{\sin \theta}$$
$$= -\operatorname{cosec} \theta \cdot \cot \theta.$$

i.e., $\dfrac{d}{d\theta} (\textbf{cosec } \theta) = -\textbf{ cosec } \theta \textbf{ cot } \theta.$

The student can now prove that
$$\frac{d}{d\theta} \sec \theta = \sec \theta \tan \theta$$

and $\dfrac{d}{d\theta} \cot \theta = -\operatorname{cosec}^2 \theta.$

6. The differentiation of the trigonometric functions has been performed on the supposition that the angles are measured in radians.

If the angles are given in degrees, we must convert to radians and then differentiate.

Example 1

If
$$y = \sin x°$$
$$y = \sin \frac{\pi x}{180}$$
$$\therefore \frac{dy}{dx} = \frac{\pi}{180} \cos \frac{\pi x}{180}$$
$$= \frac{\pi}{180} \cdot \cos x°.$$

Example 2
$$z = \cos 3t°$$
$$= \cos \frac{\pi t}{60}$$

$$\therefore \quad \frac{dz}{dt} = -\frac{\pi}{60} \sin \frac{\pi t}{60}$$

$$= -\frac{\pi}{60} \sin 3t°.$$

EXERCISE 36

Differentiate the following functions:

1. $\tan \theta$.

2. $\sec x$.

3. $\operatorname{cosec} z$.

4. $\cot y$.

5. $\tan 3\theta$.

6. $\sec \dfrac{\theta}{2}$.

7. $\operatorname{cosec} 3x$.

8. $3 \cot 4\theta$.

9. $5 \sec \left(2\theta + \dfrac{\pi}{2} \right)$.

10. $3 \tan (\theta + \pi)$.

11. $\sin 3x°$.

12. $3 \cos \frac{1}{2}x°$.

13. $2 \tan x°$.

7. Products and Quotients

Example 1

$$y = x^3 \sin x$$

$$\frac{dy}{dx} = 3x^2 \sin x + x^3 \cos x.$$

Example 2

$$y = 3x^4 \cos 2x$$

$$\frac{dy}{dx} = 3[4x^3 \cos 2x - 2x^4 \sin 2x] \quad . \quad . \quad . \quad (1)$$

$$\left(\text{Notice } \frac{d}{dx} (\cos 2x) = -2 \sin 2x \right)$$

(1) may be written

$$\frac{dy}{dx} = 6x^3(2 \cos 2x - x \sin 2x).$$

Example 3

$$z = \frac{3 \sin 5t}{t^3} \quad \cdot \quad \cdot \quad \cdot \quad \cdot \quad \cdot \quad \cdot \quad (2)$$

$$\frac{dz}{dt} = \frac{3[5t^3 \cos 5t - 3t^2 \sin 5t]}{t^6}$$

$$= \frac{3}{t^4} (5t \cos 5t - 3 \sin 5t).$$

Notice that (2) may be differentiated as a product, thus:

$$z = 3 \sin 5t \cdot t^{-3}$$

$$\frac{dz}{dt} = 3[5 \cos 5t \cdot t^{-3} - 3t^{-4} \sin 5t]$$

$$= \frac{3}{t^4} (5t \cos 5t - 3 \sin 5t).$$

8. The Differentiation of Powers of the Trigonometrical Functions

Example 1

Suppose
$$y = \sin^2 x$$
$$= u^2 \text{ (where } u = \sin x)$$
$$\frac{dy}{du} = 2u \text{ and } \frac{du}{dx} = \cos x.$$

$$\therefore \frac{dy}{dx} = \frac{dy}{du} \cdot \frac{du}{dx} = 2u \cdot \cos x$$
$$= 2 \sin x \cos x$$
$$= \sin 2x.$$

If the formal aspect of differentiation has been grasped, the substitution of u for $\sin x$ will be unnecessary.

If
$$y = \sin^2 x$$
$$\frac{dy}{dx} = \frac{dy}{d(\sin x)} \cdot \frac{d(\sin x)}{dx}$$
$$= 2 \sin x \cdot \cos x$$
$$= \sin 2x.$$

Example 2

Similarly, if $\qquad y = \cos^3 2x$

$$\frac{dy}{dx} = \frac{dy}{d(\cos 2x)} \cdot \frac{d(\cos 2x)}{d(2x)} \cdot \frac{d(2x)}{dx}$$

$$= 3 \cos^2 2x \cdot (-\sin 2x) \cdot 2$$

$$= -6 \cos^2 2x \cdot \sin 2x.$$

EXERCISE 37

Differentiate the following products and quotients:

1. $x^2 \sin x.$

2. $2x^3 \sin x.$

3. $x^4 \sin 2x.$

4. $2x^6 \cos 3x.$

5. $\dfrac{\sin 2x}{x^2}.$

6. $\dfrac{3 \cos 4x}{x^4}.$

7. $\sin \theta \cos 2\theta.$

8. $3 \sin 2\theta \cos 4\theta.$

9. $\dfrac{\sin \theta}{\cos 2\theta}.$

10. $4 \sin 3\theta \cdot \cos 4\theta.$

11. $\sin 2\pi t \cdot \cos \pi t.$

Differentiate the following:

12. $\sin^2 x.$

13. $3 \sin^3 x.$

14. $\cos^3 \theta.$

15. $5 \cos^2 3\theta.$

16. $2 \sin^3 4x.$

17. $\dfrac{\cos^2 x}{\sin x}.$

18. $2 \cos^3 x - 3 \sin^2 2x.$

9. Applications of Differentiation

Example 1

At this point it would be well for the student to read again Section 2 of Chapter 7, see p. 137.

Suppose two sides of a triangle are measured accurately, but there is a small error in the included angle. Find the relative error in the calculated area.

The area of a triangle is given by

$$x = \tfrac{1}{2}bc \sin A \quad \ldots \quad \ldots \quad (1)$$

$$\therefore \quad \frac{dx}{dA} = \frac{1}{2}bc \cos A$$

or $\qquad dx = \tfrac{1}{2}bc \cos A \cdot dA.$

Refer Section 2, Chapter 6; see p. 122.

Hence the relative error $= \dfrac{dx}{x} = \dfrac{\text{error}}{\text{calculated area}}$

$$= \frac{\frac{1}{2}bc \cos A \, . \, dA}{\frac{1}{2}bc \sin A}$$

$$= \cot A \, . \, dA \quad . \quad . \quad . \quad (2)$$

In the above work the angle must be given in radians.

Thus, suppose $A = 35° \, 25'$, and suppose there is an error of $5'$ in A.

$$5' = \frac{5\pi}{60 \times 180} \text{ radians}$$

$$= \frac{\pi}{2160} \text{ radians} \quad . \quad . \quad . \quad . \quad (3)$$

From (2) and (3), the relative error

$$= \cot 35° \, 25' \times \frac{\pi}{2160} \text{ (approx.)}$$

$$= 0 \cdot 00205.$$

The % error = relative error × 100

$$= 0 \cdot 205$$

$$= \tfrac{1}{5}\%.$$

Example 2

Maxima and Minima.
Find the turning points on the curve

$$y = 2 \sin \theta + \cos \theta \quad . \quad . \quad . \quad (1)$$

and distinguish the maxima from the minima.
We have

$$\frac{dy}{d\theta} = 2 \cos \theta - \sin \theta.$$

$\therefore$ Turning points are given by

$$2 \cos \theta - \sin \theta = 0$$

i.e., $\qquad 2 \cos \theta = \sin \theta$

or $\qquad \tan \theta = 2.$

Now observe that between 0° and 360° there are two angles XOP and XOP_1 whose tangent is 2, XOP in the first quadrant and XOP_1 extending to the third quadrant.

Both sin XOP and cos XOP are positive, whilst both sin XOP_1 and cos XOP_1 are negative.   Fig. 71 (a).

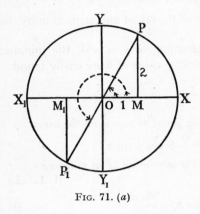

FIG. 71. (a)

FIG. 71. (b)

The + values substituted in (1) give the maximum ordinates, the − values the minimum.   See Fig. 71 (b) for the values.

The maximum values of y are $\dfrac{4}{\sqrt{5}} + \dfrac{1}{\sqrt{5}} = \sqrt{5}$.

The minimum values of y are $-\dfrac{4}{\sqrt{5}} - \dfrac{1}{\sqrt{5}} = -\sqrt{5}$.

It is to be observed that this example could equally well be worked in the following way, i.e., by writing y as the sine of a compound angle.

If $\qquad\qquad y = 2 \sin \theta + \cos \theta$ . . . . (2)

Put $\qquad\qquad r \cos \alpha = 2$

$\qquad\qquad\qquad r \sin \alpha = 1$

Then, squaring and adding,

$$\therefore \quad r^2 = 5 \text{—} i.e., r = \sqrt{5}.$$

and $$\tan \alpha = \tfrac{1}{2}.$$

From (2)

$$\therefore \quad y = \sqrt{5} \sin (\theta + \alpha) \quad . \quad . \quad . \quad (3)$$

The maximum value of the sin of any angle is unity, and the minimum — 1.

Hence the minimum value of y is $\sqrt{5}$, the minimum — $\sqrt{5}$. The corresponding value of θ are easily found.

Example 3

Show there is a turning point at $x = \dfrac{\pi}{3}$ *on the curve*

$$y = \sin x + \cos x \sin x.$$

Is the point on the curve a maximum or minimum?

(U.L.C.I.)

We have $$y = \sin x + \frac{\sin 2x}{2} \quad . \quad . \quad . \quad . \quad (1)$$

$$\therefore \quad \frac{dy}{dx} = \cos x + \cos 2x \quad . \quad . \quad . \quad . \quad (2)$$

Putting $$\cos x + \cos 2x = 0,$$

we get $$\cos 2x = - \cos x = \cos (\pi - x).$$

Hence $$2x = \pi - x$$

i.e., $$3x = \pi$$

and $$x = \frac{\pi}{3} = 60°.$$

Differentiating (2) we get:

$$\frac{d^2y}{dx^2} = - \sin x - 2 \sin 2x.$$

If $x = \dfrac{\pi}{3}$, $\dfrac{d^2y}{dx^2}$ is negative. Hence y is a maximum.

From (1) (putting $x = 60°$)

$$y = \frac{\sqrt{3}}{2} + \frac{\sqrt{3}}{4} = \frac{3\sqrt{3}}{4}$$

$\therefore$ The point $\left(\dfrac{\pi}{3}, \dfrac{3\sqrt{3}}{4}\right)$ is a maximum point.

10. Simple Harmonic Motion (SHM)

At this point the student may well refer to Section 5 of Chapter 8, which deals with periodic functions. The word "harmonic" in the heading above is used because motion according to the definition given later in this section can give rise to a pure musical note—a point at the end of a tuning-fork prong moves with SHM, although the motion is too rapid for the eye to follow. A point moving with SHM is continually changing its position and its velocity, but both positions and velocity return to the same values periodically.

Natural periodic motions all tend to approximate to the simple harmonic: if such a motion is slow enough to be observed it gives an impression of smooth perfectly controlled movement. A simple way of producing a harmonic motion slow enough to be watched is to suspend a mass from a long flexible spiral spring and to start it into vertical oscillation. On a large scale it used to be possible to watch the slow crosshead motion of the great horizontal steam engines used to drive textile mills. Although the movement was constantly reversing its direction, it appeared to be perfectly smooth; the reversal was without shock; the crosshead appeared to dwell on the dead centre, although it was not stationary for any measurable length of time. Today there are no mill engines to watch, but slow-speed open-type vertical engines for pumping water can still be found. It is not surprising that we proceed to begin the study of SHM by considering a point which is moving along a circular path, for notice that an engine crankpin, like a bicycle pedal, moves up and down and also from side to side. Each combines two reciprocating motions.

Suppose a point P describes a circle of radius a with uniform angular velocity ω. Let PM be the perpendicular on the horizontal diameter XOX_1, where O is the centre. The foot of the ordinate, M, is said to move with simple harmonic motion—*i.e.*, with SHM.

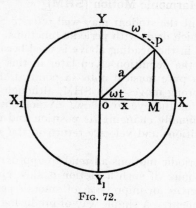

Fig. 72.

Suppose P was at X when $t = 0$—*i.e.*, at zero time.

In t secs, $\angle XOP = \omega t$.

Let $OM = x$

Then

$$x = a \cos \omega t \quad \ldots \quad (1)$$

$$\frac{dx}{dt} = -a\omega \sin \omega t \quad \ldots \quad (2)$$

$$\frac{d^2x}{dt^2} = -a\omega^2 \cos \omega t$$

$$= -\omega^2 x \quad \ldots \quad (3)$$

From (3) notice that the acceleration of M, $\dfrac{d^2x}{dt^2}$, varies as the distance of M from O.

The negative sign shows that this acceleration is directed towards O.

Observe equation (2). This gives the velocity

$$\frac{dx}{dt} = - \omega . a \sin \omega t$$

$$= - \omega . \text{MP}$$

$$= - \omega y \text{ if we put MP} = y.$$

If a point moves as described in a straight line with an acceleration always directed to a fixed point in the line, and varying as the distance from that point, it is said to have SHM. This is the formal definition.

The motion is an oscillation along XOX_1.

The distance OX (or OX_1) is called the amplitude of the motion, and is equal to the radius of the circle.

The time of a complete oscillation is the time taken by P to describe the circle, and

$$= \frac{2\pi}{\omega}$$

where ω is measured in rad/sec.

This is called the periodic time. It is independent of the radius of the circle—*i.e.*, of the amplitude, and varies with ω only.

We have so far been considering the motion of a geometrical point. In practice we are likely to be concerned with the motions of machine parts, or perhaps of projectiles, even of planets. Such bodies have mass, and are acted upon by forces. In dealing with the example that follows, and many similar problems, the data to be used in the solution must include not only the particulars given in the statement of the problem, but general truths of Physics and Mechanics. In connection with Example 1 which follows, but not in all cases, the additional data are quoted in the solution.*

* In general, reference might be made to Walker's *Mechanical Engineering Science*, or to Fisher's *Engineering Science and Calculations*, both published by the English Universities Press.

Example 1

A cylindrical spiral spring supports a weight of 35 lb and is made to vibrate vertically. The stiffness of the spring is such that when stretched 1 in. it would support a stationary weight of 10 lb. Show that when vibrating the acceleration of the weight is proportional to its displacement from mid-position, and is directed towards the mid-position, so that the vibration satisfies the definition of SHM.

Determine the periodic time.

Let AB be the natural length and BO the extension of the spring when the 35-lb weight hangs at rest.

The 35-lb " weight " is, of course, a piece of metal whose *mass* is 35 lb. Its weight is the force which gravity exerts upon it.

Since the mass is given in pounds it will be best to use the foot-pound-second system of units. Therefore, all masses should be stated as *numbers of pounds*, all lengths or distances as *numbers of feet*, all time periods as *numbers of seconds*: force must then appear as foot-pound-second units (or poundals) in order that the equation

$$\text{force} = \text{mass} \times \text{acceleration}$$

may be satisfied.

Fig. 73.

To work this, and many similar examples on SHM, it is necessary to know the law of the spring, that is, exactly how the force exerted by the spring in its effort to recover depends upon the extension. We are clearly expected to assume that **within the limits of the experiment** the force exerted by the spring is proportional to the instantaneous extension of the spring. We are, in fact, told that the effort to recover is a force of 10 lb wt for every inch of extension.*

---

* Experiment could show that this was true for small extensions. Clearly it can not be true for very large ones, since the spiral form of the spring would change appreciably, and at the same time the material of the spring might pass its Elastic Limit.

If the effort to recover is proportional to the actual elongation of the spring (BO in the figure) it is also proportional to the elongation expressed as a fraction of the original length—that is to the ratio $\dfrac{BO}{AB}$. It is a little better to think of elongation as proportional to $\dfrac{BO}{AB}$ than as proportional to BO, simply because this brings in the general properties of the spring used, and not merely the extension on this particular occasion.

A common method of denoting the characteristics of a spiral spring is to give the value of the force which will make the ratio $\dfrac{\text{elongation}}{\text{original length}}$ equal to one. This force, which is of course some number of poundals, is given the symbol λ. We can work out its value for the spring of the question because we know the unstretched length AB ft, the elongation OB ft which is $\dfrac{3 \cdot 5}{12}$ ft or $\dfrac{7}{24}$ ft and the tension, which is 35 g poundals when the spring is supporting a mass of 35 lb.

We have $\dfrac{OB}{AB}\lambda = 35$ g poundals, where $OB = \dfrac{7}{24}$ ft.

So $\qquad \lambda = \dfrac{35 \text{ g AB}}{\frac{7}{24}}.$

When the mass is in the position O (Fig. 73) the forces acting upon it are balanced. If the mass is oscillating about the position O it will have no acceleration when it is at O but will have its maximum velocity upwards or downwards. If the mass is displaced below O by an additional elongation of the spring x feet, then the resultant force acting upon it is

$$-\frac{\lambda x}{AB}$$

the negative sign indicating that the force is opposite in direction to the displacement. Thus the motion of the suspended mass satisfies the definition on p. 261 of Simple Harmonic Motion.

To find the periodic time of this SHM

Let x ft be the distance (of the oscillating mass) below O at time t sec after the mass has left O (the position of zero force). Then

$$\text{mass} \times \text{acceleration} = 35 \frac{d^2x}{dt^2} = \frac{-\lambda}{\text{AB}} \times x.$$

Thus

$$\frac{d^2x}{dt^2} = -\frac{\lambda}{\text{AB}} \times \frac{x}{35}.$$

But for SHM $\frac{d^2x}{dt^2} = -\omega x.$ See p. 260, where the acceleration at any point in SHM was derived from consideration of a point moving in a circular path with constant angular velocity ω. It was there shown that the Time Period for the SHM was $\frac{2\pi}{\omega}$. For our problem

$$\omega^2 \text{ corresponds to } \frac{\lambda}{35\text{AB}}, \text{ i.e., } \frac{24 \text{ g}}{7}$$

and $\qquad \frac{2\pi}{\omega} \qquad ,, \qquad ,, \qquad 2\pi\sqrt{\dfrac{7}{24 \text{ g}}}.$

So the Time Period is $2\pi\sqrt{\dfrac{7}{24 \text{ g}}}$ sec = 0·6 sec.

In the study of Example 1 mass and dimensions have been introduced so that the answer relates to a particular problem. Do not, however, let the arithmetic obscure the important fact that whenever a vibrating mass is controlled by any sort of spring its motion will be simple harmonic. The property of Elasticity, summarised in Hooke's Law, ensures that there is always a force urging the mass *back* to a central position (the position of rest); and that this force is proportional to the displacement of the mass, say x ft.

Since acceleration $= \dfrac{\text{force}}{\text{mass}}$, the acceleration, like the force, will be towards the centre and proportional to the displacement. Using ω^2 as a constant of proportionality, in all such cases we have

$$\frac{d^2x}{dt^2} = - \omega^2 x.$$

Example 2

A particle is known to have SHM about a fixed point O. When 2 ft from O its velocity is 12 ft/sec and its acceleration 4 ft/sec². What is the amplitude?

The answer may be simply obtained by using Fig. 72. From the question we get that:

$$4 = 2\omega^2$$
$$\therefore \quad \omega = \sqrt{2}.$$

Hence (refer to Fig. 72), in the triangle OPM:

$$OM = 2, \quad MP = \frac{12}{\sqrt{2}}$$
$$\therefore \quad OP^2 = 4 + \tfrac{144}{2} = 76$$
$$\therefore \quad OP = \sqrt{76}.$$

Note that it was unnecessary to specify the sign of the velocity.

EXERCISE 38

1. Obtain approximate values for
    (a) cos 60° 1', (b) tan 45° 1', (c) sin 29° 59'.

2. In a triangle ABC, $a = 40$ ft, B = 72°, A = 40°. Find the error in calculating b, if there is an error of 10' in measuring B.

3. Given that $i = k \tan \theta$, where k is constant find the error in i, due to a small error in reading θ.
    Find the percentage error in the current i, due to an error of 30' when θ is taken as 45°.

4. The angle of elevation of a chimney is observed from

a point 100 ft from its base as 63° 13′ subject to an error of 5′. Calculate the error in the height.

5. Find the turning points in the following curves between 0° and 360° and state which are maxima:

(1) $y = \sin \theta + \cos \theta$. (2) $y = \sin 2x + \cos x$.

(3) $y = \cos 2x + \sin x$. (4) $y = \sin^3 \theta$.

6. A mass is secured at one end of a spring blade the other end of which is gripped between the jaws of an ordinary bench vice. What will be the effect on the time period of this vibrator if (a) the free length of the blade is reduced by holding it shorter in the vice, or (b) the attached mass is increased? Justify your answers by reference to the various equations for SHM used in the preceding pages.

7. The lift of a valve moving with SHM is $\frac{3}{16}$ in., and the total time occupied by the opening and closing of the valve is $\frac{1}{20}$ sec.

Find the accelerating forces at the ends of the stroke of the valve per lb weight of the valve. (U.L.C.I.)

8. A cylindrical spiral spring supports a weight of 20 lb and is set vibrating. If a force of 15 lb is necessary to stretch it 1 in., find the period of vibration. (U.L.C.I.)

9. In an SHM along a straight line show the acceleration at any point is directly proportional to the distance of the point from the mid-point of the motion.

If a piston move with SHM, and has a stroke of 2 ft, find the force necessary to overcome the inertia of the reciprocating parts at the ends of the stroke, and also when the crank has turned through 45° from either dead centre. The reciprocating parts weigh 500 lb and the crank-shaft makes 120 revolutions per minute. (U.E.I.)

10. What is meant by SHM?

A spring increases 1 in. in length when a load of 21 lb is suspended from it. If a weight of 56 lb is attached to this spring, drawn below its position of rest and then released, how many vibrations per minute will it make? (U.E.I.)

11. A point in a mechanism moves in a straight path, and its distance s in. from a fixed point O of the path is given by $s = 4 \sin t + 2 \cdot 5 \cos t$, where t sec is the time measured from a fixed instant. Find the velocity and acceleration when $t = \dfrac{\pi}{6}$ and find the maximum displacement from O.   (U.L.C.I.)

12. A child playing on a garden swing has a motion resembling SHM, although in a curved path. A friend is willing to help the swinger to increase the amplitude. Instruct the friend as to how he may make his assistance most effective, adding explanations.

11. Integration of the Circular Functions

We have found that if $y = \sin \theta$

$$\frac{dy}{d\theta} = \cos \theta$$

i.e.,

$$dy = \cos \theta \cdot d\theta.$$

Reversing the process we get:

$$\int \cos \theta \cdot d\theta = \sin \theta + \mathbf{C} \quad \cdot \quad \cdot \quad \cdot \quad \cdot \quad (1)$$

Similarly,

$$\int \sin \theta \cdot d\theta = -\cos \theta + \mathbf{C} \quad \cdot \quad \cdot \quad \cdot \quad (2)$$

It is essential that the formal aspect of these integrations should be grasped.

Thus (1) becomes:

$$\int \cos \text{ (any angle) } d \text{ (angle)} = \sin \text{ (angle)} + \text{C.}$$

Suppose we require $\displaystyle\int \sin 3\theta \cdot d\theta$.

To get this in correct " form," we have:

$$\int \sin 3\theta \cdot d\theta = \tfrac{1}{3} \int \sin 3\theta \cdot d(3\theta)$$

$$= -\frac{\cos 3\theta}{3} + \text{C.}$$

Observe that constants may be taken outside the integral sign.

Generalising, we get:

$$\int \cos a\theta . d\theta = \frac{1}{a}\int \cos a\theta . d(a\theta) = \frac{\sin a\theta}{a} + C \qquad . \quad (3)$$

and

$$\int \sin b\theta . d\theta = \frac{1}{b}\int \sin b\theta . d(b\theta) = - \frac{\cos b\theta}{b} + C \quad . \quad (4)$$

Once we know these integrals we need not go through the process of putting them in " form."

Example 1

$$\int \sin 5x . dx = - \frac{\cos 5x}{5} + C.$$

Example 2

$$\int 3 \cos 4\theta . d\theta = \tfrac{3}{4} \sin 4\theta + C.$$

Example 3

$$\int \sin \left(\theta + \frac{\pi}{3} \right) d\theta = - \cos \left(\theta + \frac{\pi}{3} \right) + C.$$

Notice that the " form " of the integrand is correct. {Integrand = expression to be integrated.}

Example 4

$$\int \sin \left(2kt + \frac{\pi}{6} \right) dt = - \frac{1}{2k} \cos \left(2kt + \frac{\pi}{6} \right) + C.$$

EXERCISE 39

Integrate the following:

1. $\cos \theta$.
2. $\sin \theta$.
3. $\sin 3\theta$.
4. $3 \sin 2\theta$.
5. $2 \cos 4\theta$.
6. $\cos \tfrac{1}{2}\theta$.

7. $\dfrac{3}{4}\sin\dfrac{2\theta}{3}$.   8. $3\sin 2\theta - 4\cos 5\theta$.

9. $\sin(\theta + \alpha)$.   10. $\cos\left(3\theta + \dfrac{\pi}{7}\right)$.

11. $2\sin\left(\dfrac{\pi}{5} - \theta\right)$.   12. $3\cos\left(\alpha - \dfrac{\theta}{2}\right)$.

EXERCISE 39A—MISCELLANEOUS

Refer to the general note on p. 160 which applies equally to the questions which follow.

1. (*a*) Find $\dfrac{dy}{dx}$ if:

   (i) $y = \dfrac{1}{2\sqrt{x}} + \dfrac{2}{x^3}$;   (ii) $y = 2x^2 \sin(3x + 2)$;

   (iii) $y = \log_e \sin x$.

(*b*) The stiffness of a beam of rectangular section is proportional to the product of the breadth and the cube of the depth. Find the lengths of the sides of the stiffest beam of rectangular section having a given perimeter of 24 in.

(Rugby.)

2. In a certain firm the cost of producing x articles per day is $(20x^2 + 2x + 375)$ shillings, and the price at which each article can be sold is $(210 - x^2)$ shillings. Show that the profit per day (P shillings) is given by

$$P = 208x - (x^3 + 20x^2 + 375)$$

Hence find the number of articles per day which must be produced for maximum profit, and show that the selling price per article is then £9 14s.   (Sunderland.)

3. (*a*) Evaluate the following:

   (i) $\displaystyle\int \dfrac{3x^2}{5x^3 - 1}\,dx$;   (ii) $\displaystyle\int \dfrac{(2x^3 - 7x^2 + 7x - 3)}{2x - 1}\,dx$;

   (iii) $\displaystyle\int \dfrac{x + 16}{(x - 2)(x + 4)}\,dx$.

(b) If $\dfrac{d^2y}{dx^2} = 4 \sin 4x + 2 \cos 2x$ and $y = 1\frac{1}{2}$

$\dfrac{dy}{dx} = 2$, when $x = 0$

express y as a function of x.   (Worcester.)

4. (a) If $x = 3t - t^3$ and $y = \sqrt{t^2 - 5}$ find the value of $\dfrac{dy}{dx}$ when $t = 3$.

(b) The displacement x of a body is given by $x = e^{-t} \sin t$. Find an expression for its velocity and evaluate this velocity when $t = \dfrac{\pi}{2}$.

(Handsworth.)

5. (a) Find the area of the triangle whose vertices are the points $(5, 4)$, $(3, -2)$ and $(-7, 3)$.

(b) Two cylinders of diameters 15 in. and 19 in., lying side by side, are strapped together.

Calculate the length of the strap ignoring overlap.

(E.M.E.U.)

6. (a) Prove that $(\sec^2 A - 1)(\operatorname{cosec}^2 A - 1) = 1$.

(b) Express $3 \sin 4\omega t \sin \left(\omega t + \dfrac{\pi}{2} \right)$ as a difference of two sines.

(c) Solve for values of θ from $0°$ to $360°$

$$5 - 5 \cos \theta - 3 \sin^2 \theta = 0. \quad \text{(E.M.E.U.)}$$

7. (a) Calculate the area of the circle which can be inscribed in a triangle of sides 4 in., 5 in. and 6 in. in length.

(b) If $\tan \phi = \dfrac{\sqrt{3}(W_1 - W_2)}{W_1 + W_2}$

show that

$$\cos \phi = \dfrac{W_1 + W_2}{2 \times \sqrt{W_1^2 - W_1 W_2 + W_2^2}}.$$

(E.M.E.U.)

8. An open coal bin with vertical sides is to have a volume of 36 cubic feet and is to measure 2 ft from front to back.

Its ends are to be trapezoidal in shape, the back height being 4 ft. If the material from which the bin is made costs 3s. 6d. per square foot, find the length and front height so that the cost is least, and find the least cost.

(Burton-upon-Trent.)

9. (a) Differentiate with respect to x and simplify your results:

(i) $\dfrac{3x^{\frac{5}{2}} + 4x^{\frac{7}{4}} + \sqrt{x}}{3x^3}$;

(ii) $e^{3x} \sin 2x + 7$;

(iii) $\dfrac{\log_e x^2}{x^2} + 14x$;

(iv) $\dfrac{1}{\sqrt{x^2 - 1}} + \tan 2x$.

(b) If $i = \dfrac{E}{R} + Ae - \dfrac{Rt}{L}$, where A, E, R, L are constants, show that

$$L\frac{di}{dt} + Ri = E.$$
(Stafford.)

10. (a) Find $\dfrac{dy}{dx}$ in the following cases:

(i) $y = \sqrt{x^2 + 16}$;

(ii) $y = \sin 3x \cos 5x$;

(iii) $x^2 + y^2 - 16x + 12y - 30 = 0$.

(b) Evaluate the integrals:

(iv) $\displaystyle\int (3x + 7)^4 dx$;

(v) $\displaystyle\int 70 \cos 50\pi t . dt$.

(S.W. Essex.)

11. (a) If a current is given by the expression

$$i = 100 \sin 50\pi t + 12 \cos 100\pi t,$$

find the approximate change in current that takes place while t increases from 0·005 to 0·0053 sec.

(b) A road OB runs due north. On a cross-road OA running due West a machine-gun post is situated at A 80 yd from O. A motor-cyclist C is travelling along the road OB at 70 m.p.h. Find at what rate he is moving out of range of the machine-gun 3 sec after he has passed the point O.
(S.W. Essex.)

12. (a) A parabola whose equation is of the type

$$y = ax^2 + bx + c,$$

where a, b and c are constants, passes through the points $(-1, 6)$, $(2, 3)$ and $(3\frac{1}{2}, 8\frac{1}{4})$. Find the values of a, b and c.

(b) Find, to two decimal places, the value of x which satisfies the equation $3 + \sqrt{x + 3} = 2x$, where $\sqrt{x + 3}$ signifies only the positive square root. (U.L.C.I.)

13. Prove the formula for the sum of the first n terms of a geometric progression.

In a long-term survey a company estimates that, at the end of 20 years, £50,000 will be required for re-equipping. To redeem the £50,000 a sum of £X is invested at the beginning of each of the 20 years, and allowed to accumulate at $3\frac{1}{2}\%$ per annum compound interest. Find the value of X. (Sunderland.)

14. (a) State and prove the Cosine Rule for the solution of triangles.

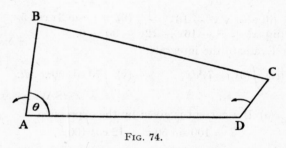

Fig. 74.

(b) The diagram shows a two-crank mechanism. If AB = 2·0 ft, DC = 1 ft, AD = 4·5 ft, BC = 5·0 ft and $\angle$ADC = 125°, calculate the angle θ. (S.W. Essex.)

15. (a) The relation $y = a + bx^n$ is satisfied by the following pairs of values:

x	3	9	27
y	4	9	36

Show that $n = \dfrac{\log 5 \cdot 4}{\log 3}$.

(b) Solve the equation $\sqrt{8 + 6x} + 2\sqrt{1 + x} = 2\sqrt{1 - x}$. Of the two values of x obtained only one satisfies the given equation. What is the equation which the other value satisfies?   (Stafford.)

16. (a) Resolve into partial fractions $\dfrac{2x - 3}{(x - 1)^2}$.

(b) An open cylindrical container is to be made from 48π sq in. of metal. Find its dimensions when its volume is maximum.   (Burton-upon-Trent.)

17. (a) In a fairground a big wheel is mounted with its hub 45 ft above the ground. The radius of the wheel is 40 ft. Find an expression of the height h of a point on the circumference of the wheel above the ground, when the radius joining it to the hub is inclined at an angle of $\theta°$ to the horizontal. How much does this point rise vertically when θ increases from 37° to 37° 10'?

(b) Find the vertical component of the velocity of this point at the moment when $\theta = 53°$, if the wheel is making one revolution every 40 sec.   (S.W. Essex.)

18. The teeth of a 3-in.-diameter cutter (A) are to have a clearance angle θ of 6° at the cutting edge. The clearance faces are to be ground by the vertical face of the cup grinding wheel (G).

Give a distance or *length* measure by means of which the cutter may be set to present the clearance faces to the wheel at the correct *angle*; and explain how the information may be used. See Fig. 75, p. 274.

19. (a) A battery of n cells with x cells in series per row, and $\dfrac{n}{x}$ rows in parallel sends a current i through an external resistance R. Given that $i = \dfrac{xe}{\dfrac{x^2 r}{n} + R}$, where n, e, r and

R are constants, find the value of x which makes the current a maximum.

(b) The displacement, S ft, of a moving body after t sec. is given by $S = 9 . \sqrt[3]{t^2} - 27 . \sqrt[3]{t}$.

Find the velocity and acceleration of the body after 8 sec. (Shrewsbury.)

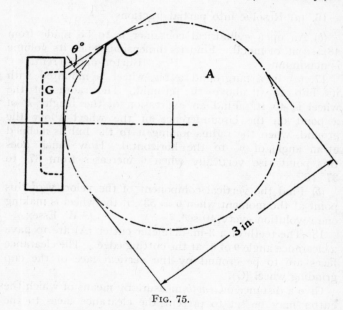

Fig. 75.

20. (a) Differentiate with respect to x, expressing each result in as simple a form as possible:

(i) $e^{-2x} \cos 3x$ (ii) $\log_e (1 + 2x^2)$

(iii) $\dfrac{(x - 1)^2}{x^2 + 1}$ (iv) $\sin^4 3x$

(b) A balloon rises vertically at the uniform rate of 6 m.p.h. from a spot 1 mile distant from an observer with a telescope. Find the rate at which he must rotate the telescope to keep the balloon in the field of view when the balloon is 3 miles high.   (Halifax.)

21. Fig. 76 shows half a symmetrical roof truss.

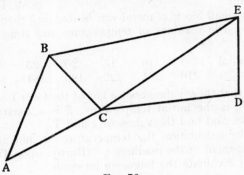

FIG. 76.

If AB = 7·3 ft, AC = 6·8 ft, CD = 8·7 ft, $\angle$BAC = 40°, $\angle$BCE = 98°, $\angle$ECD = 28° and $\angle$BEC = 23°, find the lengths of the remaining members of the framework.
                                                  (S.W. Essex.)

22. (a) Evaluate u where $u^2 = (3·024)^{6·23}$.

(b) If a body is projected with a velocity U ft per sec up a plane, angle β, so that its direction of motion makes an initial angle α with the horizontal, the range R is given by

$$R = \frac{2u^2 \cos \alpha \sin (\alpha - \beta)}{g \cos^2 \beta}.$$

Calculate u when R = 44·74, α = 58°, β = 33° 15′, g = 32.

(c) Solve the equation

$$3^{2x} \cdot 5^x = 7^{(3x + 1)}$$

giving x correct to two places of decimals.   (Worcester.)

23. (a) Explain carefully how you would find and distinguish between maximum and minimum values of a function.

(b) A window is to have a perimeter of 20 ft. It is in the form of a rectangle with a semi-circle described on its upper side as a diameter. Find to what dimensions the window should be made in order that its area may be a maximum.

(S.W. Essex.)

24. A small block of metal was heated and then allowed to cool. The readings of temperature and time were as follows:

t (min)	5	10	15	20	25	30
$T°$ C.	310	261	222	189	161	139

Show that these values obey a law of the form $T = T_0 e^{-kt}$, where T_0 is the initial temperature, k is a constant and $e = 2\cdot718$, and find the values of k and T_0.

Find by calculation the temperature 40 min after the commencement of the readings. (Burton-upon-Trent.)

25. (a) Evaluate the following integrals:

(i) $\int \left(x + \dfrac{3}{x} \right)^2 dx$ (ii) $\int \dfrac{\cos x \cdot dx}{\sin^3 x}$.

(b) Find the mean value of $\sin 3x$ between $x = \dfrac{\pi}{6}$ and $x = \dfrac{\pi}{3}$.

(S.W. Essex.)

26. (a) Find all values of θ in the range 0–360° which satisfy the equation

$$\sin 2\theta = 2 \tan \theta + 3 \sin \theta$$

(b) Express $4 \sin \theta + 5 \cos \theta$ in the form $r \sin (\theta + \alpha)$.

Hence, or otherwise, find values of θ, in degrees and minutes, between 0° and 360° which satisfy the equation

$$4 \sin \theta + 5 \cos \theta = 6.$$

(c) Prove that

$$\cos 3x = 4 \cos^3 x - 3 \cos x$$

Hence, or otherwise, find

$$\int \cos^3 x \, dx$$

(Halifax.)

27. A casting is in the shape of a frustum of a cone. The diameters of its end faces are 3 in. and 5 in., and the distance between them is 6 in. Find the position of its centre of gravity. (S.W. Essex.)

28. A mass m is free to move on a smooth horizontal wire, and initially is at rest at point A on the wire. Vertically above a point O on the wire is a ring B, so fixed that $OB = a$. Through this ring is threaded a string which is attached to mass m, and when the distance AB has been adjusted to equal $2a$ the loose end of the string is pulled horizontally at a constant velocity V. For values of $t < a/V$ find the distance of m from O in terms of a, V and t. Hence deduce the velocity of m at any time, and show that its initial velocity is $2V/\sqrt{3}$. (Sunderland.)

29. (a) The length of the crank of a vertical-cylinder reciprocating engine is 6·0 in. and the length of the connecting-rod is 24·0 in. Find the angle through which the crank has turned when the piston has moved 2·5 in. from top dead centre.

(b) Calculate the magnitude and direction of the resultant of forces of 17 lb weight and 23 lb weight which act on a point, and whose lines of action are inclined at 64° to each other. (S.W. Essex.)

30. The displacement x of a vibrating body at time t sec is given by the equation

$$x = 2e^{-t} \sin 5t,$$

where the angle $5t$ is in radians. Plot a graph of x vertically against t horizontally for values of t going from 0 to 2 sec at intervals of 0·2 sec. (Stafford.)

31. (a) Differentiate the following functions with respect to x:

(i) $(1 - 2x)^{10}$;

(ii) $\dfrac{5x^2}{1 + x^2}$;

(iii) $\sin^3 2x$;

(iv) $\log \sqrt{\dfrac{1 - x}{1 + x}}$.

(b) If $y = x^2 e^{3x}$, show that

$$\frac{dy}{dx} = 2xe^{3x} + 3y.$$

(Halifax.)

32. A container having a volume of 24·5 cu in. is to be welded out of sheet metal and is to be in the form of a match box (i.e., a tray plus an outer casing) having the ends square in section. If x in. is the depth of the tray, show that the area A, in sq in., is given by

$$A = \frac{171·5}{x} + 2x^2$$

Calculate the minimum area of sheet metal required, neglecting the thickness of the metal and any overlap. Show mathematically that the value you obtain does give a minimum and not a maximum. (Nuneaton.)

33. (i) The annual insurance premium on the machinery in a factory is 0·1% of its estimated value. If the machinery was originally worth £3000, and the value depreciated at 5% per annum, find the insurance payable after 10 years use.

(ii) (a) Expand $\sqrt{1 - 2x}$ in ascending powers of x to the fourth term, simplifying the expansion as far as possible.

(b) Given that $1 - x^3 = (1 - x)(1 + x + x^2)$, expand $\frac{1}{1 + x + x^2}$ as far as the term in x^{10}, and hence find the value of $\frac{1}{1·24}$ correct to 4 decimal places. (Cheltenham.)

34. (a) Write down the first four terms of the expansion of $(a + x)^n$ in ascending powers of x.

(b) Find, using the binomial theorem, the cube root of 0·97 correct to 4 decimal places.

(c) In the formula $n = \frac{T^{\frac{1}{2}} m^{-\frac{1}{2}} l^{-1}}{2}$, l is subject to an error of $+ 1\%$, T is subject to an error of $- 3\%$ and m is subject to an error of $+ 2\%$. Show that the approximate percentage error in n is $3\frac{1}{2}\%$ too small. (Stafford.)

35. From A, the top of a pole 6 ft high, a string is stretched taut under a small pulley C at ground level, x ft from B, the foot of the pole, and on to a fixed point, D, 20 ft from B. B, C and D are in a straight line and on the same level.

Find an expression for the length of the string in terms of x. Hence, without finding the actual length of string between A and D, find the change in its length when x is increased from 8·25 to 8·3 ft. Find also the rate at which the length of the string is changing at the instant when x is 10 and is increasing at the rate of 0·25 ft per sec. (S.W. Essex.)

36. (i) Given $P = P_0 e^{rt/100}$, calculate what value of t will make $P = 1\frac{1}{2}P_0$ when $r = 3$. (Take e to be the base of Naperian log 2·718.)

(ii) If $P_1 V_1{}^\gamma = P_2 V_2{}^\gamma$ and $\dfrac{P_1 V_1}{T_1} = \dfrac{P_2 V_2}{T_2}$,

find an expression for $\dfrac{T_2}{T_1}$

    (1) in terms of V_1, V_2 and γ only,

    (2) in terms of P_1, P_2 and γ only. (West Riding.)

37. (a) Express $7 \sin x + 24 \cos x$ in the form $r \sin (x + \theta)$, determining the values of r and θ.

(b) Solve the equation $7 \sin x + 24 \cos x = 15$ for x in the range 0–360°.

(c) Plot a graph of $[7 \sin x + 24 \cos x]$ in the range 0–360°, and by drawing a suitable straight line to intersect this, obtain, as accurately as your graph permits, alternative graphical solutions to the equation of part (b).

(Halifax.)

38. (a) Using the binomial theorem, expand $\sqrt{(1 - 2x^2)}$, giving the first 4 terms of the series.

(b) By drawing the graphs of $y = x^3$ and $y = 8 - 4x$ between $x = 0$ and $x = 2$, show that the equation $x^3 + 4x - 8 = 0$ has a root near to 1·4.

Use a method of approximation with this value to obtain a nearer value of the root. (Handsworth.)

39. The Shear Force S at a point P, x ft from one end A of a loaded beam AB, is given by

$$S = \frac{19}{2} - \frac{x}{16} - \frac{x^2}{16}.$$

(i) If $S = \dfrac{dM}{dx}$, where M is the bending moment at P, obtain an expression for M, given that $M = 141\frac{1}{3}$ when $x = 8$.

(ii) If the bending moment is a maximum where the shear force is zero, find the value of x at which maximum bending moment occurs.   (Coventry.)

40. O is a fixed point and A is a moving point distant $3 \sin 2\pi t$ from O where $2\pi t$ is an angle in radians. The rod AB of length 12 in. slides in a groove free to turn about a pivot at C. If CD is 3 in. and OD is 6 in., find (i) the angle θ, (ii) the distance x in. of B above the path of A when the time $t = 1\cdot18$ sec. What is the vertical displacement of B as A moves from end to end of its path?

          (Stafford.)

41. Differentiate the following with respect to x, expressing the results in their simplest forms:

(a) $\left(\dfrac{1+2x}{1+x}\right)^2$;   (b) $\log \sin 2x$;

(c) $e^{x \sin x}$;   (d) $\cos 2x - \frac{1}{3}\cos^3 2x$.

          (Cheltenham.)

42. (a) Write out the usual expansions for $\sin (A \pm B)$, $\cos (A \pm B)$, $\tan (A \pm B)$, and from these deduce those for $\sin 2A$, $\cos 2A$, $\tan 2A$.

(b) Show that $2 \cos A \cos B = \cos (A + B) + \cos (A - B)$.

(c) Evaluate:

(i) $\displaystyle\int_0^{\pi/4} \cos 3x \cos 5x \, dx$;   (ii) $\displaystyle\int_0^{\pi/2} \sin^2 2x \, dx$.

(d) Without using trigonometrical tables, find the value of $\tan 15°$ to three significant figures.   (Halifax.)

43. (a) Find $\frac{dy}{dx}$ in the following cases: (i) $y = x^3 \cos 5x$;

(ii) $y = \frac{7x + 3}{\sin x}$.

(b) If $y = x^2 \sin x$, find an expression in terms of x for
$$\frac{d^2y}{dx^2} + \frac{3dy}{dx} - 7y.$$
(S.W. Essex.)

44. (a) The acceleration of a piston, f, is given approximately by the formula

$$f = -21\{\cos \theta + \tfrac{2}{7} \cos 2\theta\}.$$

(i) Find the value of f when $\theta = 0°$ and $\theta = 180°$.

(ii) Find, to the nearest half degree, the values of θ when the acceleration is zero. Only positive angles less than $360°$ need be considered.

(b) If $z = \frac{2dy}{dx} + 3y$ and $y = \sin 2x$, express z in the form $R \sin (2x + \alpha)$ giving the value of α lying between $-180°$ and $+180°$.

(c) State the maximum value of z in part (b).
(Nuneaton.)

45. Differentiate

$$x^2 \sin^2 x; \quad \log (1 + e^x).$$

Obtain

$$\int_0^1 \frac{x^3 - \sqrt{x}}{\sqrt{x}}dx; \quad \int (\sin x + \cos 2x)dx.$$
(Sunderland.)

46. A man has 120 ft of fencing and uses it to form three sides of a rectangular pen of which the fourth side is part of a long wall. Show that the maximum area which can be enclosed is 1800 sq ft.

If, instead of a rectangle, the pen is in the form of an isosceles triangle with the fencing used for the equal sides, find the maximum area now enclosed. (Sunderland.)

47. (a) A machine component to be turned in a lathe

includes a tapered length measuring 1 in. axially, and having parallel diameters of $1\frac{5}{8}$ in. and 1 in. respectively at the two ends. What will be the contour of an ordinary lathe form tool in a plane such as AB perpendicular to the clearance faces of the tool? The front clearance to be provided is 6°, and the breast of the tool lies in a horizontal plane passing through the centre line of the work-piece. See Fig. 77.

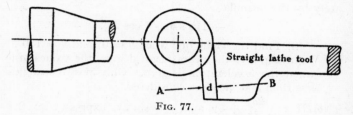

Fig. 77.

(b) It will be clear from the very slight divergence of the tool contour from that of the component that accurate work is in question, so that if many components are to be made many sharpenings of the tool will be needed, a fact which suggests the use of a circular form tool (see pp. 236–238). If the diameter of this circular cutting tool is large its radial contour may well be the same as that of the straight tool on the plane AB. But a large circular tool would be costly and might well prove impossible to mount on a standard machine tool. Because of this a form tool with a maximum diameter of 2 in. is to be used. Determine its contour on a radial plane if the minimum clearance is to be 4°.

48. Reduce to simplest terms:

(a) $\dfrac{d}{dx}\left(\dfrac{1}{2a}\log_e\dfrac{x-a}{x+a}\right)$;   (b) $\dfrac{d}{dx}\sqrt{(2x^2+4x-1)}$;

also (c) If $y=\sin\theta\cos\theta$ and $\dfrac{d^2y}{d\theta^2}=-1$, find the possible value of θ between 0 and 2π.   (Worcester.)

49. (a) Find all the values between 0° and 360° for which
$12 \sin (3\theta + 12°) - 7 \cos (3\theta - 28°) = 6.5$.

(b) A current is given by $i = 60 \sin 20\pi t - 35 \sin 40\pi t$.
Find the smallest positive value of t for which $i = 0$.

(c) Find the rate at which the current in (b) is increasing
when $t = 0.02$ sec.

50. (a) Differentiate FOUR of the following:

(i) $x^3 \cos (2x + 3)$;

(ii) $\dfrac{3x - 1}{2 + x^2}$;

(iii) $\dfrac{1}{\sqrt{(3 - 5x)}}$;

(iv) $e^{4x} - 3e^{-x} + \dfrac{1}{\sqrt{e^x}}$;

(v) $x^2 . \log (2x + 1)$;

(vi) $\dfrac{x^{2.1} - 3x^{-1.2}}{\sqrt{x}}$.

(b) If $pv^{1.4} = C$ is a constant, find $\dfrac{dp}{dv}$ and $\dfrac{dy}{dp}$, both in
terms of v.

(c) The percentage efficiency E of a petrol engine with an
expansion ratio of R is given by the expression

$$E = \left\{ 1 - \frac{1}{R^{0.28}} \right\}.$$

Find $\dfrac{dE}{dR}$.   (Dudley.)

51. (a) There are two points A and B which are not
visible to one another, but which may both be seen from C.
The distance AC is 250 yd, and BC is 300 yd. The angle
between AC and BC is 50° 18′. Calculate the distance AB.

(b) The current in a circuit at time t sec. is

$$(4.8 \sin 100\pi t - 2.0 \cos 100\pi t) \text{ amp.}$$

Express this in the form of a single sine wave. Hence find
the maximum value of the current and the least positive
value of t for which this maximum is attained.

                                    (Worcester.)

52. (a) A taper plug gauge is to have an included angle
of 5° and a length of 4 in. The ends are to be finished flat
and square to the centre line. If the diameter at the small

end is 1 in., what should be the diameter at the large end
if the taper is correct? Give an answer correct to four
significant figures.

(b) Axially adjustable centres are available whose
points lie on a line XY. By skilful work the device has
been adjusted so that the line of centres XY is exactly
parallel to the base AB, which has been finished as a true
plane.

Explain how, by the use of the above device, a sine bar,
and a finely graduated set of truly parallel blocks, you
might ascertain the included angle of the gauge. Give all
instructions and calculations.

53. (a) Differentiate with respect to x,

(i) $(1 - x^2)\sqrt{1 - x^2}$;   (ii) $\dfrac{2x}{x^2 + 3}$;   (iii) $e^{3x} \sin 2x$.

(b) The radius of curvature of a curve is given by the
formula

$$R = \frac{\left[1 + \left(\dfrac{dy}{dx}\right)^2\right]^{\frac{3}{2}}}{\dfrac{d^2y}{dx^2}}$$

If $y = \dfrac{1}{x}$, find an expression for R in terms of x, and evaluate
it when $x = 2$.   (Stafford.)

54. (a) Find $\dfrac{dy}{dx}$ when

(i) $y = \dfrac{x^2}{3x + 5}$;   (ii) $y = x^3 \sin 5x$;

(iii) $x^2 + 3y^2 - 2x + 7y - 15 = 0$.

(b) If, in a simple harmonic motion the displacement of
the body is given by $s = 50 \sin (200t + 0.03)$, find the
velocity and acceleration when $t = 0.0037$.

                                                   (S.W. Essex.)

55. (a) Find $\dfrac{dy}{dx}$ when

$$\text{(i) } y = \frac{2x^2 - 3}{(3x + 5)}; \quad \text{(ii) } y = e^{2x}(2x + 1),$$

simplifying your answer wherever possible.

(b) If $x = 6 \sin 3t + 2 \cos 3t$, find the value of $\dfrac{d^2x}{dt^2} + 9x$.

(c) Find the co-ordinates of the points on the curve $xy = 3$ at which the gradient is $-\frac{1}{3}$.

(Burton-upon-Trent.)

56. (a) Differentiate the following functions with respect to x:

$$\text{(i) } \frac{x^3}{3} - 5\sqrt{x} - \frac{2}{x^2}; \qquad \text{(ii) } \log_e (4 - 3x^2);$$

$$\text{(iii) } 0.5 \sin 4x - 5 \cos 0.3x; \qquad \text{(iv) } \frac{e^{\frac{x}{2}}}{4x + 3}.$$

(b) A solid metal cube expands uniformly when heated. The length of each edge, originally 2 in., increases at the rate of 0·4 in. per hour. Write down a formula for the length of the edge, l, after t hours and calculate the rate at which the volume is increasing after 5 hours.

(Coventry.)

57. The section of an open channel is in the shape of a trapezium with sloping sides and horizontal base each of length 10 ft. The sloping sides are equally inclined at the angle θ to the horizontal. Show that the area of the section is $100 \sin \theta(1 + \cos \theta)$ sq ft. Find the angle θ so that the area shall be a maximum and verify that this value of the angle θ gives a maximum and not a minimum.

(E.M.E.U.)

58. The vibration in a machine component results from the addition of two simple harmonic oscillations:

$$\sin\left(4t + \frac{\pi}{6}\right) \quad \text{and} \quad \sqrt{3} \cdot \cos\left(4t - \frac{\pi}{6}\right)$$

Express the vibration in the form R sin $(4t - \alpha)$, and hence determine the smallest positive values of t for which the displacement caused by the vibration reaches the algebraic maximum and minimum values.

(Cheltenham.)

59. (a) Write down the expansion of $(1 + x)^n$ as far as the term in x^4 and state the conditions for this expansion to be valid.

(b) By using the Binomial expansion, find $\sqrt{26}$ correct to 4 places of decimals.

(c) The period (t) of a simple pendulum and its length (l) are related by the formula $t = 2\pi\sqrt{\dfrac{l}{g}}$.

Find the approximate percentage change in period if the length is increased by 2%.   (Rugby.)

60. (i) Differentiate the following with respect to x, expressing the results in their simplest forms:

(a) $(x + \sin x)^7$;   (b) $\log_e \left(\dfrac{1 + x}{1 - x}\right)$;

(c) $e^{-x} \cos 3x$;   (d) x^x.

(ii) The distance, V, of the image from a concave mirror, radius r, of an object distant U from the mirror is given by

$$\frac{1}{V} + \frac{1}{U} = \frac{2}{r}.$$

If the object approaches the mirror at a speed of 5 cm/min, find the rate at which the image moves away from the mirror when $r = 12$ cm and V = 8 cm.

(Cheltenham.)

61. (a) Two forces, P and Q, act at an angle θ. Find the magnitude of their resultant force R and show that if $P = Q = T$, $R = 2T \cos \frac{1}{2}\theta$.

(b) Simplify the fraction $\dfrac{\sin 5A - \sin A}{\cos 5A + \cos A}$.

(c) Express the function $9 \cos \theta + 2 \sin \theta$ in the form

$R \cos (\theta - a)$, finding R and a. Hence, or otherwise, solve the equation $9 \cos \theta + 2 \sin \theta = 6$ for values of θ which lie between $0°$ and $360°$. (E.M.E.U.)

62. (a) If $y = A \cos (pt + \alpha)$ where A, p, α are constant, show that

$$\frac{d^2y}{dt^2} + p^2y = 0.$$

(b) In a potentiometer circuit a resistance R is given by

$$\frac{1}{R} = \frac{1}{x} + \frac{1}{a-x},$$

where a may be regarded as constant. Rearrange this making R the subject, and find the value of x which gives a maximum value of R. Show clearly that a maximum is given and determine this maximum value. Illustrate your answer with a sketch graph of R against x.

(Handsworth.)

63. A particle is oscillating about a fixed point, O, in a resisting medium. Its displacement, x in., from O after t sec. is given by the equation

$$x = 6e^{-0.0231t} \sin \left(\tfrac{2}{3}\pi t + 0.98\right)$$

the angle concerned being in radians. Determine the displacement after 6 sec. (Coventry.)

64. (i) Prove that $\cos \theta = \dfrac{\cos 3\theta}{2 \cos 2\theta - 1}$, and hence show

that $\cos 15° = \dfrac{\sqrt{3} + 1}{2\sqrt{2}}$. Derive corresponding values for $\sin 15°$ and $\tan 15°$.

(ii) The value of a periodic function is given by the sum of its first four harmonic terms, $\sin \theta$, $\sin 2\theta$, $\sin 3\theta$ and $\sin 4\theta$. Find the 3 smallest non-zero positive values of θ for which the function is zero. (Cheltenham.)

65. The displacement in feet of a particle from a fixed point O, after t sec is given by $d = 3 \sin wt - 7 \cos wt$.

Express this displacement d in the form $r \sin (wt - \alpha)$, and hence determine:

  (i) the algebraic maximum and minimum values of the displacement;

  (ii) the smallest value of t, when $w = \pi$, for which the displacement has these maximum or minimum values;

  (iii) the smallest value of t, when $w = \pi$, for which the displacement is equal to 3 ft.   (Cheltenham.)

66. (a) The displacement S ft of a particle from a fixed point at time t sec is given by

$$s = ut + \tfrac{1}{2}ft^2$$

where u and f are constants.   Find the value of $\dfrac{ds}{dt}$ and $\dfrac{d^2s}{dt^2}$ and state their meanings.

  (b) Find the value of $\dfrac{dy}{dx}$ when

  (i) $y = x \sin 3x$;   (ii) $y = (x^2 + 1)^5$;
  (iii) $y = \log_e \sin x$.

  (c) If $x = e^{2t} + \cos 2t$, show that $\dfrac{d^2x}{dt^2} + 4x = 8e^{2t}$.

                                        (Nuneaton.)

67. (a) Transform the expression $12 \cos \theta - 5 \sin \theta$ into the form $R \cos (\theta + \alpha)$.   Hence solve the equation

$$12 \cos \theta - 5 \sin \theta = 6 \cdot 6,$$

giving the possible values of θ between $0°$ and $360°$.

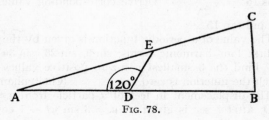

Fig. 78.

(b) In Fig. 78, p. 288, AB = 5 ft, AE = 3 ft, DE = 1 ft, BC = 1½ ft, and ADE is 120°. Find the length of AC, given that $\widehat{C}$ is acute.   (Coventry.)

68. In the accompanying figure the crank OP, of length r, rotates about the fixed centre O while one end P of the connecting-rod EP of length L is pin-jointed at P, the other end E being constrained to move along the line CAO.

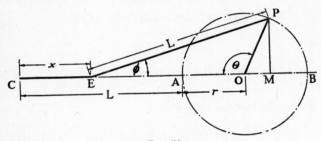

FIG. 79.

When the crank makes an angle θ with OA the rod is inclined at an angle ϕ to CAO as shown.

Prove that   (i) $\cos \phi = \left[1 - \dfrac{r^2}{L^2} \sin^2 \theta \right]^{\frac{1}{2}}$,

and (ii) the distance x of the end E of the rod from its extreme position C is given by

$$x = L + r - L \cos \phi - r \cos \theta.$$

(Halifax.)

CHAPTER 12

THE DEFINITE INTEGRAL. MEAN VALUES.
SIMPSON'S RULE *

1. It will be recalled that, if

$$y = f(x),$$

$\dfrac{dy}{dx}$ is also a function of x, often denoted as $f'(x)$,

thus $$\frac{dy}{dx} = f'(x)$$

or, using the differential notation:

$$dy = f'x \,.\, dx$$

Reversing the process we get:

$$\int f'(x) \,.\, dx = f(x) + C. \quad . \quad . \quad . \quad (1)$$

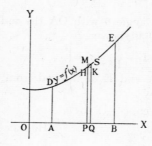

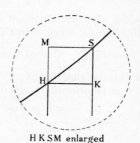

H K S M enlarged

FIG. 80.

Let us suppose that the equation of the curve DSE, Fig. 80, is $y = f'(x)$

If   OA $= a$,   AD $= f'(a)$.
Let   OP $= x$ and   PQ $= \Delta x$.

* Refer also to Section 2 of Chapter 7, p. **137**.

Complete the rectangles PQKH and PQSM.

It will be seen that the area PQSH lies between the areas of the rectangles PQKH and PQSM.

The rectangle HKSM has an area HK × KS and as Δx, or PQ, $\longrightarrow 0$, this area will vanish, since it is the product of two infinitesimals.

We shall then take the rectangle PQKH and the figure PQSH as becoming equal in area when $\Delta x \longrightarrow 0$.

Let the area   APHD $= z$

Then   PQSH $= \Delta z$

i.e., $\Delta z \longrightarrow f'(x) \,.\, \Delta x$ as $\Delta x \longrightarrow 0$

i.e., $Lt \,.\, \dfrac{\Delta z}{\Delta x} = f'(x)$.   .   .   .   (2)

We infer from (2) that z is a function of x whose differential coefficient is $f'(x)$;

$$\therefore \quad z = \int f'(x) \,.\, dx = f(x) + C \quad . \quad . \quad (3)$$

subject to the condition that $z = 0$ when $x = a$, since the area APHD vanishes when $x = a$. From (3) we get, on substituting these values for z and x,

$$0 = f(a) + C,$$

i.e., $C = -f(a).$

Hence from (3) we get that the area APHD is given by

$$z = f(x) - f(a) \quad . \quad . \quad . \quad (4)$$

If OB $= b$ the area ABED is given by $f(b) - f(a)$, which is obtained from (4) by putting b for x—*i.e.,* by supposing that P moves up to coincidence with B.

The results are summarised in Fig. 81.

To find the area ABED between the curve, $y = f'(x)$ the x-axis and two ordinates at $x = a$, and $x = b$, first find

$$\int f'(x) \,.\, dx = f(x) \text{ (do not put in a constant).}$$

Then put $x = b$ and get $f(b)$.

Next put $x = a$ and get $f(a)$.

The area is given by $f(b) - f(a)$.

The notation for this result is

$$\int_a^b f'(x)dx = \Big[f(x) \Big]_a^b = f(b) - f(a).$$

In Section 2 of Chapter 7, to which reference was made at the head of this chapter, the evaluation and interpretation of the definite integral was dealt with in a more elementary and descriptive way.

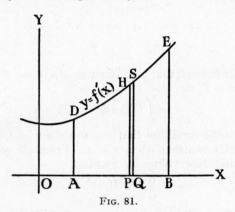

FIG. 81.

2. The integral $\int_a^b f'(x)dx$ is called a definite integral; a and b are called its limits, a being the lower limit, b the upper limit. Notice that the word limit as used here merely means a boundary.

The integral $\int_a^b f'(x)dx = f(b) - f(a)$ is called definite, since its value is definite, in contrast with that of

$$\int f'(x)dx = f(x) + c,$$

which contains the constant of integration.

3. We have seen that the definite integral can be interpreted as an area.

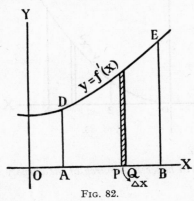

FIG. 82.

If ABED represents the area, it may be regarded as the sum of elementary areas like the one shaded in Fig. 82.

i.e., $\int_a^b f'(x) \cdot dx$ may be read thus:

" Find the sum of the rectangles like $f'(x) \cdot dx$ as x increases from a to b." The integral sign $\int$ may be regarded as a letter s, the initial letter of the word sum.

If reference to areas is not desired the expression $\int_a^b f'(x)dx$ is best translated by the words " Sum the infinitesimals like $f'(x)dx$, as x increases from a to b."

Example 1

Find the area between the curve $y = x^3$, the x-axis and the ordinates at $x = 2$ and $x = 4$.

The required area $= \int_2^4 x^3 dx = \left[\dfrac{x^4}{4} \right]_2^4 = 64 - 4$

$\qquad\qquad\qquad\qquad = 60$ square units.

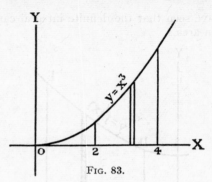

Fig. 83.

Example 2

Find the area between one arch of the curve $y = \sin \theta$ and the x-axis.

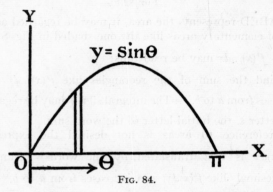

Fig. 84.

We see first that $y = 0$, when $\theta = 0$, and when $\theta = \pi$.
The small strip has the area $y d\theta$, *i.e.*, $\sin \theta d\theta$.

$$\therefore \quad \text{Area required} = \int_0^{\pi} \sin \theta d\theta = \left[-\cos \theta \right]_0^{\pi} = 1 + 1$$
$$= 2 \text{ square units.}$$

Notice $\cos \pi = -1$ and $-(-1) = +1$.

Example 3

Evaluate $\int_{-2\cdot9}^{2\cdot9} (1\cdot7x^3 - 4\cdot3x + 5)dx$ *and* $\int_{1}^{2} 3(x-1)^3 dx$.

(U.L.C.I.)

(i)

$$I = \int_{-2\cdot9}^{2\cdot9} (1\cdot7x^3 - 4\cdot3x + 5)dx = \left[1\cdot7\frac{x^4}{4} - 4\cdot3\frac{x^2}{2} + 5x\right]_{-2\cdot9}^{2\cdot9}$$

Observe that we do not need to substitute for the even powers of x in this case, since $(2\cdot9)^4 = (-2\cdot9)^4$ etc.

$$\therefore \quad I = 5\{2\cdot9 - (-2\cdot9)\}$$
$$= 5 \times 5\cdot8$$
$$= 29.$$

(ii) $I = \int_{1}^{2} 3(x-1)^3 dx = 3\left[\frac{(x-1)^4}{4}\right]_{1}^{2} = \frac{3}{4}.$

Example 4

Evaluate $\int_{1}^{3} (x-3)^2 dx$ *and* $\int_{a/b}^{b/a}\left(1 + \frac{1}{x^2}\right)dx$.

(N.C.T.E.C.)

We have $\int_{1}^{3} (x-3)^2 dx = \left[\frac{(x-3)^3}{3}\right]_{1}^{3}$

$$= 0 - (-\tfrac{8}{3})$$
$$= \tfrac{8}{3}$$

and $\int_{a/b}^{b/a}\left(1 + \frac{1}{x^2}\right)dx = \left[\left(x - \frac{1}{x}\right)\right]_{a/b}^{b/a}$

$$= \left(\frac{b}{a} - \frac{a}{b}\right) - \left(\frac{a}{b} - \frac{b}{a}\right)$$
$$= \left(\frac{b}{a} - \frac{a}{b}\right)$$
$$= \frac{2}{ab}(b^2 - a^2).$$

4. To Find a Volume of Revolution

Suppose the area ABED is rotated about the x-axis. In a complete revolution the ordinate PS describes a circle whose area is πy^2.

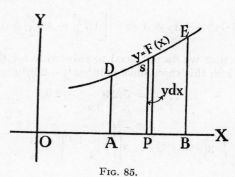

FIG. 85.

The rectangle ydx will describe a cylinder whose volume is $\pi y^2 dx$, and the required volume, V, generated by ABED in a complete revolution will be given by:

$$V = \int_a^b \pi y^2 dx$$

where OA $= a$ and OB $= b$.

We now substitute for y in terms of x.

Example 1

The part of the curve $y = x(x - 1)$ below the x-axis is rotated about that axis. Find the volume generated in a complete rotation.

We have $y = x(x - 1)$. First find the limits of integration. The curve cuts the x-axis where $x = 0$ and $x = 1$.

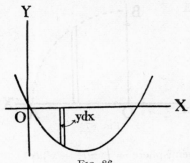

FIG. 86.

Hence the volume $= \int_0^1 \pi y^2 dx$ [y is $-$ve, but y^2 is $+$ve]

$$= \pi \int_0^1 (x^2 - x)^2 dx \text{ [Since } y = x^2 - x]$$

$$= \pi \int_0^1 (x^4 - 2x^3 + x^2) dx$$

$$= \pi \left[\frac{x^5}{5} - \frac{x^4}{2} + \frac{x^3}{3} \right]_0^1$$

$$= \pi \left[\frac{1}{5} - \frac{1}{2} + \frac{1}{3} \right] = \frac{\pi}{30} \text{ cubic units.}$$

Example 2

Find the volume of a sphere of radius r.

Regard the sphere as formed by rotating through four right angles the semi-circle whose bounding diameter is along the x-axis.

Let $x^2 + y^2 = r^2$ be the equation of the boundary curve AB.

Vol. of hemisphere $= \int_0^r \pi y^2 dx.$

Now $\qquad\qquad y^2 = r^2 - x^2.$

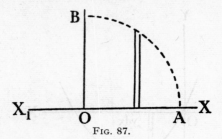

Fig. 87.

$$\therefore \text{ Vol. of hemisphere} = \int_0^r \pi(r^2 - x^2)dx$$

$$= \pi\left[\left(r^2x - \frac{x^3}{3}\right)\right]_0^r$$

$$= \pi\left(r^3 - \frac{r^3}{3}\right)$$

$$= \tfrac{2}{3}\pi r^3$$

$$\therefore \quad \tfrac{4}{3}\pi r^3 = \text{vol. of sphere.}$$

Example 3

Find the volume of a right circular cone of height h whose base has the radius r.

Regard the volume as generated by rotating the right-angled triangle OAB through four right angles.

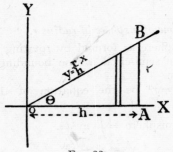

Fig. 88.

The equation of OB is $y = x \tan \theta = \dfrac{r}{h}x$.

$$\therefore \quad \text{The vol.} = \int_0^h \pi y^2 dx$$

$$= \int_0^h \pi \cdot \frac{r^2}{h^2}x^2 dx$$

$$= \frac{\pi r^2}{h^2}\left[\frac{x^3}{3}\right]_0^h$$

$$= \frac{\pi r^2}{h^2} \cdot \frac{h^3}{3} = \frac{1}{3} \cdot \pi r^2 \cdot h$$

i.e., $\frac{1}{3}$ area of base $\times$ *ht*.

EXERCISE 40

1. Evaluate the following integrals:

    (a) $\displaystyle\int_1^2 (u^2 + 3u - 5)du.$ (b) $\displaystyle\int_1^2 \left(\sqrt{v} + \frac{6}{\sqrt{v}}\right)dv.$

    (c) $\displaystyle\int_0^{\pi/3} \sin x\,dx.$ (d) $\displaystyle\int_0^{\pi/4} \cos 2t\,dt.$

    (U.L.C.I.)

2. Evaluate:

    (1) $\displaystyle\int_1^3 \left(u^2 - \frac{1}{u^2}\right)du.$

    (2) $\displaystyle\int_0^2 \pi y^2 dx$, when $y = 2x^{1\cdot5}$.

    (3) $\displaystyle\int_2^6 p\,dv$, where $pv^{0\cdot9} = 450$.

    (4) $\displaystyle\int_0^{\pi/2} (\cos t - \sin 2t)dt.$ (U.L.C.I.)

3. The shear force in tons taken by the web of a certain girder is given by

$$0\cdot6\int_{-9}^9 (3\cdot9 - 0\cdot013y^2)dy.$$

Calculate the shear.   (U.E.I.)

4. Evaluate:

(1) $\int_{-2\cdot9}^{2\cdot9} (7x^3 - 3x + 5)dx.$ (2) $\int_1^2 (x - 1)^3 dx.$

(3) $\int_{-1}^{+3} 3(x - 3)^2 dx.$

5. Evaluate:

(1) $\int_1^2 \left(x^2 - \frac{1}{x^2} + 2\right)dx.$ (2) $\int_1^3 (3 - x)^2 dx.$

(3) $\int_0^{\pi/6} (\sin 3t - \cos t)dt.$ (4) $\int_0^{\pi/2} \sin^2 \theta d\theta.$

(5) $\int_0^5 (2t^3 - 16t + 15\sqrt{t})dt.$

6. Show by integration that $\int_0^6 (x^2 - 5x + 3)dx = 0$, and given an explanation by means of a graph. (U.L.C.I.)

7. Evaluate:

(a) $\int_0^1 (x^2 + 4)dx.$ (b) $\int_4^6 \sqrt{x}(x - 4)dx.$

(c) $\int_0^{\pi/4} \cos\left(2\theta + \frac{\pi}{4}\right)d\theta.$ (d) $\int_0^{\pi/6} \cos 3x dx.$

(U.L.C.I.)

8. Find:

(1) $\int_1^9 \left(2\sqrt{x} - \frac{5}{x^2}\right)dx.$ (2) $\int_1^{10} v^{-0\cdot8} dv.$

(3) $\int_0^{\pi/6} \sin 3t dt.$ (4) $\int_0^{\pi/4} \cos\left(\tfrac{1}{2}t + 1\right)dt.$

(U.L.C.I.)

9. Evaluate:

(1) $\int_{-2}^{+1} (2x + 1)^2 dx.$ (2) $\int_{-m/n}^{m/n} \left(\frac{x^4 + 1}{x^3}\right)dx.$

(3) $\int_{-3}^{-1} \left(x - \frac{1}{2x^2}\right)dx.$ (N.C.T.E.C.)

10. For the curve $y = 3 + 2x + 3x^2$, find the area between the curve, the x-axis and the ordinates at $x = 1$ and $x = 4$.   (U.L.C.I.)

11. If $y = x^2$, show by a geometric illustration that $\int_a^b y\,dx$ will give the area between the curve the x-axis and the ordinates at $x = a$ and $x = b$.   Evaluate

$$\frac{\pi}{10}\int_1^2 (2h^{\frac{1}{2}} - h)\,dh.$$

(U.L.C.I.)

12. A curve whose equation is $\dfrac{y}{x^2 + 3} = m$, where m is a constant, passes through the point $(2, 3\cdot5)$.   Find the area bounded by the curve, the x-axis and the two ordinates at $x = 2$ and $x = 6$.   (U.L.C.I.)

5. Mean Values of a Function of One Variable

In Fig. 89, suppose that CD is part of the graph of $y = f(x)$.

Let   OA $= a$, and OB $= b$.

Then the area ABCD is represented by

$$\int_a^b f(x)\,dx \quad . \quad . \quad . \quad . \quad . \quad . \quad (1)$$

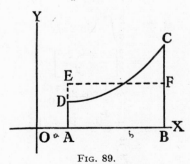

FIG. 89.

Now suppose that ABFE is a rectangle whose area equals that given by the integral (1).

The height of this rectangle—viz., AE or BF—is called the mean value of the function $f(x)$ between $x = a$ and $x = b$.

We then have, since $AB = (b - a)$

$$(b - a) \times AE = \int_a^b f(x)dx$$

$$\therefore \quad AE = \text{mean value} = \frac{1}{b - a} \cdot \int_a^b f(x)dx \quad . \quad (2)$$

Example 1

Find the mean value of x^2 between $x = 2$ and $x = 4$.

By the formula

$$\begin{aligned}
\text{M.V.} &= \frac{1}{4 - 2}\int_2^4 x^2 dx \\
&= \frac{1}{2}\left[\frac{x^3}{3}\right]_2^4 \\
&= \tfrac{1}{6}(4^3 - 2^3) \\
&= \tfrac{56}{6} = 9\tfrac{1}{3}.
\end{aligned}$$

Example 2

Find the mean value of $\sin 2x$, between $x = 0$ and $x = \frac{\pi}{2}$.

Here,

$$\begin{aligned}
\text{M.V.} &= \frac{2}{\pi}\int_2^{\pi/2} \sin 2x dx \\
&= \frac{2}{\pi}\left[-\frac{\cos 2x}{2}\right]_0^{\pi/2} \\
&= -\frac{1}{\pi}[\cos 2x]\frac{\pi/2}{0} \\
&= -\frac{1}{\pi}[(-1) - (1)] \\
&= \frac{2}{\pi}.
\end{aligned}$$

Since $\sin 2x = \sin 2(x + \pi)$, the period is π, and we have found the M.V. of $\sin 2x$ over half a period.

Example 3

Suppose a SHM is given by $x = 3 \cos 2t$.
Find the mean value of the velocity from $t = 2$ to $t = 5$.

$$\text{velocity} = \frac{dx}{dt} = -6 \sin 2t$$

$$\therefore \quad \text{M.V.} = \frac{1}{5-2} \int_2^5 (-6 \sin 2t) dt$$

$$= -2 \int_2^5 \sin 2t \, dt$$

$$= -2 \left[-\frac{\cos 2t}{2} \right]_2^5$$

$$= [\cos 2t]_2^5$$

$$= \cos 10 - \cos 4$$

(the unit angle is a radian in this result)
$$= 0 \cdot 187 \text{ ft/sec.}$$

6. Sometimes it is necessary to find the R.M.S. (root mean square) of a given function.

First find the M.V. of the square of the function. Then find the square root of the result.

Example

Find the R.M.S. of $\sin pt$ over one period.

We have, $\sin pt = \sin (pt + 2\pi) = \sin p\left(t + \frac{2\pi}{p}\right).$
Hence the period is $\frac{2\pi}{p}.$

$$\text{Mean Square} = \frac{p}{2\pi} \int_0^{2\pi/p} \sin^2 pt\,dt$$

$$= \frac{p}{2\pi} \int_0^{2\pi/p} \left(\frac{1 - \cos 2pt}{2}\right) dt$$

$$= \frac{p}{2\pi} \left[\frac{t}{2} - \frac{\sin 2pt}{4p}\right]_0^{2\pi/p}$$

$$= \frac{p}{2\pi} \times \frac{2\pi}{2p} = \frac{1}{2}$$

$$\therefore \text{R.M.S.} = \frac{1}{\sqrt{2}} = \frac{\sqrt{2}}{2} = 0\cdot707.$$

EXERCISE 41

1. Find the mean values of the following functions:

    (a) $\sin x$ from $x = 0$ to $x = \pi$.

    (b) $\sin^2 x$ from $x = 0$ to $x = \pi$.

    (c) x^2 from $x = 0$ to $x = 2$.

2. If $v = u + gt$, where u is the velocity at zero time, and $g = 32$ ft/sec^2, find (1) the average value of v during the first five seconds starting from rest, (2) during the first five seconds when $u = 36$ ft/sec.

3. A quantity of gas expands according to the law $pv^{1\cdot2} = $ const. from a volume of 2 cu ft to a volume of 5·5 cu ft. If $p = 140$ lb per sq in. when $v = 2$ cu ft, find the average of p from $v = 2$ to $v = 5\cdot5$.   (U.L.C.I.)

4. Find by means of the calculus:

    (a) The area between the curve $16x^2 = y - 1$, the x-axis and the ordinates at $x = 0$ and $x = 4$.

    (b) The mean value of y between $x = 0$ and $x = 4$.

                                                        (U.L.C.I.)

5. Given $x = a \cos wt$, find the mean value of the velocity over a quarter period for equal intervals of distance.

6. If $y = 2 \sin 3t$, find the M.V. of y^2, for the period $t = 0$ to $t = \dfrac{2\pi}{3}$.

7. Find the R.M.S. of

    (1) $2 \sin 3\theta$.   (2) $3 \cos 2x$.   (3) $\cos a\theta$.

    (4) $\sin (a\theta + \alpha)$, each taken over a period.

8. Given that $i = c + k \sin a\theta$, find the R.M.S. of i, where c, k and a are constants.

9. Find the R.M.S. of $3 \sin 2t + 2 \sin 3t$.

10. If $E = 2 \cdot 75 \sin 80\pi t$, the angle being in radians, the mean value of E over a period is given by $80 \displaystyle\int_0^{1/80} E\,dt$ and the root mean square value is given by $\sqrt{80 \displaystyle\int_0^{1/80} E^2\,dt}$. Find, by integration, the mean value and root mean square value of this function. Hence determine the Form Factor as $\dfrac{\text{Root mean square value}}{\text{Mean value}}$.   (Coventry.)

See also Miscellaneous Examples, Exercise 55.

7. Simpson's Rule

Suppose that we require the area between the curve CD, the ordinates AD and BC, and the x-axis.

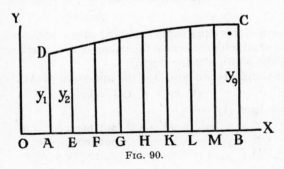

Fig. 90.

Divide the area into an even number of strips (eight in Fig. 90) by equidistant ordinates. Suppose

$$AE = EF = \ldots = MB = h.$$

Simpson's Rule states that the approximate area is

$$\frac{h}{3}[y_1 + y_9 + 4(y_2 + y_4 + y_6 + y_8) + 2(y_3 + y_5 + y_7)]$$

i.e., $\frac{h}{3}$ [(first + last) ordinates + 4 (sum of even ordinates)

$$+ \ 2 \ (\text{sum of remaining odd ordinates})] \quad . \quad (1)$$

8. We shall now show that Simpson's Rule is accurate when the boundary curve of the area is a parabola.

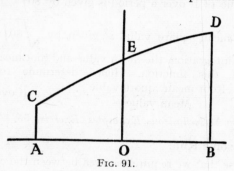

Fig. 91.

If we take the equation of CD as

$$y = a + bx + cx^2 \ (\text{a parabola}) \quad . \quad . \quad (1)$$

the form of this equation is unaltered wherever the origin O is taken, although of course the values of a, b, c will depend upon the position of the origin.

For simplicity suppose O is the mid-point of AB.

Let $\qquad\qquad OA = - h, \ OB = h.$

Then from (1)

$$AC = y_1 = a - bh + ch^2 \ (\text{putting } x = - h)$$
$$OE = y_2 = a \qquad\qquad (\text{putting } x = 0)$$
$$BD = y_3 = a + bh + ch^2 \ (\text{putting } x = h)$$

Hence $AC + BD + 4 \cdot OE = (y_1 + y_3 + 4y_2)$
$$= 6a + 2ch^2 \quad . \quad . \quad . \quad (2)$$

Also area $ABDC = \int_{-h}^{h} (a + bx + cx^2)dx$

$$= \left[ax + \frac{bx^2}{2} + \frac{cx^3}{3} \right]_{-h}^{h}$$

$$= 2ah + \frac{2ch^3}{3}$$

$$= \frac{6ah + 2ch^3}{3}$$

$$= \frac{h}{3}(6a + 2ch^2) \quad . \quad . \quad . \quad . \quad (3)$$

From (2), this result is exactly what we get for the area by Simpson's Rule.

In Fig. 90 we apply the result to each pair of strips, and so get the rule (1).

Thus area ABCD (Fig. 90).

$$= \frac{h}{3}[(y_1 + y_3 + 4y_2) + (y_3 + y_5 + 4y_4) + (y_5 + y_7 + 4y_6)$$
$$+ (y_7 + y_9 + 4y_8)]$$

$$= \frac{h}{3}[y_1 + y_9 + 4(y_2 + y_4 + y_6 + y_8) + 2(y_3 + y_5 + y_7)].$$

In applying the rule to a specific area it may happen that the curve cuts the horizontal line OX.

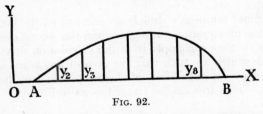

FIG. 92.

In the above case $y_1 = 0$ and $y_9 = 0$, and the area

$$= \frac{h}{3}[4(y_2 + y_4 + y_6 + y_8) + 2(y_3 + y_5 + y_7)].$$

Example

Suppose a curve passes through the points given in the table below:

x . .	1	1·5	2	2·5	3	3·5	4	4·5	5
y . .	2	2·6	2·9	3·1	3·3	3·0	2·9	2·3	2·1

Find the area between the curve, the x-axis and the ordinates at x = 1, x = 5.

In the above example, $h = 0·5$.
Area (approx.)

$$= \frac{0·5}{3}[(2 + 2·1) + 4(2·6 + 3·1 + 3 + 2·3)$$
$$+ 2(2·9 + 3·3 + 2·9)]$$
$$= \tfrac{1}{6}[66·3] = 11·05 \text{ sq units.}$$

9. If there are only three ordinates,

$$\text{Area} = \frac{h}{3}(y_1 + y_3 + 4y_2)$$
$$= 2h\left(\frac{y_1 + 4y_2 + y_3}{6}\right).$$

Hence $\dfrac{y_1 + 4y_2 + y_3}{6}$ may be regarded as the mean ordinate, whilst $2h$ is the distance between the bounding ordinates.

10. Since Simpson's Rule is accurate when the bounding curve has an equation not higher than the second degree, it follows that we can apply it to the calculation of volumes of solids which are such that the area of any plane section is given by an expression of degree not higher than the second. This area can be treated as an ordinate.

Example 1

To find the volume of the frustrum AB*ba* of a cone of height L, and base-radius R.

The area of any section LM, where ON $= x$, varies as x^2,

for $$\frac{\text{LN}}{x} = \frac{\text{AD}}{\text{DO}} = \frac{R}{h}.$$

$$\therefore \quad \pi\text{LN}^2 = \text{area of section} = \frac{\pi R^2}{h^2} \cdot x^2.$$

If $ad = r$, the radius of the mid-section $= \dfrac{R + r}{2}$.
Let the length D$d =$ H

Here $y_1 = \pi r^2$, $y_2 = \pi\left(\dfrac{R + r}{2}\right)^2$, $y_3 = \pi R^2$.

$$\therefore \quad \text{Vol. of frustum} = H\left[\pi r^2 + \frac{4\pi}{4}(R + r)^2 + \pi R^2\right]$$

$$= \frac{\pi H}{6}[2r^2 + 2R^2 + 2Rr]$$

$$= \frac{\pi H}{3}[r^2 + rR + R^2].$$

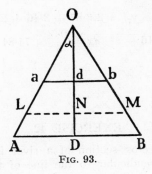

FIG. 93.

Example 2

Suppose that the areas of three cross-sections of a railway cutting 20 yd apart are 110, 140 and 172 sq yd respectively; what is the volume excavated?

The average section $= \frac{1}{6}[110 + 172 + 4 \times 140]$
$$= \frac{842}{6} \text{ sq yd.}$$

$$\therefore \text{ Volume} = \frac{40 \times 842}{6}$$

$$= 5613 \text{ cu yd.}$$

11. Simpson's Rule Applied to a Definite Integral

Use Simpson's Rule to evaluate $\int_0^4 \sqrt{16 - x^2} \, . \, dx$.

The boundary curve is $y = \sqrt{16 - x^2}$.

Divide the interval $x = 0$ to $x = 4$ into eight strips each $\frac{1}{2}$ unit wide.

x .	.	0	0·5	1	1·5	2	2·5	3	3·5	4
y .	.	4	3·97	3·87	3·71	3·46	3·12	2·65	1·92	0

We have, $y_1 + y_9 = 4 + 0 = 4$

$$4(y_2 + y_4 + y_6 + y_8) = 4[3 \cdot 97 + 3 \cdot 71 + 3 \cdot 12 + 1 \cdot 92]$$

$$= 50 \cdot 88$$

$$2(y_3 + y_5 + y_7) = 2[3 \cdot 87 + 3 \cdot 46 + 2 \cdot 65] = 19 \cdot 96$$

$$\therefore \int_0^4 \sqrt{16 - x^2} \, . \, dx = \frac{0 \cdot 5}{3} \times 74 \cdot 84 = 12 \cdot 47.$$

EXERCISE 42

1. A vertical cross-section of a river is considered in a direction perpendicular to the line of the flow of the current. The following table gives the depths d ft at distances x ft from the point on one bank which lies in this section.

x ft distance	0	40	80	120	160	200	240	280	320	360	400
d ft depth .	4	14	20	23	25	24	22	18	12	4	0

Use some approximate method of integration to find the area of the cross-section at this point and calculate the flow in gallons per minute if the speed of flow at this place is 0·6 ft per sec (1 ft³ = 6¼ gallons).   (E.M.E.U.)

2. Sketch the curve $y = 2 \sin x$ between $x = 0$ and $x = \pi$. State the period and the amplitude of the curve, and evaluate the area contained between this part of the curve and the axis of x.   (Handsworth.)

3. (i) Show that the parabola $y = x - x^2$ is symmetrical about the line $x = \frac{1}{2}$.

(ii) Find the area bounded by the x-axis and that part of the above parabola which lies in the first quadrant. Find also the volume of the solid of revolution when the area is rotated about the x-axis.   (Halifax.)

4. Ordinates at a common distance apart of 10 ft are of length 5, 6·5, 9, 13, 18·5, 22, 23, 22, 18·5 and 14 ft. By any method find the area bounded by curve, the axis of x and the end ordinates. Describe a second method by which the result could be verified.   (U.L.C.I.)

5. Sketch the graph of the curve $y = \frac{1}{2}(x^2 - 1)$ from $x = 0$ to $x = 3$.

(a) Calculate the area bounded by the axes of x and y, the curve and the line $y = 4$.

(b) Calculate the volume swept out when the area defined in (a) is rotated through four right angles about the y axis.   (E.M.E.U.)

6. Sketch the curve $xy = 4$ for positive values of x and find the area enclosed by this curve and the x-axis between the ordinates at $x = 1$ and $x = 4$. Find the value of k such that $x = k$ divides this area into two equal parts.

(Cheltenham.)

7. Evaluate by Simpson's Rule

$$(1) \int_0^2 \sqrt{8 + x^3} \, . \, dx. \qquad (2) \int_0^1 \sqrt{1 + x^4} \, . \, dx.$$

8. p is the pressure of a gas when its volume is v.

p . . .	70·2	32·5	20·3	15·4	12·5
v . . .	2	4	6	8	10

Find the work done as the gas expands from 2 to 10 units of volume. p is measured in pounds per sq ft and v in cu ft.

9. Find (1) by integration, (2) by Simpson's Rule the value of $\int_2^4 \frac{10}{x^2}dx$. For (2) use six strips.

10. The area of the cross-section of a tree trunk is A sq in. at x in. from one end. Plot A against x and estimate the volume of the trunk, whose total length is 140 in.

x . . .	0	20	40	60	80	100	120	140
A . . .	108	110	114	120	118	123	135	153

(N.C.T.E.C.)

See also Miscellaneous Examples, Exercise 55.

CHAPTER 13

PHYSICAL APPLICATIONS OF INTEGRATION

1. The Centroid, the Mass Centre, the Centre of Gravity

A circle, a circular area, a spherical surface, and a solid sphere, all have *centres*. Every other figure has an unique point which has many of the properties of a centre and which we may call the **Centroid.** The positions of the centroid of a square or cube, and of many other figures, are obvious on inspection.

If there is *mass* uniformly distributed along the length of a linear figure, over the area of a surface, or throughout the volume of a solid, the centroid will be the **Mass Centre** of the figure—length, area or volume as the case may be.

Since mass is acted upon by gravity, and has weight proportional to itself, the mass centre will be the **Centre of Gravity,** which is thus also at the centroid of any figure over or throughout which mass is uniformly distributed. Many readers will know that a simple way of finding the centroid of a plane figure is to cut it out in sheet metal or card of uniform thickness, and then by trial find the centre of gravity, which will always, if free to do so, set itself directly under the point of suspension (see Fig. 94 (*a*)).

To think first of the centroid, then of the mass centre and lastly of the centre of gravity, is logical for the student of mathematics. This, however, is the opposite order to that in which these terms and what they denote became of interest and importance to practical men. Long ago everyday handling of heavy weights left people in no doubt that there was a centre of weight, or in the language of Physics, a " Centre of Gravity." The man in charge of lifting on structural work, or in an engine shop, can still (often at the first attempt) get his lift so accurately " over the weight " that the piece of machinery can be lifted subsequently with no tilting or sideway shift (and thus safely) and lowered exactly into the position desired. His experienced judgment tells him what and where the centre of gravity is.

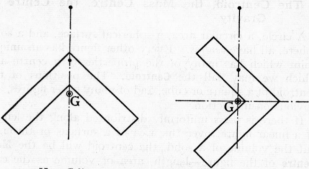

Here G lies actually outside the L-shaped area
FIG. 94 (a).

Because of its long familiarity, therefore, it is very common for writers to use the term " centre of gravity " rather than the more correct " centroid " in cases where there is neither mass nor weight but simply geometric form. We must accept this as natural although we shall endeavour to use the terms more precisely ourselves.

To illustrate these points Fig. 94 (b), and the accompanying table of dimensions, and properties are extracted from a British Standard.* It will be seen that the figures in the table all relate directly to the size and shape of the channel section drawing—in itself a mere figure which certainly has neither weight nor mass. The headings, however, refer to " gravity " and " inertia." The Standards Committee de-

* B.S. 4, published by the British Standards Institution, British Standards House, 2 Park St., London, W.1.

CHANNELS

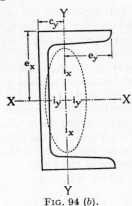

$c_x \, c_y$ Distance of centre of gravity from X axis and back line of channel.

$J = ai^2$ Moment of inertia.

$i = \sqrt{\dfrac{J}{a}}$ Radius of gyration.

$e_x \, e_y$ Distance of outer fibres from X and Y axes.

$Z = \dfrac{J}{e}$ Modulus of section.

FIG. 94 (b).

EXTRACTS FROM TABLE OF DIMENSIONS AND PROPERTIES

1	2	3	4	8	9	10	11	12
		Standard thickness		Sectional Area	Centre of gravity		Moments of inertia	
Reference No.	Size A × B	Web t_1	Flange t_2	a	c_x	c_y	J_x	J_y
	inches	inches		inches	inches		inches	
BSC 101 .	3 × 1½	0·20	0·28	1·35	0	0·48	1·82	0·26
BSC 101A .	3 × 1½	0·25	0·28	1·50	0	0·48	1·94	0·30
BSC 102 .	4 × 2	0·24	0·31	2·09	0	0·60	5·06	0·70

liberately use terms which convey their meaning rapidly to a great number of practical people.

As students, if we happen to be dealing with an area, we shall seek its " centroid " rather than its " centre of gravity "; if in this book we integrate the second moments of elements of an area (see p. 332) we shall say so, rather than speak of the " moment of inertia " of the area. The nomenclature of questions quoted from published examination papers has **not,** however, been revised.

Centre of Gravity

Having traced the origin of the idea of a weight centre, and having also discussed the common use of the term " centre of gravity " where " centroid " would in fact be more appropriate, we can now consider the problem of locating the C.G. in simple cases by the application of mathematical methods.

Any finite body may be regarded as an aggregate of particles, whose weights form a system of parallel forces. Assuming each force to act at a point about which the mass of the particle is distributed, the resultant of this system of parallel forces passes through a centre, called the centre of gravity of the body, at which the weight of the body can be taken as acting.

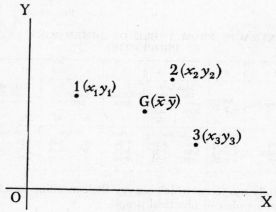

Fig. 95.

Suppose first that the particles to be considered are in one plane, and that the co-ordinates of two of them are respectively x, y and $x_2 y_2$. Let their respective weights be the forces P_1 and P_2.

Let the plane be horizontal—of course setting the plane in a particular position will not affect the position of the centre of gravity of the particles. Then the moments about the y axis of the particle weights will be P_1x_1 and P_2x_2: the moments about the x-axis will be P_1y_1 and P_2y_2. If the total weight is taken as acting at the point G whose co-ordinates are $\bar{x}$ and $\bar{y}$, then

$$P_1x_1 + P_2x_2 = (P_1 + P_2)\bar{x},$$

also $$P_1y_1 + P_2y_2 = (P_1 + P_2)\bar{y},$$

since the moment of the whole weight must be equal to the sum of the moments * of its parts.

Extending our consideration to cover any number of particles, and adopting the usual notation for a sum of similar terms, we have

$$\bar{x} = \frac{P_1x_1 + P_2x_2 + \ldots}{P_1 + P_2 + \ldots} = \frac{\Sigma Px}{\Sigma P} \quad . \quad . \quad (1)$$

and $$\bar{y} = \frac{P_1y_1 + P_2y_2 + \ldots}{P_1 + P_2 + \ldots} = \frac{\Sigma Py}{\Sigma P} \quad . \quad . \quad (2)$$

In the solution of most problems it is sufficient to consider particles in a plane and their two co-ordinates x and y. Often the centre of gravity of a solid can be seen to lie in a particular plane by reason of symmetry. The L form of Fig. 126 could equally well represent a thin sheet or a length of angle bar. In the latter case the centre of gravity would be at the point G in a cross-section half-way along the bar.

Since the forces P_1, etc., are the weights of particles m_1, etc., and the weight of a mass of 1 lb is mg poundals, we may write

$$\bar{x} = \frac{\Sigma mg \cdot x}{\Sigma mg} = \frac{\Sigma mx}{\Sigma m} \quad . \quad . \quad . \quad (3)$$

and $$\bar{y} = \frac{\Sigma mg \cdot y}{\Sigma mg} = \frac{\Sigma my}{\Sigma m} \quad . \quad . \quad . \quad (4)$$

It will be clear, also, from (3) and (4) that g cancels throughout the fractions, as also does m if the particles

* For moments, see as previously Walker's *Mechanical Engineering Science*, or Fisher's *Engineering Science and Calculations*, both published by the English Universities Press.

considered are all of the same mass. If instead of heavy particles the system comprised elements of area, the unit of area would similarly cancel out. Thus the detail of the arithmetic will be the same whether the purpose of the calculation is to find a centre of gravity, a mass centre, or a centroid. This is a reason, though hardly a justification, for the rather indiscriminate use of these terms.

$\Sigma P \cdot x$, Σmx, and the corresponding expressions involving ordinates are often called the *first moments* of the system about the axes of y and of x respectively.

Hence we may write:

$$\bar{x} = \frac{\text{First moment of the system about OY}}{\text{Sum of the forces (or masses, area, etc.)}}$$

and

$$\bar{y} = \frac{\text{First moment of the system about OX}}{\text{Sum of the forces (or masses, area, etc.)}}$$

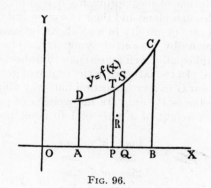

Fig. 96.

2. To find the centroid of an area bounded by a given curve, the x-axis and two ordinates, proceed as follows:

Let $y = f(x)$ be the equation of the curve DC of Fig. 96. Required, the centroid of the area ABCD.

Let OA = a and OB = b.

Consider the strip PQST, where OP = x, PT = y, and PQ = dx.

The area of the strip = PT . PQ = $y . dx$ (nearly).

The centre of area of this strip is at R, its mid-point, and we shall regard $\left(x, \dfrac{y}{2}\right)$ as the co-ordinates of R.

To apply formula (3) of p. 317 the elementary weights mg are replaced by the elements of area ydx, which we may treat as concentrated at positions R.

Thus,
$$\bar{x} = \frac{\int ydx . x}{\int ydx} \qquad \ldots \quad \ldots \quad (1)$$

replacing the sign Σ by the sign of integration, since we are summing the elements of a continuous area.

Similarly,
$$\bar{y} = \frac{\int ydx . \dfrac{y}{2}}{\int ydx} \qquad \ldots \quad \ldots \quad (2)$$

Thus to find the centroid of the area under DC of Fig. 96 it is now only necessary to substitute $f(x)$ for y, and put in the limits of integration.

Example 1

Find the centroid of the area between the curve $y = x^3$, *the x-axis and the line* $x = 3$.

ydx is the element at R.   OB = 3, and the line BC is $x = 3$.   See Fig. 97.

$$\bar{x} = \frac{\int ydx . x}{\int ydx} = \frac{\int_0^3 x^4 dx}{\int_0^3 x^3 dx} \text{ (substituting for } y\text{)}.$$

Hence $\bar{x} = \dfrac{\left[\dfrac{x^5}{5}\right]_0^3}{\left[\dfrac{x^4}{4}\right]_0^3} = \dfrac{3^5}{5} \times \dfrac{4}{3^4} = \dfrac{12}{5}$ units.

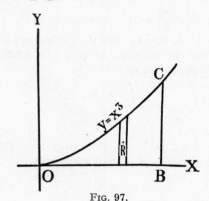

FIG. 97.

Similarly,

$$\bar{y} = \frac{\int y\,dx \cdot \dfrac{y}{2}}{\int y\,dx} = \frac{\dfrac{1}{2}\displaystyle\int_0^3 x^6\,dx}{\displaystyle\int_0^3 x^3\,dx} = \frac{1}{2} \cdot \frac{3^7}{7} \cdot \frac{4}{3^4} = \frac{54}{7} \text{ units.}$$

Example 2

Find the centre of mass of a hemisphere of radius a.

Consider the hemisphere generated by the revolution of the quadrant of the circle OAB about OX.

The bounding curve is $x^2 + y^2 = a^2$.

The volume of the element formed by rotating the area PQRS about OX is $\pi y^2 dx$, where OP $= x$, and PS $= y$.

The centre of volume of the element is on OX, and distant x from O.

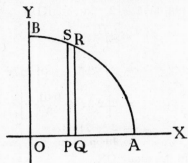

FIG. 98.

By symmetry $y = 0$ and

$$\bar{x} = \frac{\int_0^a \pi y^2 \cdot dx \cdot x}{\tfrac{2}{3}\pi a^3} = \frac{\int_0^a x(a^2 - x^2)dx}{\tfrac{2}{3}a^3}.$$

The numerator

$$= \left[\frac{a^2 x^2}{2} - \frac{x^4}{4}\right]_0^a = \frac{a^4}{4} \quad \therefore \quad \bar{x} = \frac{3a}{8}.$$

The numerator above was obtained by integrating first moments of elements of volume. The resulting value of $\bar{x}$ thus indicates the position of the centroid of the hemisphere. If this solid is of uniform density its centre of mass will be at the centroid thus determined.

Example 3

The lamina ABCD shown in the diagram, Fig. 99, is bounded by the y-axis, the line $x = 9$ and the two curves $y = 2 \cdot 5 + 0 \cdot 01x^2$ and $y = -2 \cdot 5 - 0 \cdot 01x^2$ the unit of length along each axis of reference being 1 in. Find the area of the lamina and the distance of its centroid from AB. (U.L.C.I.)

Notice that the area is symmetrical about OX.

The area of the vertical strip $= y dx$.

L

$\therefore$ Total area $= 2 \times$ area OKDA

$$= 2 \int_0^9 y \, dx$$

$$= 2 \int_0^9 (2 \cdot 5 + 0 \cdot 01 x^2) \, dx$$

$$= 2 \left[2 \cdot 5x + \frac{0 \cdot 01}{3} x^3 \right]_0^9$$

$$= 2 \times 24 \cdot 93$$

$$= 49 \cdot 86 \text{ sq in.}$$

The centroid lies along OX.

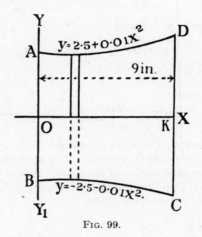

$y = 2 \cdot 5 + 0 \cdot 01 x^2$

9 in.

$y = -2 \cdot 5 - 0 \cdot 01 x^2.$

Fig. 99.

Let its co-ordinate be $\bar{x}$.

Then

$$\bar{x} = \frac{\int_0^9 2 \cdot y \, dx \cdot x}{\int_0^9 2y \, dx}.$$

The denominator has just been found and is **49·86** sq in.

The numerator

$$= 2\int_0^9 (2 \cdot 5 + 0 \cdot 01x^2)x \, dx$$

$$= 2\left[\frac{2 \cdot 5x^2}{2} + \frac{0 \cdot 01x^4}{4}\right]_0^9$$

$$= 2[101 \cdot 25 + 16 \cdot 40]$$

$$= 235 \cdot 30.$$

Hence $\bar{x} = \dfrac{235 \cdot 30}{49 \cdot 86}$

$$= 4 \cdot 72 \text{ in.}$$

In this example the lamina is an ideal figure whose out-
lines are defined mathematically. If this had been an
actual lamina cut out from sheet metal to assigned
dimensions it is unlikely that its area would be known to
the one hundredth part of a square inch. It would be
unwise to imply that the area was known with such
accuracy by writing 49·86 sq in. A preferred value would
then be: " 50 sq in., correct to two significant figures."

Example 4

*A solid is formed by rotating about the axis of x the area
under the graph of the function* $\left(2 - \dfrac{3x^{\frac{1}{2}}}{4}\right)$ *between* $x = 0$ *and*
$x = 4$. *Find the volume of the solid, and the distance of its
centre of gravity from the origin.*   (N.C.T.E.C.)

It is to be assumed that the solid is of uniform density.

The volume $= \displaystyle\int_0^4 \pi\left(2 - \frac{3x^{\frac{1}{2}}}{4}\right)^2 dx$ . . . . (1)

$$= \pi\int_0^4 (4 - 3x^{\frac{1}{2}} + \tfrac{9}{16}x) \, dx$$

$$= \pi\left[4x - 2x^{\frac{3}{2}} + \frac{9}{16} \cdot \frac{x^2}{2}\right]_0^4$$

$$= \pi(16 - 16 + \tfrac{9}{2})$$

$$= \frac{9\pi}{2} \text{ cu units.}$$

If x = distance of the centroid of the solid from the origin

$$\frac{9\pi}{2} . \bar{x} = \int_0^4 \pi\left(2 - \frac{3x^{\frac{1}{4}}}{4}\right)^2 . x\,dx$$

$$= \pi\int_0^4 (4x - 3x^{\frac{3}{2}} + \tfrac{9}{16}x^2)dx$$

$$= \pi[2x^2 - \tfrac{6}{5}x^{\frac{5}{2}} + \tfrac{3}{16}x^3]_0^4$$

$$= \pi[32 - \tfrac{6}{5} . 32 + 12]$$

$$= \pi(12 - \tfrac{32}{5})$$

$$= \frac{28\pi}{5}$$

$$\therefore \quad \bar{x} = 1.24 \text{ units, approx,}$$

if the solid is of uniform density, its C.G. is at the centroid thus found.

In this solution we have assumed that $x^{\frac{1}{4}} = +\sqrt{x}$, not $\pm\sqrt{x}$.

EXERCISE 43

1. Find the centroid of the area between the curve $y^2 = 4x$ and $x = 4$.

2. Find the centroid of that half of the above curve which lies in the first quadrant.

3. Find the centroid of the area between $y = 4x^2$, the x-axis and $x = 4$.

4. Find the centroid of the area between $y = x^3$, the axis of y and $y = 1$.

5. The curve $y = a + bx + cx^2$ passes through the points $(0, 2)$ $(1, 5)$ $(-1, 3)$. Find the area between the curve, the x-axis, and the ordinates at $x = 0$ and $x = 3$. Find also the co-ordinates of the centroid.   (U.L.C.I.)

6. A uniform elliptical disc of metal, thickness 0.2 in., has major and minor axes of 10.6 and 7 in. An equilateral triangular slab of the same material, and of thickness 0.3 in. has an edge of 4.5 in. The slab is placed flat on the disc

symmetrically about the major axis with a vertex at the centre of the ellipse. Find the centroid of the combination
(U.L.C.I.)

7. A solid is formed by rotating about the x-axis the area between the graphs of $\left(1 + \dfrac{x^2}{8}\right)$ and $\dfrac{x}{4}$ for values of x from $x = 2$ to $x = 4$. The unit is one inch along each axis.

Calculate (1) the volume of the solid, (2) the distance of its centroid from the smaller end face. (N.C.T.E.C.)

8. The distance x of the centroid of a sector of a circle from the centre is given by

$$x = \frac{\frac{2}{3}a\displaystyle\int_0^B \cos A\, dA}{\displaystyle\int_0^B dA}.$$

Where B is the half angle of the sector in radians and a is the radius. Find x when a is 2 in. and the angle of the sector is 120°. (U.E.I.)

9. The dimensions of a triangular piece PQR of metal are PQ = 8 in., QR = 12 in., and RP = 10 in. M and N are mid-points of PQ and PR, and are joined by a straight line. The part PMN is cut away. Find the position of the centroid of the remaining part. (U.L.C.I.)

10. In order to design a tipping device of inverted cone shape to tip when loaded above a certain level, it is necessary to find the centroid of a cone of uniform density of vertical height H and base area A. Find this by integration. (U.E.I.)

11. Find the centroid of an area formed by the parabola $y^2 = 4x$ and bounded by the chord perpendicular to the axis of x where $x = 9$. (U.E.I.)

12. A quadrant of the ellipse $\dfrac{x^2}{36} + \dfrac{y^2}{52} = 1$ rotates about the x-axis. Find the position of the centroid of the solid generated.

13. A trapezium is formed by the axes of co-ordinates, and the straight lines $y = 2 + 3x$, $x = 3$. Find the co-ordinates of its centroid.

14. If the above trapezium is rotated about OX, find the centroid of the frustum of the cone which it generates.

15. A spherical cap of height 4 in. is cut from a solid sphere of radius 6 in. Find the position of its centroid.

16. The cross-sectional area of a solid of revolution at a distance of x in. from one end, A, of its axis is $\left(\dfrac{x}{4} + 3\sqrt{x}\right)$ sq in. The length of the axis is 4 in. Find the volume of the solid and the distance from A of its centroid. (N.C.T.E.C.)

3. The Theorems of Pappus, or Guldinus

Theorem I

If a curve, lying in the x-y plane, but which does not cut the x-axis, be rotated about that axis, a SURFACE is generated, the AREA of which is

LENGTH OF GIVEN CURVE × Distance travelled by its CENTROID.

Suppose AB is the curve of length l, P is any point on it, and Q an adjacent point such that $PQ = ds$, where $AP = s$.

Let y be the ordinate of P.

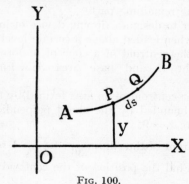

FIG. 100.

The surface generated by ds in a complete revolution about OX is $2\pi y \cdot ds$.

$\therefore$ The total surface $= \int 2\pi y ds$

$$= 2\pi \int y ds \quad . \quad . \quad . \quad . \quad (1)$$

If $\bar{y}$ be the ordinate of the centroid of the curve AB

$$\bar{y} = \frac{\int y ds}{\int ds} = \frac{\int y ds}{l}$$

i.e., $$l \cdot y = \int y ds$$

$\therefore$ substituting in (1) we get

total surface $= 2\pi y \cdot l$, which proves the proposition.

If y does not perform a complete rotation, but moves through an angle θ, the surface generated

$$= \int y\theta \cdot ds$$

$$= \theta \int y ds$$

$$= y \cdot \theta \cdot l$$

i.e., surface = distance travelled by centroid × length of curve.

Theorem II

If an area, lying in the x-y plane, but not cut by the x-axis, be rotated about that axis, a SOLID FIGURE is generated, the VOLUME of which is

The given AREA × DISTANCE TRAVELLED BY ITS CENTROID.

The proof is similar to that given for the first theorem.

In the diagram, Fig. 101, suppose A to represent the area enclosed by the curve.

Let $d\mathrm{A}$ be an element of area, surrounding a point B, whose ordinate is y.

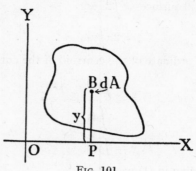

FIG. 101.

In turning through a complete revolution about OX the volume generated by $d\mathrm{A}$ is $2\pi y d\mathrm{A}$.

∴ The total volume generated by the area is $\int 2\pi y d\mathrm{A}$.

i.e., $\qquad\qquad 2\pi \int y d\mathrm{A}$ . . . . . (1)

But $\qquad\qquad \int y d\mathrm{A} = \bar{y} \cdot \mathrm{A}$

Hence (1) becomes $\qquad 2\pi \bar{y} \cdot \mathrm{A}$

If the area turns through an angle θ,

$\qquad$ vol. generated $= y \cdot \theta \cdot \mathrm{A}$ . . . (2)

Example 1

A cylindrical hole of diameter 1 in. is drilled axially through a solid right circular cone of height 8 in. and base diameter 4 in. By the theorems of Guldinus, or by any other method, find the volume and the outside curved surface area of the solid remaining. (U.L.C.I.)

Let OA be the centre line of the cone, and OBA a half-section passing through the centre line. Then by definition OA = 8 in. and AB = 2 in. Also AD = $\frac{1}{2}$ in.

By Pythagoras' theorem OB = $\sqrt{68}$ in. = $2\sqrt{17}$ in. The original cone was generated by rotating the area OAB about OA; what is left can be regarded as being generated by rotating CDB about OA.

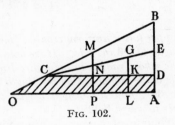

Fig. 102.

BD = $\frac{3}{2}$ in. and AB = 2 in.

$$\therefore \quad \frac{\text{Area BCD}}{\text{Area BOA}} = \frac{9}{16}$$

i.e.,   area BCD = $\frac{9}{16}$. 8 sq in.

$$= \frac{9}{2} \text{ sq in.} \quad \cdot \quad \cdot \quad \cdot \quad (1)$$

If G is the centroid of the triangle CDB,

$$\text{GK} = \frac{2}{3} \times \text{DE} = \frac{2}{3} \times \frac{3}{4} \text{ in.}$$
$$= \frac{1}{2} \text{ in.}$$
$$\therefore \quad \text{GL} = 1 \text{ in.} \quad \cdot \quad \cdot \quad \cdot \quad (2)$$

Hence using Guldinus' theorem, with (1) and (2) we get that the required volume

$$= 2\pi \times 1 \times \frac{9}{2}$$
$$= 9\pi \text{ cu in.}$$

For the surface, note that this is generated by CB.

Also   CB = $\frac{3}{4} \times$ OB
$$= \frac{3}{4} \times 2\sqrt{17}$$
$$= \frac{3}{2} \times \sqrt{17}.$$

M is the mid-point of CB, *i.e.*, it is its centroid.

$$MN = \tfrac{1}{2}BD = \tfrac{3}{4} \text{ in.}$$

$$\therefore \quad MP = 1\tfrac{1}{4} \text{ in.}$$

$$
\begin{aligned}
\therefore \quad \text{Required surface} \quad &= 2\pi \times MP \times CB \\
&= 2\pi \times \tfrac{5}{4} \times \tfrac{3}{2}\sqrt{17} \\
&= \frac{15\sqrt{17} \cdot \pi}{4} \text{ sq in.}
\end{aligned}
$$

Example 2

A length of copper has a uniform cross-section which is that of a regular hexagon of 0·6 in. side. It is bent into the form of an arc of a circle whose radius to the centre line of copper is 9 ft 3 in. If the angle subtended by the length of bent copper at the centre be 36°, find the weight of the copper. Take 1 cu in. of copper to weigh 0·32 lb. (U.L.C.I.)

Clearly, the volume of copper is approximately* that generated by the area of the hexagon turning through 36° about an axis 9 ft 3 in. from its centroid.

$$\text{The area} = 6 \times \frac{\sqrt{3}}{4} \times (0·6)^2 \text{ sq in.}$$

$$= 0·54 \times \sqrt{3} \text{ sq in.}$$

The rotation of 36° is $\tfrac{1}{10}$ that of a complete rotation.

$$\therefore \quad \text{vol. of copper} = \tfrac{1}{10} \times 2\pi \times 111 \times 0·54 \times \sqrt{3} \text{ cu in.}$$

$$
\begin{aligned}
\text{and the weight} \quad &= \frac{0·32}{10} \times 2\pi \times 111 \times 0·54 \times \sqrt{3} \text{ lb} \\
&= 20·86 \text{ lb.}
\end{aligned}
$$

EXERCISE 44

1. The section of an oil ring is shown in the sketch. Find the volume of the ring which is formed by rotating the area about the horizontal line shown.

---

* " approximately " because the bending will slightly distort the section from its original hexagon form.

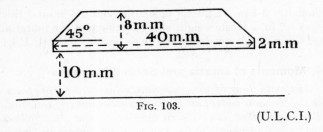

FIG. 103.

(U.L.C.I.)

2. Establish the theorem of Guldinus for volumes.

Hence determine the position of the centroid of a semi-circular lamina of radius 5·5 in.   (U.E.I.)

3. An isosceles triangle has a base 4 in. and height 6 in. It is placed with the base parallel to the x-axis, and 12 in. away from it, its vertex being towards the axis. The triangle generates a ring by rotation about the x-axis.

Find the volume of the ring.

4. Use Guldinus' theorem to find:

(1) The centroid of a semi-circular arc of radius a.
(2) The centroid of a semi-circle of radius a.

5. A semi-circle has its bounding diameter, 8 in. long, parallel to the x-axis (and 6 in. from it). Its circular boundary is remote from the axis. Find the volume generated in a complete rotation about the x-axis.

6. An anchor ring is generated when a circle of radius r rotates about an axis in its plane. If the axis is distant a from its centre, show that the surface area of the ring is $4\pi^2 ar$, and its volume $2a\pi^2 r^2$.

7. Find the area bounded by $y^2 = ax$, the x-axis and the straight line $x = b$. By rotating this area about the x-axis and using Guldinus' theorem find the y-co-ordinate of the centroid of the area.

8. Establish the theorem of Guldinus for volumes. The head of a rivet is in the form of the frustum of a cone, base

diameter 3·7 in., diameter of smaller end 2·8 in. and thickness 1·2 in.   If the weight of a cubic inch of the material is 0·28 lb find the weight of 100 rivet heads.   (U.E.I.)

4. Moments of Inertia and Second Moments

Determination of these quantities for various purposes is one of the most important physical applications of integration. The study takes its origin in mechanics, and there follows a brief revision note.   Refer also to a note under the heading Simple Harmonic Motion on p. 259.

At an early stage in the study of Mechanics, students learn in regard to linear motion that a force (say P) acting upon a mass (m) produces an acceleration (f) where

$$P = mf$$

if the units in which P, m and f are measured are suitably chosen.   If the force in question is the weight of the mass (m) we know that in foot-pound-second units the acceleration will be g, since this is the acceleration of a body falling freely.   In other words the weight of mass (m lb) is (mg) foot-pound-second units, or, to use a common nomenclature, (mg) poundals.

We know that a similar equation holds good in regard to angular motion.   For force we may write turning moment or torque.   For linear acceleration we may write angular acceleration.   Mass, however, must be replaced by some expression that takes account of the distribution of mass as well as of its total amount.   This expression has been given the descriptive name " Moment of Inertia."   If there are particles of mass m_1, m_2 . . . at radii r_1, r_2 . . . from the chosen axis, then the Moment of Inertia of the body about that axis is the sum of all the elementary *second* moments mr^2 . . .

It is easy to see that any small element of mass has an influence in regard to angular acceleration which depends upon the square of its distance from the axis of rotation.

Any given angular acceleration will demand a linear (tangential) acceleration proportional to the radius of the particle considered. Further, the force needed to maintain this linear acceleration has a moment about the axis which again is proportional to the radius of the particle.

For a thin plate or a solid body respectively elements of area or of volume may replace elements of mass in forming the second moments for summation. Of course where there is no mass there can be no moment *of inertia*. But the mathematical summation of second moments is the same whether or not they concern inertia.

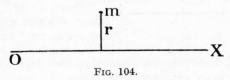

FIG. 104.

Turning now to Fig. 104.

If m be an element of mass, distant r units from a fixed axis OX, mr^2 is called the moment of inertia of the mass m about the given axis.

The term second moment is also used because the product involves r^2. The first moment of m about OX is mr.

If we have a number of particles of masses m_1, m_2, m_3, etc., at distances r_1, r_2, r_3, etc., from OX their combined moment of inertia is

$$m_1r_1^2 + m_2r_2^2 + m_3r_3^2 + \ldots$$

i.e., writing I for the total moment of inertia, we get:

$$\text{I} = \Sigma mr^2 \qquad \ldots \ldots \quad (1)$$

If M be the total mass of the particles, we put:

$$\text{I} = \Sigma mr^2 = \text{M}k^2 \qquad \ldots \ldots \quad (2)$$

k is called the radius of gyration of the system of masses about the given axis.

Suppose B is any continuous body.

If dm be an element of mass surrounding the point A, whose ordinate is y, its M.I. about OX is y^2dm and the M.I. of the body B about OX is $\int y^2dm$.

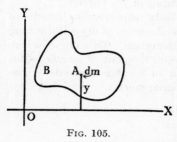

FIG. 105.

The word " inertia " refers to mass, whilst the word " moment " is used in the sense of " important," as when we speak of a " momentous occasion " or of " things of great moment." " Moment of inertia " (about a given axis) therefore means the " importance of the manner in which the mass is distributed with respect to the given axis," and this importance is measured by Mk^2.

When we are not dealing with mass, as for instance in problems on the bending of beams, where we deal with the areas of sections, we speak of the " second moment " of the section, usually about an axis through its centroid, known as the neutral axis.

Example 1

To find the second moment of the line AB about an axis through one end perpendicular to AB.

Suppose $AB = 2a$. Let m be its linear density. If $AP = x$, let $PQ = dx$.

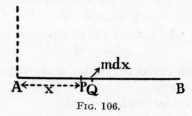

FIG. 106.

Then $mdx \cdot x^2$ is the second moment of the element dx.

$$\therefore \quad I = \int_0^{2a} mx^2 \cdot dx \text{ is the second moment of AB}$$

$$I = \left[\frac{mx^3}{3}\right]_0^{2a} = \frac{8}{3} ma^3 \qquad \cdot \quad \cdot \quad \cdot \quad \cdot \quad \cdot \quad (1)$$

The total mass of AB $= m \cdot 2a$.

$$\therefore \quad 2amk^2 = \frac{8}{3} ma^3$$

i.e.,
$$k^2 = \frac{4a^2}{3} = \frac{(2a)^2}{3} = \frac{(\text{length})^2}{3}.$$

Squares of the radii of gyration, k^2, together with the axes to which they refer, for different bodies, should be remembered.

We deduce at once the k^2 for AB when the axis is taken through its mid-point O.

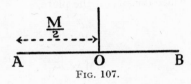

FIG. 107.

The axis is an axis through the end of half the rod. Hence

$$Mk^2 = 2 \times \frac{M}{2} \cdot \frac{a^2}{3}$$

i.e.,
$$k^2 = \frac{a^2}{3} = \frac{(\frac{1}{2} \text{ length})^2}{3}.$$

Example 2

To find the M.I. of a rectangle of uniform surface density m [*m units of mass per unit of area*]

    (1) *About one side.*

    (2) *About an axis parallel to one side through the C.G. of the rectangle.*

Let ABCD be the rectangle in which AB = 2a and AD = 2b.

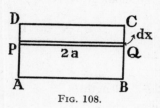

FIG. 108.

To find the M.I. about AD.

Since we know the area and therefore the mass of the rectangle, all we require is the appropriate k^2.

Let AP = x, and suppose the breadth of the strip PQ is dx, where PQ is perpendicular to AD. Using the previous result, the second moment of the strip PQ $= \dfrac{4a^2}{3} \cdot 2a\,dx$.

$$\therefore \text{ M.I. of rectangle} = \frac{4a^2}{3}\int_0^{2b} 2a \cdot dx \cdot m,$$

where m = surface density of the plate,

$$= \frac{4a^2}{3} \cdot (2a \times 2b \times m)$$

$$= \text{M} \times \frac{(2a)^2}{3}.$$

Hence k^2 (about a side) $= \dfrac{(\text{other side})^2}{3}.$

Similarly, k^2 about an axis through the C.G. parallel to AD, is given by $\dfrac{(\frac{1}{2}\,\text{other side})^2}{3}.$

Example 3

The moment of inertia of a ring of negligible radial width about an axis through its centre perpendicular to its plane is clearly Ma^2, where M = mass of the ring and a is its radius.

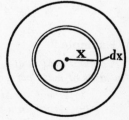

FIG. 109.

We can use this result to find the M.I. of a circular disc of radius a, about its axle.

The axle is perpendicular to the plane of the paper through O. m is the surface density.

The M.I. of the ring of radius x, width dx is

$$2\pi x dx \cdot m \times x^2 = 2\pi m x^3 dx$$

$$\therefore \quad \text{M.I. of disc} = 2\pi m \int_0^a x^3 dx$$

$$= 2\pi m \frac{a^4}{4}$$

$$= \pi a^2 m \times \frac{a^2}{2}.$$

Hence $\qquad k^2 = \dfrac{a^2}{2} = \frac{1}{2} \text{ (radius)}^2.$

Example 4

To find the M.I. of a solid sphere of uniform density m about a diameter.

Let the sphere have a radius $= a$, and suppose it is generated by the rotation of a semi-circle about its bounding diameter.

Suppose OA is the diameter about which we require the M.I.

The M.I. of the whole $=$ twice that of the hemisphere.

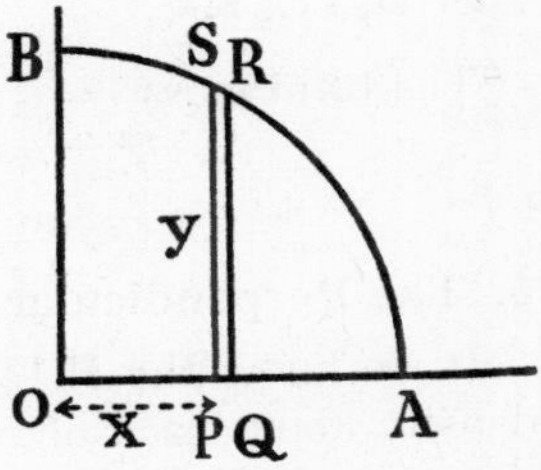

Let the bounding circle be

FIG. 110.

$$x^2 + y^2 = a^2 \quad . \quad . \quad . \quad . \quad . \quad (1)$$

The strip PQRS generates a disc whose radius is y and thickness dx.

Since m = the density of all parts of the sphere

M.I. of disc = $\pi y^2 dx \cdot m \times \dfrac{y^2}{2}$ (*i.e.*, mass $\times \frac{1}{2}$ radius^2)

$$= \frac{\pi m}{2} y^4 dx$$

$$= \frac{\pi m}{2} (a^2 - x^2)^2 dx \text{ from (1).}$$

$\therefore$ M.I. of sphere $= 2 \displaystyle\int_0^a \frac{\pi m}{2} \cdot (a^2 - x^2)^2 dx$

$$= \pi m \int_0^a (a^4 - 2a^2 x^2 + x^4) dx$$

$$= \pi m \left[a^4 x - \frac{2a^2 x^3}{3} + \frac{x^5}{5} \right]_0^a$$

$$= \pi m \left(a^5 - \frac{2}{3} a^5 + \frac{a^5}{5} \right)$$

$$= \pi m \cdot \tfrac{8}{15} a^5.$$

This is the answer to the question propounded. We go on to express it in the standard form for a Moment of Inertia, *i.e.*, Mk^2.

The total mass $= \frac{4}{3}\pi a^3 m =$ M
$\therefore \quad k^2 = \frac{2}{5} a^2.$

5. The Perpendicular Axes Theorem

If we know the M.I. of a lamina of uniform superficial density about each of two perpendicular axes in its plane, we can write down its M.I. about an axis perpendicular to its plane through the point of intersection of the other two.

A is the area of the lamina; P any point of the area whose co-ordinates with respect to axes OX, OY are (x, y).

Let I_x, I_y be the second moments (supposed known) of the lamina about OX and OY respectively.

If m be the mass of an element of area surrounding P, we have

$$I_x = \Sigma my^2$$

and

$$I_y = \Sigma mx^2$$

But

$$x^2 + y^2 = r^2$$

$$\therefore \quad \Sigma mx^2 + \Sigma my^2 = \Sigma mr^2.$$

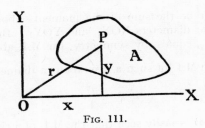

FIG. 111.

Now, Σmr^2 is the M.I. of the lamina about an axis through O perpendicular to the plane of the paper; call this I_z.

Hence

$$I_x + I_y = I_z$$

i.e., knowing the moments about each of two perpendicular axes in a plane, adding them gives us the moment about an

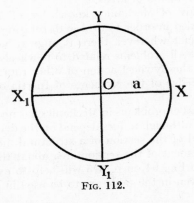

FIG. 112.

axis perpendicular to the plane through the intersection of the other two.

Example

The M.I. of a disc radius a of uniform density about its axle is $\dfrac{Ma^2}{2}$.

This must be the sum of the moments about the two perpendicular diameters XOX_1, and YOY_1. But the M.I. about XOX_1, equals, by symmetry, the M.I. about YOY_1.

Hence the M.I. of such a disc about a diameter $= \dfrac{Ma^2}{4}$,

giving
$$k^2 = \frac{a^2}{4}.$$

Similarly, it is easily seen that the M.I. of a ring about a diameter gives

$$k^2 = \frac{a^2}{2}$$

where $a =$ the radius of the ring.

6. Further Note on Moments of Inertia of massive parts and Second Moments of areas.

In the study of Mechanics knowledge of Moments of Inertia is needed in order to deal with rotating bodies and systems—in fact wherever there is angular velocity and acceleration. All problems related to flywheels or balance wheels, or to the flywheel action of other rotating bodies, call for knowledge of the Moments of Inertia of the parts concerned.

Another class of problems in Mechanics has no connection with rotation, although it does depend on the determination of the centroid of the section of a structural member, and the second moment of the section area about the centroid. A reference to Fig. 94 on p. 315 will help to explain this. The values given in the table are to be used in calculating the resistance to bending (for any permissible stress in the material) for certain channel sections. Tables are published giving similar figures for all the many steel sections that have been standardised. The important figures are those giving the x and y co-ordinates of the centroid, and the second moments of the section area about axes through the centroid and respectively parallel to the x- and y-axes. Both are given because the channel section might experience bending either edge-wise or flat-wise.

Now as a fact calculations about flywheels were made by earlier engineers than those who began to design structures in steel. Engineering practice had to make great advances before steel ingots could be produced and rolled into girders. When this happened the structural people took the nomenclature already in use by the engine-builders and spoke of Moments of Inertia. It is all very confusing for the young mathematician. In this book, as far as possible, we avoid speaking of moments of inertia where there is no mass, and of centres of gravity where weight does not enter into the problem. But in fact the student who finds words used loosely in technical literature should not, with this explanation, find any difficulty.

Example

· *Establish the formula* $I = \frac{1}{12}(BD^3 - bd^3)$ *for the second moment about the neutral axis* NA *of the section of Fig.* 113.

Fig. 114 represents, very much out of proportion, one of the I-form beam sections used in structural engineering. It is accepted to speak of the Moment of Inertia of such a section (or more often just to use the symbol I) meaning the sum of the second moments of its elements about an axis through its centroid. This axis is known as the Neutral Axis because ordinary loading of the beam gives rise to tension in the lower flange, compression in the upper flange, but no stress in longitudinal fibres passing through this axis. The proportions of such a beam as used in practice may be inferred from those of the channel section of Fig. 94.

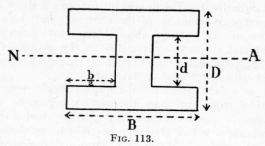

Fig. 113.

The section may be considered as a rectangle D by B from which two rectangles d by $b/2$ have been cut.

$$\text{M.I. of first} = \text{BD} \times \frac{\left(\dfrac{\text{D}}{2}\right)^2}{3} = \frac{\text{BD}^3}{12} \qquad . \quad . \quad . \quad (1)$$

$$\text{M.I. of each of others} = \frac{bd}{2} \times \frac{\left(\dfrac{d}{2}\right)^2}{3} = \frac{bd^3}{24}$$

$$\therefore \quad \text{M.I. of both} = \frac{bd^3}{12} \qquad . \quad . \quad . \quad . \quad (2)$$

Take the difference between (1) and (2), and the result follows.

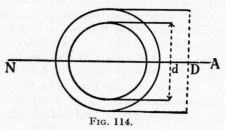

Fig. 114.

Whenever the Moment of Inertia is, in fact, a sum or difference, a similar method may be followed.

If the diagram of Fig. 115 represents a section across a hollow shaft * its second moment about the neutral axis is the difference between the moments of the two circles whose diameters are given, *i.e.*,

$$I = \frac{\pi D^2}{4} \cdot \frac{\left(\dfrac{D}{2}\right)^2}{4} - \frac{\pi d^2}{4} \cdot \frac{\left(\dfrac{d}{2}\right)^2}{4}$$

$$= \frac{\pi}{64}(D^4 - d^4).$$

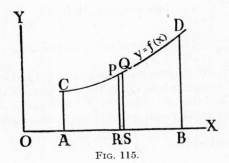

FIG. 115.

In regard to Figs. 113 and 114, students should note that although Moments of Inertia about NA can be added or subtracted, the same does not apply to values of Z, the section Modulus. Why is this so?

7. We now find the second moment of an area bounded by a curve whose equation is given. See Fig. 115.

* This, like the preceding examples, deals with the properties of the member when used to resist *bending*. Shafts are more often used to transmit twisting actions, in which case the polar moment of inertia is to be used. See Example 3, p. 336.

Suppose $y = f(x)$ is the equation of the curve CD.

Let $OA = a$ and $OB = b$.

Suppose we require the second moment about OX of the area bounded by the curve, the axis of x, and the ordinates at $x = a$, and $x = b$.

This is the area ABCD shown in the figure. Consider any strip on RS as base.

If $OR = x$, $RP = y = f(x)$, and $RS = dx$. Consider the strip as a rectangle.

Its area $= ydx$.

Its "k^2" $= \dfrac{y^2}{3}$, about RS, *i.e.*, about OX.

$\therefore \dfrac{y^3 dx}{3}$ is its second moment about OX.

$\therefore \displaystyle\int_a^b \dfrac{y^3 dx}{3}$ is the second moment of the area.

Thus suppose the curve is given by $y = 2x^2$ and we require the second moment about OX of the area between the curve, the x-axis and the two ordinates at $x = 0$ and $x = 2$.

Using the above result, putting $2x^2$ for y we get

$$\text{second moment} = \int_0^2 \frac{(2x^2)^3}{3}\, dx = \frac{8}{3}\left[\frac{x^7}{7}\right]_0^2$$

$$= \frac{1024}{21} \text{ (in.)}^4$$

if the unit of length $= 1$ in.

7. The Parallel Axis Theorem

Suppose I_g is the M.I. of a body about an axis through its C.G., and I the M.I. about a parallel axis, whose distance from the first is h units. If m is the mass of the body then

$$I = I_g + mh^2 \quad \dots \dots \quad (1)$$

or

$$k^2 = k_g^2 + h^2 \quad \dots \dots \quad (2)$$

where k is the radius of gyration of the body about any axis, k_g the radius of gyration about a parallel axis through the C.G., and h the distance between the axes.

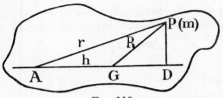

FIG. 116.

Suppose the axes are perpendicular to the paper through A and G, where G is the C.G. of the body, the section of which by the paper, we will take as the area bounded by the wavy line in the diagram above.

P is any point of the area, and m the mass of a small element of area surrounding P.

Let PD be perpendicular to AG.

Let $GD = x$, and $GA = h$.

Using a well known geometrical theorem, we have

$$AP^2 = GP^2 + AG^2 + 2AG \cdot GD$$

i.e.,
$$r^2 = R^2 + h^2 + 2hx$$

$$\therefore \ mr^2 = mR^2 + mh^2 + 2mhx$$

and
$$\Sigma mr^2 = \Sigma mR^2 + \Sigma mh^2 + \Sigma 2mhx \quad . \quad . \quad (3)$$

if we sum for every element.

Notice that the last term on the right-hand side of (3) is
$$\Sigma 2mhx = 2h\Sigma mx,$$

since $2h$ is a constant and is a factor of every term of
$$\Sigma 2mhx.$$

But $\dfrac{\Sigma mx}{\Sigma m}$ = the x-co-ordinate of the C.G. of the body, referred to G as origin.

$$\therefore \ \frac{\Sigma mx}{\Sigma m} = 0, \ i.e., \ \Sigma mx = 0. \ \therefore \ \Sigma 2mhx = 0.$$

Hence from (3)

$$\Sigma mr^2 = \Sigma mR^2 + h^2\Sigma m$$

i.e., $$I = I_g + Mh^2$$

where M is the mass of the total area of uniform density m.

If we divide throughout this last equation by M, we get:

$$k^2 = k_g{}^2 + h^2.$$

Example 1

(1) *A rectangular section has sides 14 in. by 6 in. Find its second moment about an axis parallel to the 6 in. side, and 9 in. from it.*

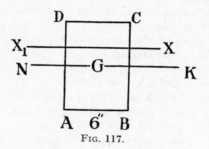

Fig. 117.

Let ABCD be the section. AB = 6 in., AD = 14 in. NK is the axis through the C.G.

Let X_1X be a parallel axis, 2 in. from NK.

For axis NK, $k_g{}^2 = \frac{49}{3}$ (in.)^2.

Also $h = 2$, $\therefore h^2 = 4$ (in.)^2.

Hence if k be the radius of gyration about X_1X,

$$\begin{aligned}
k^2 &= k_g{}^2 + h^2 \\
&= (\tfrac{49}{3} + 4)\ (\text{in.}^2) \\
&= \tfrac{61}{3}\ (\text{in.})^2
\end{aligned}$$

$\therefore$ second moment $= 6 \times 14 \times \frac{61}{3}$ (in.)$^4 = 1708$ (in.^{4}).

Example 2

Find the M.I. of a circular disc of radius a and mass M about an axis through a point on its rim perpendicular to its plane.

We have $$k_g^2 = \frac{a^2}{2}$$

and $$h = a$$

$$\therefore \quad k^2 = \frac{a^2}{2} + a^2 = \frac{3a^2}{2}.$$

Hence the required M.I. $= M \cdot \dfrac{3a^2}{2}.$

EXERCISE 45

(mainly upon matter immediately preceding, but including a few examples for revision)

1. Find by integration the position of the centre of gravity, and the second moment of the area about a line through the centre of gravity parallel to the base, of the given figure.

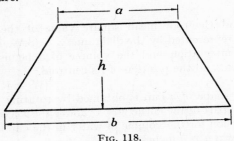

FIG. 118.

(Stafford.)

2. A groove of semi-circular section, and diameter 6 in. is turned in a metal cylinder of diameter 1 ft. Find the volume of metal removed and the surface area of the groove.   (Cheltenham.)

3. (i) A solid cap of a sphere has a base diameter of 6 in. and a height of 1 in. What is the radius of the sphere?

(ii) Find by integration (1) the volume of the cap, (2) the distance of its centre of gravity from the centre of the base.

(West Riding.)

4. (a) Find the mean value of $50 \sin 12\theta \cos 6\theta$ between $\theta = \dfrac{\pi}{12}$ and $\theta = \dfrac{\pi}{6}$.

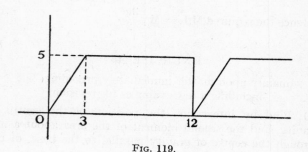

FIG. 119.

(b) Find the root mean square value of the periodic function represented by the diagram. (S.W. Essex.)

5. By integration find the volume of a hemisphere of radius 8 in. and the position of its centroid.

(West Riding.)

6. The shape of a cup is obtained by rotating *about the y-axis* the part of the curve $y = x^3$ above the x-axis. Find an expression for the volume of water in the cup when the depth of water is h inches.

If water is poured into the cup at a uniform rate of 20 cu in. per sec, find, at the instant when the depth is 8 in.: (i) the rate at which the water level is rising; (ii) the rate at which the radius of the water surface is increasing.

(Surrey.)

7. A rectangular plate ABCD in which AB = 10 in. and BC = 6 in. has a rectangular portion PQRS removed. P and Q lie in AB such that AP = QB = 2 in. and QR = 4 in.

Calculate the distance from CD of the centroid of the remainder of the plate.

Calculate the second moment of area of this remaining portion about an axis through the centroid and parallel to CD.

Deduce the radius of gyration about this axis.

(E.M.E.U.)

8. Sketch roughly the curve $y = 4x^2$ from $x = 0$ to $x = 4$.

Find by integration (i) the area between the curve, the x-axis, and the above ordinates; (ii) the co-ordinates of the centroid of this area; obtain (iii), without further integration, the volume of revolution generated by rotating the area of (i) through four right angles about the x-axis.

(West Riding.)

9. Find the area and the position of the centroid of the area bounded by the curve $y = \frac{1}{4}x^{\frac{3}{2}}$, the x-axis, and the ordinate $x = 4$. (Stafford.)

10. Sketch roughly the curve $y = 1 - \frac{1}{2}\sin x$ between $x = 0$ and $x = \pi$. Find the area between this curve, the x-axis, and ordinates at $x = 0$ and $x = \pi$.

If this area is rotated about the x-axis through 360° find the volume generated and, using Guldinus' Theorem or otherwise, calculate the y-co-ordinate of the centroid of the area. (Burton-upon-Trent.)

11. (a) Find the area enclosed by the curve $y = \sin x$ (between $x = 0$ and $x = \pi$) and the x-axis.

(b) Determine the co-ordinates of the centroid of this area.

(c) Find the volume generated when the area makes a complete revolution about the x-axis. (N.C.T.E.C.)

12. The portion of the curve $y = \sqrt{x + 5}$ which lies between $x = 0$ and $x = 10$, rotates about the axis of x. Find (a) the volume of the solid so formed, and (b) the

distance from the origin of a plane perpendicular to the axis of x, which will divide this solid into two equal volumes.   (S.W. Essex.)

13. (a) Find the area enclosed between the curve $y = 5 \cdot 3 \sin 100\pi t$, the t-axis and the ordinates at $t = 0 \cdot 002$ and $t = 0 \cdot 005$.

(b) Calculate the distance of the centroid of this area from the t-axis.

(c) Find the volume generated when this area is revolved about the t-axis.   (Stafford.)

14. Calculate the area between the curve $y = x^2 + 1$, the x-axis and the ordinates $x = 1$, $x = 4$. Find the distances of the centroid of this area from the x- and y-axes.
                                                    (U.L.C.I.)

15. Prove the formula for the moment of inertia of a uniform circular disc about an axis through its centre and perpendicular to the plane of the disc. The diagram is a section through the centre of a circular metal flywheel. The rim is a 2-in. square and the centre portion is 1 in. thick. Calculate its M.I. about axis YY given that 1 cu ft of metal weighs 450 lb.

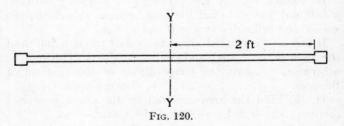

Fig. 120.

(West Riding.)

16. (a) Sketch the curve $y = 4(9 - x^2)$ between $x = -4$ and $x = +4$, and find by integration: (i) the area enclosed between the curve and the axis of x; (ii) the position of the centroid of this area.

(*b*) The work done by a gas in expanding from volume v_1 to volume v_2 is

$$\int_{v_1}^{v_2} p \, dv.$$

Calculate the work done when a quantity of gas expands according to the law $pv = 45,000$ from a volume of 5 cu ft to a volume of 15 cu ft. The pressure p is measured in pounds per square foot.   (Handsworth.)

17. Find the second moment of area of the section shown in Fig. 121 about the axis AB.

Using the parallel axis theorem, or otherwise, find the second moment of area about an axis through the centroid of the section parallel to the axis AB.

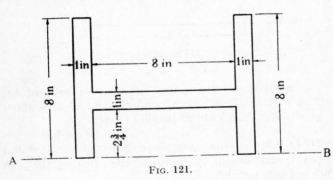

FIG. 121.

(U.L.C.I.)

18. (i) Sketch the curve $y = 16 - x^2$ indicating on it the area enclosed by the curve and the x-axis.

(ii) Determine by integration the area bounded by the curve $y = 16 - x^2$ and the x-axis.

(iii) Find by integration the co-ordinates of the centroid of this area.   (West Riding.)

19. P is the point $(x = 9, \; y = 18)$ on the parabola $y^2 = 36x$. Determine (i) the area enclosed by the curve,

the x-axis, and the ordinate through P, (ii) the position of the centroid of this area. (N.C.T.E.C.)

20. (i) The figure shows a section in the shape of a trapezium ABCD, the interior angles at A and B being equal. Find the position of the centroid of the section.

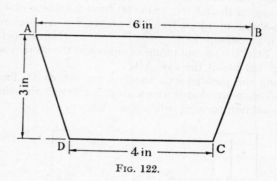

FIG. 122.

(ii) Calculate (1) the second moment of area of the section about AB; (2) the second moment of area about a line through the centroid parallel to AB.

(West Riding.)

21. (a) On the same axes, sketch the curves $y = x^3$ and $y = \sqrt{x}$, and obtain, by means of the calculus, the area enclosed between them.

(b) A spherical cap of height 8 in. is cut from a solid sphere of radius 13 in. Find its volume and the position of its centre of gravity. The sphere is of uniform density.

(Handsworth.)

22. (a) For the triangular area of Fig. 123, write down: (i) the area of the shaded element; (ii) the second moment of this area about the axis OX; (iii) the second moment of the whole triangular area about OX, in the form of an integral. Hence, obtain the second moment of area

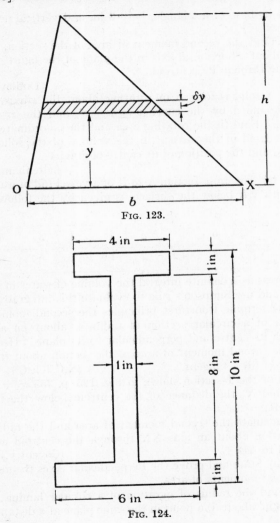

FIG. 123.

FIG. 124.

about its base of a triangle, base 6 in. and vertical height 5 in.

(b) Find the second moment of area of the section, Fig. 124, about a horizontal axis in the plane of the figure, and passing through its centroid.

(Dudley.)

23. A solid is formed by rotating, about the x-axis, the area bounded by the curve $y = 4 - x^2$, and the x- and y-axes. Find (i) the rotating area and the co-ordinates of the centroid of this area; (ii) the volume of the solid so formed and the position of its centre of gravity.

(Cheltenham.)

24. (a) The cross-section A sq ft of a vessel full of water, at depth x ft below the surface, is given by the following table:

x . .	0	1	2	3	4	5	6
A . .	6	4·2	2	1·9	1	0·7	0

Express as a definite integral the volume of water in the vessel and use Simpson's rule to evaluate this integral.

(b) Determine from first principles the second moment of area of a circular section of radius a about an axis through its centre and perpendicular to its plane. Hence find the second moment of area of the section about (i) a diameter, (ii) a tangent. (N.C.T.E.C.)

25. For the T-section shown in Fig. 125, p. 355,

(a) find $\bar{X}$, the distance of the centroid below the top edge AB;

(b) calculate the second moment of area and the radius of gyration about an axis XX through the centroid and parallel to AB. (Coventry.)

26. (a) State and prove the Perpendicular Axes theorem for second moments of area.

(b) Find the radius of gyration of a circular lamina of radius 3 in. about (i) a point in the same plane at a distance of 8 in. from the centre of the lamina, and (ii) a straight line in the same plane at a distance of 8 in. from the centre of the lamina. (S.W. Essex.)

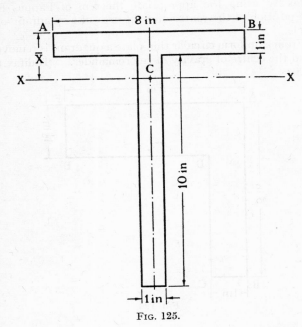

FIG. 125.

27. In a certain steam engine the work done under adiabatic expansion of the steam is

$$W = \int_{v_1}^{v_2} p \, dv. \quad \text{If } p_1 v_1^n = p_2 v_2^n,$$

where $p_2 v_2^n = 109.2$, $p_1 = 240$, $v_1 = 0.5$ and $v_2 = 2$. Calculate the value of n and hence find the work done. What work would be done if instead the expansion were according to Boyle's Law $pv = 109.2$? (Worcester.)

28. (a) Find the area bounded by the x-axis and the curve $y = 4x - x^2$. Find also the volume traced out when this area is rotated about the x-axis.

(b) By using the appropriate theorem of Pappus find the position of the centroid of the area of a quadrant of a circle.

From a uniform circular thin plate a quadrant is removed. Find the centre of gravity of the remainder.   (Halifax.)

29.

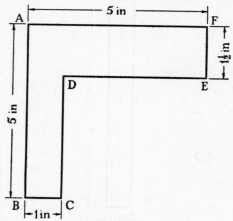

FIG. 126.

(a) Determine the position of the centroid of the section shown in the figure.

(b) Find the second moment of area of the section about an axis through the centroid: (i) parallel to the side AB; (ii) perpendicular to the plane of the section. You may assume, without proof, that k^2 for a rectangle (sides a and b) about an axis through its centroid parallel to side b, is $\dfrac{a^2}{12}$, where k stands for the radius of gyration.

(Nuneaton.)

30. (*a*) Evaluate the following integrals:

$$\text{(i)} \int_1^4 \left(2x + \frac{1}{\sqrt{x}} \right) dx \qquad \text{(ii)} \int_0^{\pi/2} \sin^2 x \, dx$$

$$\text{(iii)} \int_0^4 \frac{x}{x^2 + 4} \, dx$$

(*b*) The bending moment M at a distance x from the fixed end of a cantilever of length l is given by $W(l - x)$, where W is the load. From the relation $M = EI\frac{d^2y}{dx^2}$, where E and I are constants, find the deflection y at the free end if $\frac{dy}{dx} = 0$ and $y = 0$ when $x = 0$.   (Stafford.)

Progress Note

Readers who have followed the Examples given in the text, and worked many of the questions included in the " Exercises " may well at this point look ahead to Exercise 55 (p. 415) and make a study of what is included. All the questions of Exercise 55 are extracted from recent O.N.C. Final examination papers; moreover the Exercise is fairly representative of the total content of these papers. The reader will find that with few exceptions the questions could reasonably be attempted in the light of his studies to date.

Chapters 14, 15, 16, and 17, which follow, offer a helpful introduction to more advanced mathematical studies than are commonly specified for O.N.C. The chapters form an interesting bridge between " practical mathematics " and mathematics as a " principal " subject in an H.N.C. or block-release Course. The reader with a bent for Mathematics may well be fascinated by the new vistas opened, and should indulge himself by borrowing (or even buying) a copy of Pedoe's *Advanced National Certificate Mathematics*

(Volume 1), E.U.P., in which he will find the new work developed in a very lucid and interesting way.

Chapters 14 to 17 are reprinted without material change from earlier editions, since, as has been explained, there is no store of published questions of O.N.C. standard from which additional illustrations or examples can be drawn.

CHAPTER 14

THE EXPONENTIAL, HYPERBOLIC, AND LOGARITHMIC, FUNCTIONS

1. The Exponential Function, e^x

Suppose that the following problem is proposed for solution:

"Find a function of x whose gradient at any point is equal to the value of the function at that point, and which is such that when $x = 0$, the function has the value unity."

If $y =$ the required function we have,

$$\frac{dy}{dx} = y \qquad \dots \dots \dots \dots \quad (1)$$

and

$$y = 1 \text{ when } x = 0 \quad \dots \dots \dots \quad (2)$$

Solution.

Suppose
$$y = 1 + a_1 x + \frac{a_2}{\underline{|2}} x^2 + \frac{a_3 x^3}{\underline{|3}} + \cdots \qquad (3)$$

where the series on the right-hand side of (3) proceeds indefinitely. Notice that condition (2) above is satisfied.

Differentiating both sides of (3), we get:

$$\frac{dy}{dx} = a_1 + a_2 x + \frac{a_3 x^2}{\underline{|2}} + \frac{a_4 x^3}{\underline{|3}} + \cdots \qquad (4)$$

Condition (1) above makes (3) $\equiv$ (4).

I.e.,
$$1 + a_1 x + \frac{a_2 x^2}{\underline{|2}} + \frac{a_3 x^3}{\underline{|3}} + \cdots$$
$$\equiv a_1 + a_2 x + \frac{a_3 x^2}{\underline{|2}} + \frac{a_4 x^3}{\underline{|3}} + \cdots$$

These two series are identical.

∴ by equating coefficients of like powers of x we get:

$$1 = a_1$$
$$a_1 = a_2 = 1$$
$$\frac{a_2}{\underline{2}} = \frac{a_3}{\underline{2}}, \text{ i.e., } a_2 = a_3 = 1$$

and so on. Every a, no matter what its suffix may be, has the value 1.

Substituting these values in (3) we have:

$$y = 1 + x + \frac{x^2}{\underline{2}} + \frac{x^3}{\underline{3}} + \frac{x^4}{\underline{4}} + \cdots \qquad (5)$$

This is the function of x we set out to find.

Now in (5) write ax for x, and y_1 for y.

Then
$$y_1 = 1 + ax + \frac{a^2 x^2}{\underline{2}} + \frac{a^3 x^3}{\underline{3}} + \cdots \qquad (5a)$$

and $\frac{dy_1}{d(ax)} = y_1$, from (1).

Now $\frac{dy_1}{d(ax)} = y_1$, may be written $\frac{1}{a}\frac{dy_1}{dx} = y_1$

i.e.,
$$\frac{dy_1}{dx} = ay_1 \qquad \cdots \qquad (6)$$

Also
$$\frac{d}{dx}(y^n) = ny^{n-1}\frac{dy}{dx} = ny^n \qquad \cdots \qquad (7)$$

since
$$\frac{dy}{dx} = y \text{ (from (1)).}$$

Notice that (7) has the same form as (6) with y^n written for y_1 and n for a.

Make this substitution in (5a):

then
$$y^n = 1 + nx + \frac{n^2 x^2}{\underline{2}} + \frac{n^3 x^3}{\underline{3}} + \cdots$$

Now put $n = \dfrac{1}{x}$, so that

$$y^{\frac{1}{x}} = 1 + 1 + \frac{1}{\lfloor 2} + \frac{1}{\lfloor 3} + \cdots \quad \cdot \quad \cdot \quad (8)$$

The series on the right-hand side of (8) is denoted by e. Its value is indeterminate, but by an easy calculation is found to be 2·718 correct to three places.

From (8) then, we have:

$$y^{\frac{1}{x}} = e$$

$$\therefore \quad y = e^x = 1 + x + \frac{x^2}{\lfloor 2} + \frac{x^3}{\lfloor 3} + \cdots \quad \cdot \quad (9)$$

This function of x is called the **Exponential function.**
It may be generalised thus:
Noting that $a = e^{\log_e a}$, we get:

$$a^x = e^{\log_e a \cdot x} = 1 + x \log_e a + \frac{x^2}{\lfloor 2} (\log_e a)^2 + \cdots \quad (10)$$

The graph $y = e^{\pm x}$ is shown below.

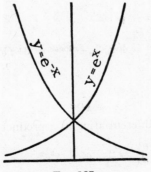

Fig. 127.

Summary

(1)
$$e^x = 1 + x + \frac{x^2}{\lfloor 2} + \frac{x^3}{\lfloor 3} + \dots$$

If $x = 1$, we get $e = 1 + 1 + \frac{1}{\lfloor 2} + \frac{1}{\lfloor 3} + \dots = 2 \cdot 718 \dots$

(2) if
$$y = e^x$$
$$\frac{dy}{dx} = e^x.$$

(3) if $y = e^{ax}$
$$\frac{dy}{dx} = \frac{dy}{d(ax)} \cdot \frac{d(ax)}{dx} = e^{ax} \cdot a = ae^{ax}.$$

Thus, if
$$y = e^{3x}$$
$$\frac{dy}{dx} = 3e^{3x}.$$

Similarly, if
$$y = 6e^{-2x}$$
$$\frac{dy}{dx} = -12e^{-2x}.$$

(4) $a^x = e^{x \log_e a} = 1 + x \log_e a + \frac{x^2 (\log_e a)^2}{\lfloor 2} + \dots$

If $y = 3^x = e^{x \log_e 3}$

$$\frac{dy}{dx} = \log_e 3 \cdot e^{x \log_e 3} = 3^x \cdot \log_e 3.$$

Example 1

Differentiate $y = x^2 e^x.$

We have, by differentiating as a product,

$$\frac{dy}{dx} = 2x \cdot e^x + x^2 e^x$$
$$= e^x (2x + x^2).$$

Example 2

Differentiate $y = 3e^{2x} \sin x.$

We have:

$$\frac{dy}{dx} = 3(2e^{2x} \sin x + e^{2x} \cos x)$$
$$= 3e^{2x}(2 \sin x + \cos x).$$

Example 3

Find $\qquad \frac{d}{dx}(e^{-2x} \sin 3x).$

Put $\qquad y = e^{-2x} \sin 3x$

then $\qquad \frac{dy}{dx} = -2e^{-2x} \sin 3x + 3e^{-2x} \cos 3x$

$$= e^{-2x}(3 \cos 3x - 2 \sin 3x)$$

Example 4

If $y = e^{ax}$, *find* y_2 *and* y_3 *and deduce the value of* y_n, *where* y_n *is the* n^{th} *differential coefficient of* y.

$$y = e^{ax}$$
$$y_1 = ae^{ax}$$
$$y_2 = a^2 e^{ax}$$
$$y_3 = a^3 e^{ax}$$

and $\qquad y_n = a^n e^{ax}.$

2. Integration of the Exponential Function

We have found that if

$$y = e^x$$
$$dy = e^x dx.$$

Hence, reversing the process:

$$\int e^x dx = y = e^x + C.$$

adding the constant of integration.

The " form " of this result should be noted as

$$\int e^{(\ )} d(\ ) = e^{(\ )} + \text{const.}$$

Thus $\qquad \int e^{2x}dx = \frac{1}{2}\int e^{2x}d(2x) = \frac{e^{2x}}{2} + C.$

Similarly, in the general case,

$$\int e^{ax}dx = \frac{1}{a}\int e^{ax}d(ax) = \frac{e^{ax}}{a} + C.$$

Thus $\qquad \int e^{-2x}dx = -\frac{e^{-2x}}{2} + C$

and $\qquad \int 3e^{-\frac{x}{2}}dx = -6e^{-\frac{x}{2}} + C.$

3. The Hyperbolic Functions cosh x and sinh x

These functions are defined below:

$$\cosh x = \frac{e^x + e^{-x}}{2} \qquad \cdot \quad \cdot \quad \cdot \quad \cdot \quad (1)$$

and $\qquad \sinh x = \frac{e^x - e^{-x}}{2} \qquad \cdot \quad \cdot \quad \cdot \quad \cdot \quad (2)$

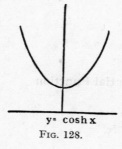

y = cosh x

FIG. 128.

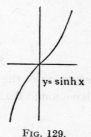

y = sinh x

FIG. 129.

By expanding e^x and e^{-x} we see that

$$\cosh x = 1 + \frac{x^2}{\lfloor 2} + \frac{x^4}{\lfloor 4} + \ldots$$

and $\qquad \sinh x = x + \frac{x^3}{\lfloor 3} + \frac{x^5}{\lfloor 5} + \ldots$

If $\qquad y = \cosh x = \dfrac{e^x + e^{-x}}{2}$

$$\dfrac{dy}{dx} = \dfrac{e^x - e^{-x}}{2}$$

$$= \sinh x \quad . \quad . \quad . \quad . \quad . \quad (3)$$

and $\qquad \displaystyle\int \sinh x\, dx = \cosh x + C \quad . \quad . \quad . \quad (4)$

Similarly, if $\qquad x = \sinh x = \dfrac{e^x - e^{-x}}{2}$

$$\dfrac{dy}{dx} = \dfrac{e^x + e^{-x}}{2} = \cosh x \quad . \quad . \quad (5)$$

and $\qquad \displaystyle\int \cosh x\, dx = \sinh x + C \quad . \quad . \quad . \quad (6)$

Also
$$\cosh^2 x - \sinh^2 x = \tfrac{1}{4}(e^x + e^{-x})^2 - \tfrac{1}{4}(e^x - e^{-x})^2$$
$$= \tfrac{1}{4}[(e^{2x} + 2 + e^{-2x}) - (e^{2x} - 2 + e^{-2x})]$$
$$= 1 \quad . \quad . \quad . \quad . \quad . \quad . \quad . \quad (7)$$

Notice the analogy between (7) and
$$\cos^2 x + \sin^2 x = 1.$$

EXERCISE 46

1. Differentiate the following:

(1) e^{3x}.   (2) e^{-4x}.   (3) $3e^{\frac{x}{3}}$.   (4) $-4e^{\frac{x}{4}}$.

(5) $\dfrac{1}{e^{2x}}$.   (6) $\dfrac{5}{e^{4x}}$.   (7) $2e^{3x} - 4e^{-2x}$.

2. Integrate:

(1) e^{2x}.   (2) e^{-4x}.   (3) $5e^{\frac{x}{4}}$.   (4) $-2e^{-3x}$.

3. Differentiate the following:

(1) $x^2 e^x$.   (2) $3x^3 e^{2x}$.   (3) $x^{-2} e^{-4x}$.

(4) $e^x \sin x$.   (5) $e^{3x} \cos 4x$.   (6) $ke^{ax} \sin bx$.

(7) $e^{-2t} \cos 3t$.   (8) $\dfrac{e^{4x}}{x^3}$.   (9) $ae^{-kt} \sin (kt)$.

4. Differentiate:

(1) $\cosh 3x$. (2) $\sinh 4x$. (3) $3 \cosh \dfrac{x}{3}$.

5. Differentiate:

(1) $e^{\sin x}$. (2) $e^{3 \sin 2x}$. (3) $\dfrac{ax^2 + bx + c}{e^x}$.

6. Differentiate:

(1) a^x. (2) 3^x. (3) 4^{2x}. (4) 5^{-3x}.

7. (1) If $y = e^{3x}$, find y_5. (2) If $y = e^{-2x}$, find y_6.

8. If $\dfrac{d^2y}{dx^2} - \dfrac{7dy}{dx} + 12y = 0$, show that $y = Ae^{4x} + Be^{3x}$.

9. If $y = 2e^x + 3e^{-2x}$, find the value of $\dfrac{d^2y}{dx^2} + \dfrac{dy}{dx} - 2y$.

10. The curve $y = c \cosh \dfrac{x}{c}$ is called the catenary. It is the form assumed when a uniform chain hangs between two fixed points.

Find the area between the curve, the x-axis, and the ordinates $x = 0$, $x = a$.

11. A curve is represented by the equation $y = 2e^x - 3e^{-x}$. Find (1) the gradient where $x = 1$, and (2) the mean value of y over the range $x = 0$, to $x = 0.5$. (U.L.C.I.)

12. Evaluate (1) $\displaystyle\int_0^1 e^{2x}dx$, (2) $\displaystyle\int_0^2 e^{-x}dx$.

4. The Logarithmic Function, $\log_e x$

If we put $\quad\quad\quad y = \log_e x \quad . \quad . \quad . \quad . \quad$ (1)

we have $\quad\quad\quad\quad e^y = x \quad . \quad . \quad . \quad . \quad$ (2)

Differentiating both sides of (2) with respect to y, we get

$$e^y = \frac{dx}{dy}$$

or, inverting, $\quad\quad\quad \dfrac{dy}{dx} = \dfrac{1}{e^y}$

$$= \frac{1}{x} \text{ from (2).}$$

Hence

$$\frac{d}{dx} \log_e x = \frac{1}{x} \quad \cdots \quad \cdots \quad (3)$$

This is an important result.

Similarly, if
$$y = \log_e ax$$
$$= \log_e a + \log_e x$$

then
$$\frac{dy}{dx} = \frac{1}{x}$$

since $\log_e a$ is a constant, and its differential coefficient is zero.   The graph of $y = \log_e x$ is shown below.

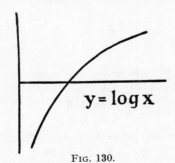

$$y = \log x$$

Fig. 130.

Example 1

$$y = \log_e 3x$$
$$\frac{dy}{dx} = \frac{1}{x}.$$

Example 2

If
$$y = \log_e (x^2 + x + 1), \text{ find } \frac{dy}{dx}.$$

Put
$$z = x^2 + x + 1.$$

Then
$$y = \log_e z$$
$$\frac{dy}{dz} = \frac{1}{z}.$$

But
$$\frac{dy}{dx} = \frac{dy}{dz} \cdot \frac{dz}{dx}$$

$$= \frac{1}{z} \cdot (2x + 1)$$

$$= \frac{2x + 1}{x^2 + x + 1}.$$

Example 3

Similarly, if $\quad y = \log_e (3 - x)$

$$\frac{dy}{dx} = \frac{1}{3 - x} \cdot \frac{d}{dx} (3 - x)$$

$$= \frac{-1}{3 - x}.$$

Example 4

Find $\dfrac{d}{dx} \log_e \dfrac{x^2 - 4x + 3}{x^2 + 3x + 1}$.

Put $\quad y = \log_e \dfrac{x^2 - 4x + 3}{x^2 + 3x + 1}$

$$= \log_e (x^2 - 4x + 3) - \log_e (x^2 + 3x + 1)$$

$$\therefore \quad \frac{dy}{dx} = \frac{2x - 4}{x^2 - 4x + 3} - \frac{2x + 3}{x^2 + 3x + 1}$$

by differentiating as in Example 2.

Example 5

Find $\dfrac{d}{dx} \log_e y$.

If $\qquad\qquad z = \log_e y$

$$\frac{dz}{dx} = \frac{1}{y} \cdot \frac{dy}{dx}$$

$$\therefore \quad \frac{d}{dx} \log_e y = \frac{1}{y} \frac{dy}{dx}.$$

This result should be noted well.

Example 6

Differentiate $e^{2x} \log_e x$.

Put $\qquad\qquad y = e^{2x} \log_e x$ (a product)

then $\qquad\qquad \dfrac{dy}{dx} = 2e^{2x} \log x + \dfrac{e^{2x}}{x}.$

Example 7

Differentiate $\qquad\qquad (5 + x)^x.$

In this example notice that the index is a variable.

Put $\qquad y = (5 + x)^x.$

Taking logs to base e, we get

$$\log_e y = x \log_e (5 + x) \quad \cdot \quad \cdot \quad \cdot \quad \cdot \quad \cdot \quad (4)$$

$$\therefore \; \frac{1}{y} \cdot \frac{dy}{dx} = \log (5 + x) + \frac{x}{5 + x}.$$

$$\therefore \; \frac{dy}{dx} = (5 + x)^x \left[\log (5 + x) + \frac{x}{5 + x} \right]$$

Notice that the right-hand side of (4) is a product. The left-hand side is differentiated as in Example 5.

N.B.   If $\qquad y = (5 + x)^n$ where n is a constant,

$$\frac{dy}{dx} = n(5 + x)^{n-1}.$$

Example 8

Differentiate $\log_{10} x$ with respect to x.

Put $\qquad y = \log_{10} x = \dfrac{\log_e x}{\log_e 10} = 0{\cdot}4343 \log_e x$

$$\therefore \; \frac{dy}{dx} = \frac{1}{x \cdot \log_e 10} = \frac{\log_{10} e}{x} = \frac{0{\cdot}4343}{x}.$$

5. Logarithmic Integrals

If $\qquad\qquad\qquad y = \log_e x$

$$dy = \frac{dx}{x}.$$

Hence $\qquad \int \dfrac{dx}{x} = y = \log_e x + \mathrm{C}$ . . . . . (1)

The " form " of (1) should be noted thus

$$\int \frac{d(\quad)}{(\quad)} = \log_e (\quad) + \mathrm{C}$$

or $\qquad \int \dfrac{d(\text{denominator})}{\text{denominator}} = \log_e (\text{denominator}) + \mathrm{C}.$

Example 1

$$\int \frac{3dx}{x+4} = 3 \int \frac{dx}{x+4}$$
$$= 3 \log_e (x+4) + \mathrm{C}.$$

Since $\qquad dx = d(x+4).$

Example 2

$$\int \frac{dx}{5-x} = \int \frac{d(5-x)}{(5-x)}$$
$$= - \log_e (5-x) + \mathrm{C}.$$

Example 3

$$\int \frac{xdx}{x^2+5} = \frac{1}{2} \int \frac{2xdx}{x^2+5}$$
$$= \tfrac{1}{2} \log (x^2+5) + \mathrm{C}.$$

Notice the method of putting the integrand into the correct " form."

Example 4

$$\int \frac{(x+2)dx}{x^2+4x+1}$$
$$= \frac{1}{2} \int \frac{(2x+4)dx}{x^2+4x+1}$$
$$= \tfrac{1}{2} \log_e (x^2+4x+1) + \mathrm{C}.$$

Example 5

$$\int \cot \theta \, d\theta$$
$$= \int \frac{\cos \theta \, d\theta}{\sin \theta}$$
$$= \int \frac{d(\sin \theta)}{\sin \theta}$$
$$= \log_e \sin \theta + C.$$

Example 6

Similarly,

$$\int \tan \theta \, d\theta$$
$$= \int \frac{\sin \theta \, d\theta}{\cos \theta}$$
$$= - \int \frac{d(\cos \theta)}{\cos \theta}$$
$$= - \log_e \cos \theta + C$$
$$= \log_e \sec \theta + C.$$

Example 7

$$\int \operatorname{cosec} \theta \, d\theta = \int \frac{d\theta}{\sin \theta}$$
$$= \int \frac{d\theta}{2 \sin \frac{\theta}{2} \cos \frac{\theta}{2}}$$
$$= \int \frac{\sec^2 \frac{\theta}{2} \cdot d \frac{\theta}{2}}{\tan \frac{\theta}{2}}$$
$$= \int \frac{d\left(\tan \frac{\theta}{2}\right)}{\tan \frac{\theta}{2}}$$
$$= \log_e \tan \frac{\theta}{2} + C.$$

We can readily prove that $\operatorname{cosec} \theta - \cot \theta = \tan \dfrac{\theta}{2}$.

Hence another form for the last result is

$$\int \operatorname{cosec} \theta d\theta = \log_e (\operatorname{cosec} \theta - \cot \theta) + C.$$

Example 8

Notice $\displaystyle\int \sec \theta d\theta = \int \dfrac{\sec \theta(\sec \theta + \tan \theta)d\theta}{\sec \theta + \tan \theta}$.

The numerator is seen to be the differential of the denominator.

Hence $\displaystyle\int \sec \theta d\theta = \log_e (\sec \theta + \tan \theta) + C.$

The last four results should be remembered.

Example 9

$$\int_0^1 \frac{dx}{4 + 3x} = \left[\tfrac{1}{3} \log (4 + 3x) \right]_0^1 = \tfrac{1}{3} \log_e \tfrac{7}{4}.$$

Example 10

$$\int_0^1 4e^x dx = \left[4e^x \right]_0^1 = 4(e - e^0) = 4(e - 1).$$

EXERCISE 47

1. Differentiate:

(1) $\log_e 3x$.   (2) $\log (5 - x)$.   (3) $\log \left(\dfrac{x + 2}{x + 5} \right)$.

(4) $\log (4 - 3x)$.   (5) $\log \dfrac{x^2 + 3x}{x + 1}$.   (6) $\log \dfrac{5 - 4x^2}{3 + 5x^2}$.

2. Differentiate:

(1) $x^2 \log x$.   (2) $3x^{-2} \log (x + 1)$.

(3) $\sin x \log x$.   (4) $\dfrac{3 \log x}{x + 1}$.

(5) $e^{3x} \log x$.

(6) $3e^{-3x} \log (1 + x)$.

(7) $\sin 3x \log (x^2 + x + 1)$.

(8) $\tan x \log x$.

(9) $\log_{10} x$.

(10) $\log_{10} (3x^2 + x + 1)$.

(11) $\log \sqrt[5]{x^2 + 1}$.

(12) $\log \dfrac{\sin x}{1 + \cos x}$.

(13) $\log \sqrt{\dfrac{1 + x}{1 - x}}$.

3. Integrate:

(1) $\dfrac{1}{x + 2}$.

(2) $\dfrac{3}{2 - x}$.

(3) $\dfrac{x}{x^2 + 1}$.

(4) $\dfrac{\cos x}{1 + \sin x}$.

(5) $\dfrac{\sin x}{1 + \cos x}$.

(6) $\dfrac{e^x}{3 + e^x}$.

(7) $\dfrac{1}{3x + 2}$.

(8) $\dfrac{5}{4 - 3x}$.

(9) $\dfrac{ax}{b + cx^2}$.

(10) $\dfrac{x + 3}{x^2 + 6x + 4}$.

(11) $\dfrac{x - 1}{x^2 - 2x + 4}$.

4. Explain what you understand by " a definite integral."
If $y = \dfrac{3}{x} + 7x^{\frac{1}{2}}$, find the value of $\displaystyle\int_a^b y\,dx$.   (U.L.C.I.)

5. Evaluate:

(1) $\displaystyle\int_0^1 \dfrac{dx}{x + 3}$.

(2) $\displaystyle\int_0^2 \dfrac{3\,dx}{5 - 2x}$.

(3) $\displaystyle\int_{-1}^2 \dfrac{dx}{4 + x}$.

(4) $\displaystyle\int_0^{\pi/2} \dfrac{\cos x\,dx}{1 + \sin x}$.

(5) $\displaystyle\int_0^1 \dfrac{(x + 3)\,dx}{x^2 + 6x + 4}$.

CHAPTER 15

SOME STANDARD METHODS OF INTEGRATION

1. If in taking a cross-country walk we find a brook, and follow it downstream, we are certain to reach in the end the main river and the sea. But if, instead, we follow the river **up**-stream, seeking its source, every confluence faces us with a decision to be made. As compared with differentiation, integration is such a reverse process, and it is this which constitutes its central difficulty. Success in evaluating a given integral depends largely on the student's knowledge of the standard integrals, and any unfamiliar integral must be reduced to one of the standard forms.

In this chapter we describe some of the methods used to reduce the unfamiliar integrals to those of a more familiar form. The practical engineer who may lack this ability to proceed by looking back may take comfort in the fact that outside the examination room he may never need do more than follow the steps of integrations which others have achieved.

2. Integration by Substitution

In using this method we introduce a new variable, and the procedure adopted will be clear from the examples which follow:

Example 1

Evaluate,
$$I = \int \frac{x\,dx}{\sqrt{x+5}}.$$

Put
$$\sqrt{x+5} = y$$

i.e.,
$$x + 5 = y^2$$
$$\therefore \quad x = y^2 - 5$$

and
$$dx = 2y\,dy.$$

Hence
$$I = \int \frac{(y^2 - 5)2ydy}{y}$$
$$= \int (y^2 - 5)2dy$$
$$= \frac{2y^3}{3} - 10y + C$$
$$= \tfrac{2}{3}(x + 5)^{\frac{3}{2}} - 10(x + 5)^{\frac{1}{2}} + C.$$

Example 2

$$I = \int \frac{x^2dx}{6 + x^3}.$$

Notice that the numerator is $\frac{1}{3}d(6 + x^3)$, or formally put,

$$6 + x^3 = z$$
$$\therefore \quad 3x^2dx = dz$$
$$x^2dx = \tfrac{1}{3}dz$$
$$\therefore \quad I = \frac{1}{3}\int \frac{dz}{z} = \frac{1}{3} \log z = \frac{1}{3} \log (6 + x^3) + C.$$

Example 3

$$I = \int \sin^3 \theta \cos \theta d\theta.$$

Notice that $\cos \theta d\theta = d(\sin \theta)$

If $\sin \theta = x$
$$\cos \theta d\theta = dx$$
$$\therefore \quad I = \int x^3dx = \frac{x^4}{4} + C$$
$$= \frac{\sin^4 \theta}{4} + C.$$

Example 4

$$I = \int \frac{dx}{\sqrt{a^2 - x^2}}.$$

Put $\quad x = a \sin \theta$

$\qquad dx = a \cos \theta d\theta$

$$I = \int \frac{a \cos \theta d\theta}{\sqrt{a^2 - a^2 \sin^2 \theta}}$$

$$= \int \frac{a \cos \theta d\theta}{a \cos \theta} = \int d\theta = \theta + C.$$

$$\therefore \quad I = \sin^{-1} \frac{x}{a} + C$$

i.e., $\qquad \int \frac{dx}{\sqrt{a^2 - x^2}} = \sin^{-1} \frac{x}{a} + C.$

This result should be memorised as it is standard. It should be observed that in order to obtain it, we made use of a substitution which rationalised the denominator of the integrand.

Many integrals can be reduced to the above form.

Example 5

$$I = \int \frac{dx}{\sqrt{3 - 2x - x^2}}.$$

" Completing the square," we get:

$$I = \int \frac{d(x + 1)}{\sqrt{4 - (x + 1)^2}}$$

$$= \sin^{-1} \frac{x + 1}{2} + C.$$

Example 6

$$I = \int \frac{dx}{a^2 + x^2}$$

Let $\qquad\qquad x = a \tan \theta \quad . \quad . \quad . \quad . \quad . \quad (1)$

$\qquad \therefore \quad dx = a \sec^2 \theta d\theta.$

Denominator $= a^2(1 + \tan^2 \theta) = a^2 \sec^2 \theta.$

$$\therefore \quad I = \int \frac{a \sec^2 \theta \, d\theta}{a^2 \sec^2 \theta} = \int \frac{d\theta}{a}$$

$$= \frac{\theta}{a} + C.$$

But from (1) $\qquad \theta = \tan^{-1} \frac{x}{a}$

$$\therefore \quad \int \frac{dx}{a^2 + x^2} = \frac{1}{a} \tan^{-1} \frac{x}{a} + C.$$

This is another standard form to which many integrals can be reduced.

Example 7

$$I = \int \frac{dx}{2 + 2x + x^2}$$

$$= \int \frac{dx}{1 + (x + 1)^2}$$

$$= \tan^{-1} (x + 1) + C.$$

Example 8

$$I = \int \frac{dx}{2x^2 + 4x + \frac{9}{2}}$$

$$= \frac{1}{2} \int \frac{dx}{x^2 + 2x + \frac{9}{4}}$$

$$= \frac{1}{2} \int \frac{dx}{(x + 1)^2 + \frac{5}{4}}$$

$$\left(\text{Here,} \qquad a = \frac{\sqrt{5}}{2} \right)$$

$$\therefore \quad I = \frac{1}{\sqrt{5}} \tan^{-1} \frac{2(x + 1)}{\sqrt{5}} + C.$$

3. The Integration of Products Involving Multiples of θ

Products such as $\sin 2\theta \cos 3\theta$, $\sin 3\theta \sin 4\theta$, or $\cos 5\theta \cos \theta$ are simply integrated by employing the trigonometrical transformations proved on p. 211 *et seq.*

Example 1

Thus $\qquad 2 \cos 3\theta \sin 2\theta = \sin 5\theta - \sin \theta.$

Hence $\qquad \int \cos 3\theta \sin 2\theta d\theta = \tfrac{1}{2} \int (\sin 5\theta - \sin \theta) d\theta$

$$= -\frac{1}{2}\left[\frac{\cos 5\theta}{5} - \cos \theta\right] + C.$$

Example 2

Evaluate $\qquad \int \sin 4\theta \sin 3\theta d\theta.$

We have

$$2 \sin 4\theta \sin 3\theta = \cos \theta - \cos 7\theta$$

$$\therefore \int \sin 4\theta \sin 3\theta d\theta = \frac{1}{2}\int (\cos \theta - \cos 7\theta) d\theta$$

$$= \frac{1}{2}\left(\sin \theta - \frac{\sin 7\theta}{7}\right) + C.$$

EXERCISE 48

1. Integrate the following:

(1) $\dfrac{1}{\sqrt{x+3}}.$ (2) $\dfrac{1}{\sqrt{5-x}}.$ (3) $\dfrac{a}{\sqrt{b+cx}}.$

2. First reduce the following expressions by division and then integrate each:

(1) $\dfrac{x}{x+4}.$ (2) $\dfrac{x^2}{x-4}.$ (3) $\dfrac{2x}{x+3}.$ (4) $\dfrac{x}{2x+3}.$

3. Integrate:

(1) $\dfrac{1}{\sqrt{4-x^2}}.$ (2) $\dfrac{1}{\sqrt{2-x^2}}.$ (3) $\dfrac{1}{\sqrt{8-2x^2}}.$

(4) $\dfrac{1}{\sqrt{8-2x=x^2}}.$ (5) $\dfrac{1}{\sqrt{12-4x-x^2}}.$ (6) $\dfrac{1}{\sqrt{8-4x-2x^2}}.$

4. Integrate:

(1) $\dfrac{1}{1 + x^2}$.   (2) $\dfrac{3}{4 + x^2}$.   (3) $\dfrac{1}{8 + 2x^2}$.

(4) $\dfrac{1}{x^2 + 2x + 5}$.   (5) $\dfrac{1}{x^2 - 4x + 8}$.

(6) $\dfrac{1}{2x^2 + 6x + 20}$.   (7) $\dfrac{1}{3x^2 + 9x + 9}$.

5. Integrate:

(1) $\sin 2\theta \cos 4\theta$.   (2) $\cos 5x \sin 3x$.   (3) $2 \sin 4t \cos 2t$.

(4) $2 \sin 5t \sin 3t$.   (5) $\cos 6x \cos 2x$.   (6) $2 \sin \tfrac{1}{2}t \cos t$.

6. Integrate:

(1) $\sin^3 \theta \cos \theta$.   (2) $\dfrac{\sin \theta}{\cos^3 \theta}$.   (3) $\cos^4 x \sin x$.

(4) $\tan^3 \theta \sec^2 \theta$.   (5) $\sin \theta (\cos^3 \theta + 1)$.

4. The Use of Partial Fractions in Integration

The addition of a given number of fractions can be readily performed. Thus:

$$\frac{2}{x} + \frac{3}{x + 5} = \frac{5x + 10}{x(x + 5)}.$$

The problem of partial fractions is to start with an expression like $\dfrac{5x + 10}{x(x + 5)}$ and to find its constituent fractions. These are called partial fractions.

Thus $\dfrac{2}{x}$ and $\dfrac{3}{x + 5}$ are the partial fractions of $\dfrac{5x + 10}{x(x + 5)}$. We deal below with one case which is useful to the student at this stage of his work.

Case I. When the denominator of the given fraction contains factors of the first degree only.

Example 1

Put $\dfrac{3x + 1}{(x + 4)(x + 5)}$ *into partial fractions.*

Observe that the numerator of the given fraction is of lower degree than the denominator.

Let
$$\frac{3x + 1}{(x + 4)(x + 5)} \equiv \frac{A}{x + 4} + \frac{B}{x + 5}$$
$$\equiv \frac{A(x + 5) + B(x + 4)}{(x + 4)(x + 5)}.$$

The numerators on both sides must be identical, since the denominators are the same

$$\therefore \quad 3x + 1 \equiv A(x + 5) + B(x + 4) \quad . \quad . \quad (1)$$

There are two ways of finding A and B from (1).

First Method.

Since (1) is an identity, it is true for all values of x.

Put $\qquad\qquad x = -4.$

Then $\qquad -12 + 1 = A(-4 + 5) + 0.$

giving $\qquad\qquad A = -11.$

Then put $\qquad\qquad x = -5.$

Then $\qquad\qquad -14 = -B.$

$$\therefore \quad B = 14.$$

Second Method.

(1) may be written

$$3x + 1 \equiv x(A + B) + 5A + 4B$$
$$\left.\begin{array}{l} \therefore \quad A + B = 3 \\ \quad 5A + 4B = 1 \end{array}\right\}$$

Solving these we get $A = -11$, $B = 14$ as before.

Example 2

Put $\dfrac{1}{x(x - 2)}$ *into partial fractions.*

$$\frac{1}{x(x - 2)} = \frac{A}{x} + \frac{B}{x - 2}.$$

Equating numerators we get:

$$1 \equiv A(x - 2) + Bx$$

Put $x = 0$, and get $A = -\frac{1}{2}$.

Put $x = 2$, and get $B = \frac{1}{2}$.

Hence $\qquad \dfrac{1}{x(x - 2)} = -\dfrac{1}{2} \cdot \dfrac{1}{x} + \dfrac{1}{2} \cdot \dfrac{1}{x - 2}.$

Example 3

Evaluate $\qquad I = \displaystyle\int \dfrac{(3x + 1)dx}{(x + 4)(x + 5)}.$

Put $\dfrac{3x + 1}{(x + 4)(x + 5)}$ into partial fractions; this has been done in Example 1.

$$\frac{3x + 1}{(x + 4)(x + 5)} = \frac{-11}{x + 4} + \frac{14}{x + 5}$$

$$\therefore \quad I = -11\int \frac{dx}{x + 4} + 14\int \frac{dx}{x + 5}$$

$$= -11 \log (x + 4) + 14 \log (x + 5) + C.$$

Example 4

Find $\qquad I = \displaystyle\int \dfrac{dx}{x(x - 2)}.$

Using the result of Example 2 above,

$$I = -\frac{1}{2}\int \frac{dx}{x} + \frac{1}{2}\int \frac{dx}{x - 2}$$

$$= -\tfrac{1}{2} \log x + \tfrac{1}{2} \log (x - 2) + C.$$

$$= \log \sqrt{\frac{x - 2}{x}} + C.$$

Example 5

Find $\qquad \displaystyle\int \dfrac{dx}{x^2 - a^2}.$

We have

$$\frac{1}{x^2 - a^2} = \frac{1}{2a}\left[\frac{1}{x-a} - \frac{1}{x+a}\right]$$

$$\therefore \int \frac{dx}{x^2 - a^2} = \frac{1}{2a}\int\left(\frac{1}{x-a} - \frac{1}{x+a}\right)dx$$

$$= \frac{1}{2a}\log\frac{x-a}{x+a} + \text{C.}$$

This is a standard form, and should be remembered. Many examples can be reduced to the above form, *e.g.*,

Example 6

Find
$$\int \frac{dx}{x^2 + 2x - 3}$$

$$\text{I} = \int \frac{dx}{(x+1)^2 - 4} = \frac{1}{4}\log\frac{x-1}{x+3} + \text{C.}$$

Example 7

$$\text{I} = \int \frac{dx}{x^2 + x - 4}$$

$$= \int \frac{dx}{(x+\frac{1}{2})^2 - \frac{17}{4}}$$

$$= \frac{1}{\sqrt{17}}\log\frac{x+\frac{1}{2} - \frac{\sqrt{17}}{2}}{x+\frac{1}{2} + \frac{\sqrt{17}}{2}} + \text{C.}$$

The logs in these examples are to base *e*.

EXERCISE 49

1. Put the following into partial fractions, and then find the integrals:

(1) $\dfrac{2x}{x^2 - 1}$.

(2) $\dfrac{2x - 3}{x^2 - 5x + 6}$.

(3) $\dfrac{2x + 3}{x^2 + x - 30}$.

(4) $\dfrac{x}{x^2 - 9}$.

(5) $\dfrac{x + 1}{3x^2 - x - 2}$.

(6) $\dfrac{2x + 1}{x^2 - 5x + 4}$.

(7) $\dfrac{4}{x(x+2)}$. (8) $\dfrac{1}{3x(x+2)}$. (9) $\dfrac{3x+1}{(x+6)(x+1)}$.

2. Find the integrals of the following functions:

(1) $\dfrac{1}{x^2 + x - \frac{1}{2}}$. (2) $\dfrac{1}{x^2 + 2x - 8}$. (3) $\dfrac{1}{x^2 + 3x + 1}$.

(4) $\dfrac{1}{x^2 + 4x + 1}$. (5) $\dfrac{1}{2t^2 + 4t + 1}$.

5. Integration by Parts

This is a method of integration which readily evaluates certain types of integrals.

Suppose u and v are two functions of x.

Then $$\frac{d}{dx}(uv) = u\frac{dv}{dx} + v\frac{du}{dx}$$

or using differentials

$$d(uv) = udv + vdu$$
$$\therefore \quad udv = d(uv) - vdu \quad \cdots \quad (1)$$

Integrating (1), we have:

$$\int udv = uv - \int vdu \quad \cdots \quad (2)$$

The form (2) should be remembered in words, after first noting that the left-hand side $\int udv$ is the integral of the product of two functions of x;

For $\int udv = \int u \cdot \dfrac{dv}{dx} \cdot dx$; both u and $\dfrac{dv}{dx}$ are functions of x.

Hence, in words (2) becomes:

"The integral of a product = first function × the integral of the second — the integral of (D.C. first × integral of second)."

It might appear from formula (2) that the integral on the

right-hand side is just as difficult to evaluate as the one on the left. In many cases, by a careful choice of our first function, this is found not to be the case.

Example 1

Evaluate $\int xe^x dx.$

Take x as the " first " function, and e^x as second

$$\int xe^x dx = xe^x - \int e^x dx$$
$$= xe^x - e^x + C$$
$$= e^x(x - 1) + C.$$

Example 2

Find $\int x^2 e^{2x} dx$

$$\int x^2 e^{2x} dx = x^2 \cdot \frac{e^{2x}}{2} - \int 2x \cdot \frac{e^{2x}}{2} dx$$
$$= x^2 \frac{e^{2x}}{2} - \int xe^{2x} dx$$
$$= x^2 \frac{e^{2x}}{2} - \left[x \cdot \frac{e^{2x}}{2} - \int \frac{e^{2x}}{2} dx \right]$$

(Notice a second application of the formula.)

$$= x^2 \frac{e^{2x}}{2} - x\frac{e^{2x}}{2} + \frac{e^{2x}}{4} + C$$
$$= \frac{e^{2x}}{4}(2x^2 - 2x + 1) + C.$$

Example 3

Find $\int x^3 \log_e x dx.$

Take $\log_e x$ as the " first " function

$$\int \log_e x \cdot x^3 \, dx = \log_e x \cdot \frac{x^4}{4} - \int \frac{1}{x} \cdot \frac{x^4}{4} dx$$

$$= \log_e x \cdot \frac{x^4}{4} - \frac{1}{4} \int x^3 dx$$

$$= \log_e x \cdot \frac{x^4}{4} - \frac{x^4}{16} + C$$

$$= \frac{x^4}{16} (4 \log_e x - 1) + C.$$

Example 4

Evaluate $\qquad \int x^2 \sin 2x dx.$

Take x^2 as the " first " function and apply the formula twice.

$$\int x^2 \sin 2x dx = x^2 \frac{(- \cos 2x)}{2} - \int \frac{2x \cdot (- \cos 2x)}{2} dx$$

$$= - \frac{x^2}{2} \cos 2x + \int x \cos 2x dx$$

$$= - \frac{x^2}{2} \cos 2x + \left[x \frac{\sin 2x}{2} - \int \frac{\sin 2x}{2} dx \right]$$

$$= - \frac{x^2}{2} \cos 2x + x \frac{\sin 2x}{2} + \frac{\cos 2x}{4} + C.$$

Example 5

Find $\qquad \int e^x \cos x dx.$

In this type of example neither function can be simplified either by differentiation or integration. The formula must be applied twice, and either function may be taken as the " first "; but, when the choice has been made, it must be retained in both applications of the formula. Notice that we return to the original integral.

Put $$I = \int e^x \cos x\, dx.$$

Then, taking e^x as " first " function

$$I = e^x \sin x - \int e^x \sin x\, dx$$

$$= e^x \sin x - \left[e^x(-\cos x) - \int e^x(-\cos x)\, dx \right]$$

$$= e^x \sin x + [e^x \cos x - I]$$

$$= e^x \sin x + e^x \cos x - I.$$

Now bringing I over to the left-hand side, we get:

$$2I = e^x \sin x + e^x \cos x$$

$$\therefore \quad I = \frac{e^x}{2}(\sin x + \cos x) + C.$$

Example 6

$$I = \int e^{-2x} \sin 3x\, dx.$$

Take e^{-2x} as the " first " function.

$$I = e^{-2x} \cdot \frac{(-\cos 3x)}{3} - \int (-2e^{-2x}) \frac{(-\cos 3x)}{3}\, dx$$

$$= -\frac{e^{-2x}}{3} \cos 3x - \frac{2}{3} \int e^{-2x} \cos 3x\, dx$$

$$= -\frac{e^{-2x}}{3} \cos 3x - \frac{2}{3} \left[e^{-2x} \frac{\sin 3x}{3} - \int -2e^{-2x} \frac{\sin 3x}{3}\, dx \right]$$

$$= -\frac{e^{-2x} \cos 3x}{3} - \frac{2}{9} e^{-2x} \sin 3x - \frac{4}{9}I.$$

Hence $\quad \dfrac{13}{9}I = -\dfrac{e^{-2x}}{9}[3\cos 3x + 2\sin 3x]$

$$\therefore \quad I = -\frac{e^{-2x}}{13}(3\cos 3x + 2\sin 3x) + C.$$

EXERCISE 50

1. Integrate the following by " parts ":

(1) xe^x.   (2) x^2e^x.   (3) x^2e^{2x}.

(4) xe^{-2x}.   (5) x^2e^{-3x}.

2. Integrate:

(1) $x \sin x$.   (2) $x \cos x$.   (3) $x^2 \sin x$.

(4) $x^2 \sin 2x$.   (5) $x \cos \tfrac{1}{2}x$.   (6) $x^2 \cos x$.

3. Integrate the following (take $\log x$ as " first "):

(1) $x^2 \log x$.   (2) $x^{-3} \log x$.   (3) $\dfrac{\log x}{x}$.

4. Integrate:

(1) $e^x \sin x$.   (2) $e^x \cos x$.   (3) $e^{2x} \sin x$.

(4) $e^{-2x} \sin x$.   (5) $e^{3x} \sin 2x$.   (6) $e^{4x} \cos 2x$.

(7) $e^{-x} \cos 3x$.   (8) $e^{-2x} \sin 3x$.

5. Integrate:

(1) $e^{ax} \cos bx$.   (2) $e^{ax} \sin bx$.

Observe that all the examples in 4 above are included in these two types.

CHAPTER 16

GRAPHS OF TRIGONOMETRICAL FUNCTIONS, AND THE GRAPHIC SOLUTION OF TRIGONOMETRICAL EQUATIONS

1. The Graphical Solution of Equations Involving Trigonometrical Functions

Example 1

Solve $\qquad \cos(x + 30) = \frac{1}{2}\sin x.$

where angles are measured in degrees.

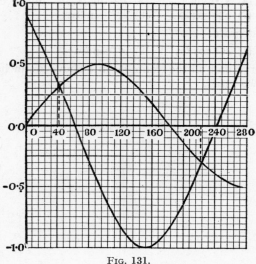

FIG. 131.

$x = 41°$ and $221°$ (nearly).

Construct the table below. Angles are measured in degrees.

x . . .	0	20	40	60	80	100	120	140	160	180
cos $(x + 30)$.	0·87	0·64	0·34	0	−0·34	−0·64	−0·87	−0·98	−0·98	−0·87
$\frac{1}{2}$ sin x . .	0	0·17	0·32	0·43	0·49	0·49	0·43	0·32	0·17	0

In making the table, observe that the values of cos $(x + 30)$ repeat themselves in reverse in order starting from $x = 160°$ to $x = 360°$.

Similarly, when we have found $\frac{1}{2}$ sin x from $x = 0°$ to $x = 80°$, the values are reversed to $x = 180°$. From 180° to 360°, the values of $\frac{1}{2}$ sin x are negative, but the same numerically as from 0° to 180°.

Take 5 squares along OX to represent 40°.
    10 „   „   OY „   „   0·5.

Now plot $y = \cos (x + 30)$⎫ Fig. 131.
and $y = \frac{1}{2} \sin x.$ ⎭

The abscissæ of the intersections give the roots.

Example 2

Tabulate values of $2 \cos x° + 3 \sin x°$ *at intervals of* 10°; *then solve graphically* $2 \cos x° + 3 \sin x° = 3·5.$

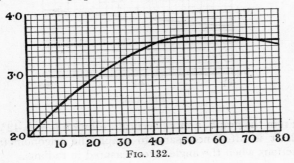

Fig. 132.

x	0°	10°	20°	30°	40°	50°	60°	70°	80°
$2 \cos x$ . . .	2	1·969	1·879	1·732	1·532	1·286	1·0	0·684	0·347
$3 \sin x$ . . .	0	0·521	1·026	1·5	1·928	2·298	2·598	2·819	2·954
$2 \cos x + 3 \sin x$.	2	2·490	2·905	3·232	3·460	3·584	3·598	3·503	3·301

To solve the equation plot

$$y = 2 \cos x + 3 \sin x \qquad . \quad . \quad . \quad (1)$$
and
$$y = 3·5 \qquad . \quad . \quad . \quad . \quad . \quad . \quad (2)$$

It will be seen that (1) cuts (2) very close to the values $x = 42°$ and $x = 70°$. To get a more accurate value for the root near 42°, make the following table:

x	41°	43°
$2 \cos x$ . . .	1·5094	1·4628
$3 \sin x$ . . .	1·9683	2·0460
$2 \cos x + 3 \sin x$.	3·4777	3·5088

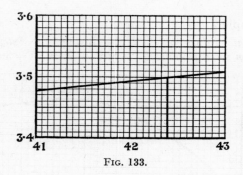

Fig. 133.

From the graph, a more accurate solution is $x = 42° 24'$.

2. It is often necessary to graph the trigonometrical functions when the angles are measured in radians.

It is, of course, always possible to change from degrees to radians or from radians to degrees.

Example 1

Plot $y = \sin \theta$ (θ in radians).

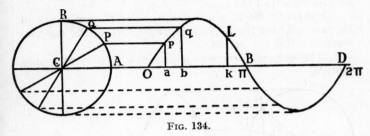

FIG. 134.

Draw a circle, any size, and call its radius one unit of length. C is its centre. Divide the four right angles round C into any number of equal parts—12 in the figure. Each angle is thus $\dfrac{\pi}{6}$.

Produce the diameter CA indefinitely. Take any point O as origin, and take any convenient length, OB to represent π radians (*i.e.*, two right angles).

Notice, that we may be using different horizontal and vertical scales.

Divide OB into six equal parts. One of these Oa is shown, and Oa represents $\dfrac{\pi}{6}$. Erect the perpendicular ap, where Pp has been drawn parallel to the diameter CA.

It is clear that $pa = \text{CP} \sin \text{ACP}$

$$= \sin \frac{\pi}{6}, \text{ since CP = unity.}$$

Similarly, $\qquad qb = \sin 2\dfrac{\pi}{6}$,

where $\qquad\quad Ob = \tfrac{1}{3}OB.$

Proceeding in this way all round the circle we get the curve in Fig. 134.

The part from B to D repeats that from O to B on the other side of the axis OBD.

The wave form clearly repeats itself to the right of D, and to the left of O.

The greatest height above OB is called the amplitude of the wave, whilst the horizontal length OD, of the *complete* wave is called the period.

3. The general form $y = a \sin (n\theta + \alpha)$ is now readily plotted.

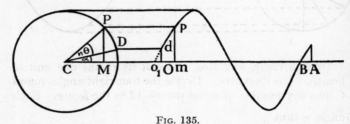

FIG. 135.

The amplitude $= a =$ radius of the circle.

The period $= \dfrac{2\pi}{n} = $ OA, measured on any convenient scale, using O as origin.

Corresponding to any angle DCP $= n\theta$ measure O$m = \theta$ (to scale).

Then PM $= pm = a \sin (n\theta + \alpha)$.

The whole curve may now be plotted by taking any number of convenient points round the circle.

Since $a \sin (n\theta + \alpha) = a \sin n\left(\theta + \dfrac{\alpha}{n} \right) = a \sin nx$

where $\qquad\qquad x = \theta + \dfrac{\alpha}{n},$

if O_1 be taken to the left of O so that $OO_1 = \dfrac{\alpha}{n}$ (to scale), we get the same curve by plotting $y = a \sin nx$, using O_1 as origin; or what is the same thing, plot $y = a \sin z$, where abscissæ are measured from O_1, and corresponding to $z = \widehat{MCP}$, take $O_1 m = \dfrac{z}{n}$ to scale. The plotting is thus reduced to that of the preceding paragraph.

4. Since $\qquad \cos \theta = \sin\left(\theta + \dfrac{\pi}{2}\right)$

then, $\qquad a \cos (n\theta + \alpha) = a \sin\left(n\theta + \dfrac{\pi}{2} + \alpha\right).$

We thus take an origin O_1, $\dfrac{1}{n}\left(\alpha + \dfrac{\pi}{2}\right)$ units to the left of O and plot $y = \sin z$, where the abscissa corresponding to any angle z is $\dfrac{z}{n}$.

Example 1

Plot $\qquad y = 3\cdot5 \cos\left(\dfrac{5\pi}{6} - 4\theta\right)$

$\qquad\qquad = 3\cdot5 \sin\left(4\theta - \dfrac{\pi}{3}\right)$

using the complement of $\dfrac{5\pi}{6} - 4\theta.$

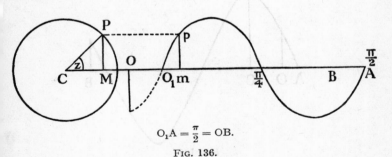

$$O_1 A = \frac{\pi}{2} = OB.$$

Fig. 136.

We plot $y = 3 \cdot 5 \sin z$, using O_1 as origin where $OO_1 = \dfrac{\pi}{12}$, measured to the *right*.

The period $= \dfrac{\pi}{2}$. Radius of circle is $3 \cdot 5$ units.

Corresponding to the angle z, measure $O_1 m = \dfrac{z}{4}$, and proceed similarly for all angles round the circle.

Example 2

Put $4 \sin \theta + 3 \cos \theta$ *in the form* $R \sin (\theta + \alpha)$ *where* R *and* α *are known. Then plot the function.*

Put $\qquad\qquad$ R cos $\alpha = 4$

and $\qquad\qquad$ R sin $\alpha = 3$

So that $\qquad\qquad$ $R = \sqrt{4^2 + 3^2} = 5$

and $\qquad\qquad$ tan $\alpha = 0 \cdot 75$.

$\qquad\qquad\qquad$ $\alpha = 36° 52'$

$\qquad\qquad\qquad\quad$ $= 0 \cdot 64$ radians (nearly).

Now plot

$$y = 5 \sin (\theta + 0 \cdot 64).$$

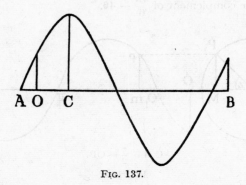

Fig. 137.

If OA $= 0.64$, we could get the curve by plotting
$$y = 5 \sin x,$$
using A as origin.   The amplitude is 5, and AC $= \dfrac{\pi}{2}$.

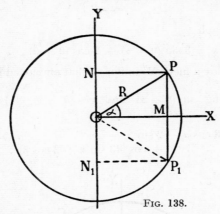

Fig. 138.

5. The method of graphing used in the preceding paragraphs is sometimes called the " crank " method, the radius of the circle becoming the " representative crank."

For such functions as $4 \sin \theta + 3 \cos \theta$ (see Example 2, par. 4) we could construct the representative crank.

On OX make OM $= 4$ units.

On OY make ON $= 3$ unit, and complete the rectangle MONP.

If
$$\widehat{\text{MOP}} = \alpha$$
$$\text{R} \cos \alpha = 4$$
$$\text{R} \sin \alpha = 3$$

$\therefore$ R$^2 = 25$, and $\tan \alpha = \frac{3}{4}$, and $\alpha = 0.64$ radians.
Hence $4 \sin \theta + 3 \cos \theta$
$$= \text{R} \cos \alpha \sin \theta + \text{R} \sin \alpha \cos \theta$$
$$= \text{R} \sin (\theta + \alpha)$$
$$= 5 \sin (\theta + 0.64).$$

This is simply 5 sin x with the origin A, Fig. 137, taken 0·64 unit to the left of O.

To plot 4 sin θ — 3 cos θ, measure $ON_1 = ON$ along the negative sense of OY. Then OP_1 is the initial position of the crank.

6. To graph

$$y = 3 \sin (\theta + \alpha) + 2 \cos (\theta + \beta) \quad . \quad . \quad (1)$$

We employ a method similar to that employed in the last paragraph.

Expanding sin $(\theta + \alpha)$ and cos $(\theta + \beta)$, (1) may be written:

$$y = \sin \theta \, (3 \cos \alpha - 2 \sin \beta)$$
$$+ \cos \theta (3 \sin \alpha + 2 \cos \beta) \, . \quad . \quad (2)$$

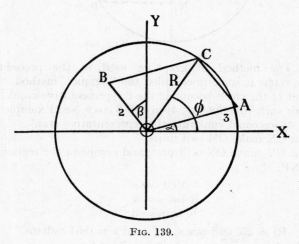

FIG. 139.

Take OA = 3 units, making α with OX, and OB = 2 units making β with OY. Complete the parallelogram AOBC.

If OC = R, and XOC = ϕ,

R cos ϕ = sum of projections of OA and AC on the y-axis.

$\quad\quad$ = $\quad$,, $\quad\quad$,, $\quad\quad$,, $\quad$ OA ,, OB ,, $\quad$,,

$\quad\quad$ = 3 cos α − 2 sin β.

Similarly, projecting OC on the y-axis

$$\text{R sin } \phi = 3 \sin \alpha + 2 \cos \beta.$$

Hence (2) becomes

$$y = \text{R} \cos \phi \sin \theta + \text{R} \sin \phi \cos \theta$$
$$= \text{R} \sin (\theta + \phi) \quad . \quad . \quad . \quad . \quad . \quad (3)$$

Read R and ϕ from the diagram, and plot, using the circle shown.

If we had to plot

$$y = 3 \sin (\theta + \alpha) - 2 \cos (\theta - \beta)$$

measure OA and α, as before; then measure OB 2 units down and rotate OB clockwise through an angle β. Complete the parallelogram OACB as before and OC is the initial position of the crank. Fig. 140.

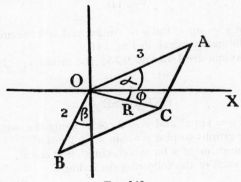

Fig. 140.

Now plot $y = \text{R} \sin (\theta + \phi)$, where R = OC, and XÔC = ϕ.

7. The method of plotting used in the following example is sometimes useful.

Example

Find, by plotting, the maximum and minimum values of $\sin x + \sin 2x$.

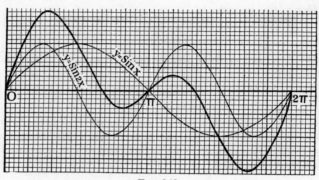

FIG. 141.

We plot $y = \sin x$, and $y = \sin 2x$, and add the ordinates, getting the heavy curve in Fig. 141.

The maxima are $1\cdot73$ and $0\cdot35$; the minima $-1\cdot73$ and $-0\cdot35$.

EXERCISE 51

1. Plot $y = \sin x°$ and $y = 2 \cos x°$ using the same axes.
Use the graphs to plot $y = \sin x° \pm 2 \cos x°$.
Find one value of x for which $\sin x° = 2 \cos x°$.

2. Plot each of the following (in radians).

(1) $3 \sin \theta$.   (2) $3 \sin 2\theta$.   (3) $3 \sin \left(\theta + \dfrac{\pi}{4} \right)$.

(4) $3 \sin \left(\theta - \dfrac{\pi}{4} \right)$.   (5) $2 \cos \left(\theta - \dfrac{\pi}{3} \right)$.   (6) $3 \cos \left(\theta + \dfrac{\pi}{5} \right)$.

3. Plot the following where the angles are given in radians

(1) $4 \sin \left(3\theta + \dfrac{\pi}{4} \right).$ (2) $4 \sin \left(3\theta - \dfrac{\pi}{4} \right).$

(3) $3 \cos \left(4\theta - \dfrac{\pi}{6} \right).$ (4) $2 \cos \left(3\theta + \dfrac{\pi}{2} \right).$

4. Express the following functions in the form

$$R \sin (\theta \pm \alpha);$$

state the values of R and α.

(1) $2 \sin \theta + 4 \cos \theta.$ (2) $3 \sin \theta - 2 \cos \theta.$
(3) $1 \cdot 5 \sin \theta + \cos \theta.$

5. On the usual axes, show the initial position of the representative crank for the functions:

(1) $y = 3 \sin \left(\theta + \dfrac{\pi}{6} \right) + 2 \cos \left(\theta + \dfrac{\pi}{3} \right).$

(2) $y = 3 \sin \left(\theta - \dfrac{\pi}{6} \right) + 2 \cos \left(\theta - \dfrac{\pi}{3} \right).$

(3) $y = 3 \sin \left(\theta + \dfrac{\pi}{6} \right) - 2 \cos \left(\theta - \dfrac{\pi}{3} \right).$

6. Find correct to three decimal places a value of x in radians satisfying $4 \sin x = 2 + 0 \cdot 82x$.

7. Solve, for one value of θ correct to three decimal places,

$$5 \cos \theta = 4 + 0 \cdot 92\theta \quad (\theta \text{ is in radians}).$$

8. The end P of a crank OP, 6 in. long, describes a circle centre O, with an angular velocity 0·5 radians per sec. If p is the projection of P at any time, t, on a vertical diameter, plot a curve showing the motion of p during one revolution of the crank.

9. A crank OP 6 in. long makes 20 revs/min. It starts from rest when OP makes 60° with the horizontal and moves counter clockwise. p is the projection of P on a vertical diameter.

Write down the equation of the curve giving the motion of p.

10. Find, by calculation, the maxima and minima of $2 \sin x + \sin 3x$ between 0 and π. Then plot

$$y = 2 \sin x + \sin 3x$$

by adding the ordinates of $y = 2 \sin x$ and $y = \sin 3x$.

11. Plot $y = \sin x \cdot \sin 2x$ (1) by plotting each sine separately and then multiplying ordinates (2) by expressing $\sin x \cdot \sin 2x$ in the form $\frac{1}{2}(\cos x - \cos 3x)$ and adding ordinates.

as an operator, which, when operating on a length such as $\overline{OP}$, rotates that length through 90° in a counter-clockwise sense.

Thus, for radii $\overline{OP} = \overline{OC}$, $\ldots$

Then $\overline{OP} = \overline{OC}$, and $\overline{OC}$, acting a second time, $\ldots$

$$j(j \cdot \overline{OP}) = \ldots$$

and

Further if $+ 3$ would be shown by the point E, $j(+ 3)$, or $j(+ 3)$ would be represented by the point C, where $\overline{OC} = \overline{OE}$, the length $\overline{OE}$ has been turned through 90° in the positive sense $\ldots \overline{OC}, \ldots$

Also the figure $(+ 3, + 3)$ and $(+ 3, \ldots)$ may represent the point whose coordinates are given as $x = + 3$, $y = + 3 \ldots$ by the points $(3, 3) \ldots$

Similarly, $- 4$ could be the point D, $(+ 4, - 4)$, the lines infer that $\ldots$ y can represent $\ldots$ the point whose $\ldots$

The number which is called a complex number. In purely mathematical, the familiar real number when $\ldots$ j is represented by $\ldots$ so that $j \times j = j^2 = j \cdot j$, $\ldots$ $\ldots = -1$, $\ldots$ these all imaginary and the $\ldots$ complex $\ldots$ counter, and $\ldots$

The student $\ldots$ and $\ldots$ in his previous work, have solved the quadratic equation $x = \frac{b}{2a} \ldots 13 \times \ldots$

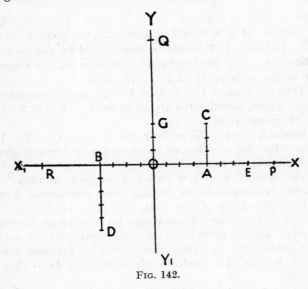

FIG. 142.

Thus he would indicate $+ 4$ either by the point A (Fig. 142), or by the length $\overline{OA}$. Similarly, -4 would be shown by the point B, or by the length $\overline{OB}$. The unit of length chosen is arbitrary.

Now (Fig. 142) let $\overline{OP} = + x$; and let "j" be defined

401

as an operator, which, when operating on a length such as $\overline{OP}$, rotates that length through 90° in the positive (anti-clockwise) sense.

Now make OP = OQ = OR.

Then $j\overline{OP} = \overline{OQ}$; and operating with j a second time, we get:

$$j(j\overline{OP}) = j\overline{OQ} = \overline{OR} \quad . \quad . \quad . \quad (1)$$

Writing jj as j^2, (1) gives (since $\overline{OP} = + x$),

$$j^2x = -x = -1 \times x,$$

i.e., $\qquad j^2 = -1.$

and $\qquad j = \sqrt{-1} \quad . \quad . \quad . \quad . \quad (2)$

Further, $(4 + 3)$ would be shown by the point E, or by $\overline{OE}$; but $(4 + j.3)$ would be represented by the point C, where AC = 3; the length AE has been turned through 90° to the position AC—*i.e.*, $j.\overline{AE} = \overline{AC}$.

Thus the symbol $4 + j.3$ (or $4 + 3j$) may represent the point whose co-ordinates are given by $x = 4$, $y = 3$—*i.e.*, by the point (4, 3).

Similarly, $-4 - 5j$ is the point D $\equiv (-4, -5)$. We thus infer that $x + jy$ can be plotted as the point whose co-ordinates are (x, y).

The symbol $x + jy$ is called a complex number. In purely mathematical, as distinct from engineering work, j is replaced by i, so that $x + j.y$, or $x + iy$, or $x + \sqrt{-1}.y$ are all notations for the same complex number, and all three have the same representative point. The student has met these numbers in his previous work. Thus, solving the quadratic equation $x^2 - 4x + 13 = 0$ we get

$$x = \frac{4 \pm \sqrt{16 - 52}}{2} = \frac{4 \pm \sqrt{-36}}{2}.$$

Now notice that $-36 = -1.36 = j^2.36$,

and $\qquad \sqrt{-36} = j.6.$

So that $\qquad x = 2 \pm j.3.$

Previously he called such roots imaginary. He can now designate them as complex roots.

In $x + jy$, x is called the real part of the complex number; y, or jy, is the imaginary part; whilst X_1OX is called the real axis, and Y_1OY the imaginary axis. A number like $3j$ represented by G, or $\overline{OG}$ (Fig. 142), is called a purely imaginary number. All such are plotted on the y-axis, just as all real numbers like 5, $-2{\cdot}6$, or $\sqrt{7}$ are on the x-axis.

EXERCISE 52

1. State the co-ordinates of the points represented by the following numbers. Plot the points on the same diagram.

(a) $2 + 3j$.   (b) $-2 + j$.   (c) 5.
(d) $-2j$.   (e) $1 - 2j$.   (f) $3j$.

2. Express the roots of the following equations as complex numbers:

(a) $x^2 + x + 2 = 0$.   (b) $2x^2 - 3x + 4 = 0$.
(c) $x^2 - 0{\cdot}7x + 2{\cdot}1 = 0$.

2. The Argand Diagram

If P represent the complex number $x + jy$, we see from Fig. 143 an alternative representation of the same number, viz. by the vector $\overline{OP}$. The student will recall that a vector involves both magnitude and direction, and that physical entities like velocity and force, whose specifications involve both magnitude and direction can be represented by straight lines. Such lines as $\overline{OP}$ are usually designated by their end letters, the order of the letters showing the sense of the vector, the *length* OP its magnitude, whilst the bar over the letters indicates that we are dealing with a vector.

From Fig. 143 we see that $x = r \cos \theta = $ OA, $y = r \sin \theta$
$=$ AP, and $\quad x + jy = r \cos \theta + jr \sin \theta$
$$= r (\cos \theta + j \sin \theta).$$

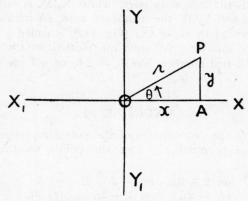

FIG. 143.—THE ARGAND DIAGRAM

This way of writing a complex number is called the
polar form. It is often abbreviated to $r \,\lfloor\theta$. We can
easily change this form into the other. Thus:

$$3 \,\lfloor 30° = 3 (\cos 30° + j \sin 30°)$$
$$= 3\left(\frac{\sqrt{3}}{2} + j \cdot \frac{1}{2}\right)$$
$$= \frac{3\sqrt{3}}{2} + j \cdot \frac{3}{2},$$

which is the form $x + jy$.

3. Modulus and Amplitude (or Argument)

In Fig. 143 (called an Argand diagram) the *length* OP—
i.e., r—is called the modulus of the complex number,
whilst θ is called its amplitude or argument; abbreviations
are mod., am. (sometimes amp.) or arg.

Another notation for mod. $(x + jy)$ is $|x + jy|$. Thus $r = +\sqrt{x^2 + y^2} = $ mod. $(x + jy) = |x + jy|$, and it should be observed that the modulus of any complex number is the length of the straight line joining the origin O to the point representing the number.

Also am. $(x + jy) = $ arg. $(x + jy) = \tan^{-1}\dfrac{y}{x} = \theta$.

Note that we get the same point P (Fig. 143) if its am. is increased or decreased by any integral multiple of 360°. To prevent ambiguity amplitudes will be taken to lie between 0° and $+ 180°$ or 0° and $- 180°$, and these values will be called the principal values of the amplitudes.

Am. $(- x)$ is taken as 180° or π.

Example 1

Plot the numbers $(2 + 3j)$ and $(- 3 - 2j)$. State their moduli and the principal value of their arms.   (See Fig. 144.)

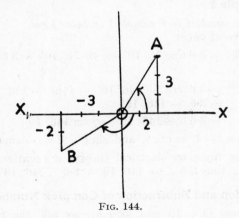

Fig. 144.

$|2 + 3j| = $ OA $= \sqrt{4 + 9} = \sqrt{13} = 3\cdot6$;
am. $(2 + 3j) = \tan^{-1}\frac{3}{2} = 56° \, 19'$;
and mod. $(- 3 - 2j) = $ OB $= \sqrt{13} = 3\cdot6$.

Am. $(-3-2j)$ = the negative angle XOB = $-(180° - X_1OB) = -(180° - \tan^{-1}\frac{2}{3}) = -(180° - 33° 41') = -146° 19'$.

Example 2

State the mod. and arg. of each of the following numbers: $-5, 3j, 2, -j$.

If the student will plot the above numbers (or imagine them on an Argand diagram) the results below will be apparent.

$|-5|\quad = 5,\quad$ arg. $(-5) = 180°$ or π.

Mod. $(3j) = 3,\quad$ arg. $(3j)\quad = 90°$ or $\dfrac{\pi}{2}$.

Mod. 2 $\quad = 2,\quad$ arg. 2 $\quad = 0°$.

$|-j|\quad = 1,\quad$ arg. $(-j) = -90°$ or $-\dfrac{\pi}{2}$.

Example 3

Put the numbers in Example 1 *in polar form.*
We have at once:

$$(2+3j) = 3\cdot6\,(\cos 56° 19' + j \sin 56° 19') = 3\cdot6\,\underline{|56° 19'}$$

and

$$(-3-2j) = 3\cdot6\,[\cos(-146° 19') + j \sin(-146° 19')]$$
$$= 3\cdot6\,\underline{|-146° 19'}$$
$$= 3\cdot6\,(\cos 146° 19' - j \sin 146° 19')$$

since $\quad \cos(-\theta) = \cos\theta$, and $\sin(-\theta) = -\sin\theta$.

In some texts on electrical theory, a negative am. is shown $\searcorner$; thus $3\cdot6\,\angle -146° 19' = 3\cdot6 \searcorner 146° 19'$.

4. Addition and Subtraction of Complex Numbers

In adding $(3+2j)$ and $(5+4j)$ we add the two real parts to get a new real part, and the two imaginary parts for a new imaginary part—*e.g.*:

$$(3+2j) + (5+4j) = (3+5) + j(2+4) = 8 + 6j.$$

Similarly, with subtraction:

$$(3 + 2j) - (5 + 4j) = (3 - 5) + j(2 - 4) = -2 - 2j.$$

The rules may be proved graphically.

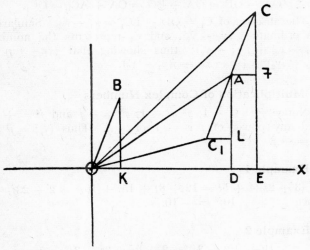

FIG. 145.

Let A (Fig. 145) represent the number $x_1 + jy_1$. Another representation is by the vector $\overline{OA}$. Similarly, B represents $x_2 + jy_2 = \overline{OB}$. From A draw AC equal and parallel to OB, so that $\overline{OB}$ and $\overline{AC}$ represent the same vector.

Then $\overline{OA} + \overline{OB} = \overline{OA} + \overline{AC} = \overline{OC}.$

Projecting OC orthogonally on the x-axis, the abscissa of C = OE = OD + AF. Now observe that the projection of AC on OX = proj. of OB on OX = x_2. Hence the abscissa of C is $x_1 + x_2$. Similarly, by projecting OC on OY we see that its ordinate is $y_1 + y_2$.

Hence

$$C \equiv \{(x_1 + x_2),\ (y_1 + y_2)\} = (x_1 + x_2) + j(y_1 + y_2).$$

Fig. 145 shows also the subtraction
$$(x_1 + jy_1) - (x_2 + jy_2).$$
For $\qquad - (x_2 + jy_2) = - \overline{OB} = \overline{BO} = \overline{AC_1}.$

$\therefore \quad \overline{OA} - \overline{OB} = \overline{OA} + \overline{BO} = \overline{OA} + \overline{AC_1} = \overline{OC_1}.$

The abscissa of $C_1 = OD - LC_1 = x_1 - x_2$. Similarly, its ordinate $= (y_1 - y_2)$, and C_1 represents the number $(x_1 - x_2) + j(y_1 - y_2)$; thus showing that $(x_1 + jy_1) - (x_2 + jy_2) = (x_1 - x_2) + j(y_1 - y_2)$.

5. Multiplication of Complex Numbers

Notice $j = \sqrt{-1}$, $j^2 = -1$, $j^3 = -j$ and $j^4 = +1$, and any power of j is ± 1 or $\pm j$. Thus $(j)^7 = j^4 \times j^3 = -j$.

Example 1

$(3 + 2j)(4 + 5j = 12 + 8j + 15j + 10j^2 = 2 + 23j$, since $\qquad 10j^2 = -10.$

Example 2

$\qquad (1 + j)(2 - 3j) = 2 + 2j - 3j - 3j^2 = 5 - j$, since $\qquad - 3j^2 = +3.$

Example 3

Evaluate $(\cos \theta_1 + j \sin \theta) \cdot (\cos_2^0 + j \sin \theta_2).$
[Notice complex numbers of the form $(\cos \alpha + j \sin \alpha)$.]
Mod. $(\cos \alpha + j \sin \alpha) = + \sqrt{\cos^2 \alpha + \sin^2 \alpha} = 1$. The am. or arg. $= \alpha$.

Hence $\qquad (\cos \alpha + j \sin \alpha) = 1 \ \underline{|\alpha}.$

$\therefore \quad (1 \ \underline{|\theta_1}) \times (1 \ \underline{|\theta_2}) = (\cos \theta_1 + j \sin \theta_1)(\cos \theta_2 + j \sin \theta_2)$
$= \cos \theta_1 \cos \theta_2 + j(\sin \theta_1 \cos \theta_2 + \cos \theta_1 \sin \theta_2)$
$\qquad\qquad\qquad\qquad\qquad\qquad + j^2 \sin \theta_1 \sin \theta_2$
$= (\cos \theta_1 \cos \theta_2 - \sin \theta_1 \sin \theta_2) + j(\sin \theta_1 \cos \theta_2$
$\qquad\qquad\qquad\qquad\qquad\qquad\qquad + \cos \theta_1 \sin \theta_2)$

$$= \cos (\theta_1 + \theta_2) + j \sin (\theta_1 + \theta_2) = 1 \ \underline{|(\theta_1 + \theta_2)}.$$

This result we shall use later.

Example 4

$$(\cos 30° + j \sin 30°) \ . \ (\cos 15° + j \sin 15°) =$$
$$\cos 45° + j \sin 45° = 1 \ \underline{|45°}.$$

6. Division of Complex Numbers

Definition:—Two complex numbers, $(x + jy)$ and $(x - jy)$, which differ only in the sign of the imaginary part, are called conjugate complex numbers.

Thus $(-3 + 4j)$ and $(-3 - 4j)$ are conjugates.

The sum and product of two conjugates are both real.

Sum $= (x + jy) + (x - jy) = 2x$.

Product $= (x + jy)(x - jy) = x^2 - (jy)^2 = x^2 + y^2 =$ the square of the mod. of either of the two numbers.

Notice the product $(\cos \theta + j \sin \theta) \ . \ (\cos \theta - j \sin \theta) = 1$.

Example 1

Consider $\dfrac{1}{3 + 2j}$. *Multiplying numerator and denominator by the conjugate number* $3 - 2j$, *we get*:

$$\frac{1}{3 + 2j} = \frac{3 - 2j}{(3 + 2j)(3 - 2j)} = \frac{3 - 2j}{13} = \frac{3}{13} - \frac{2j}{13},$$

—*i.e.*, the form $x + jy$. $[y = -\tfrac{2}{13}.]$

Example 2

Put $\dfrac{1 - 2j}{1 + 3j}$ *in the form* $x + jy$.

$$\frac{1 - 2j}{1 + 3j} = \frac{(1 - 2j)(1 - 3j)}{(1 + 3j)(1 - 3j)} = \frac{1 - 5j + 6j^2}{10}$$

$$= \frac{-5 - 5j}{10} = -\frac{1}{2} - \frac{1}{2}j.$$

Example 3

Express in the form $x + jy$, the sum $\dfrac{2 - 3j}{1 - j} + \dfrac{3 + j}{2 + 4j}$.

$$\frac{2 - 3j}{1 - j} + \frac{3 + j}{2 + 4j} = \frac{(2 - 3j)(1 + j)}{(1 - j)(1 + j)} + \frac{(3 + j)(2 - 4j)}{(2 + 4j)(2 - 4j)}$$

$$= \frac{5 - j}{2} + \frac{10 - 10j}{20}$$

$$= \left(\frac{5}{2} - \frac{j}{2}\right) + \left(\frac{1}{2} - \frac{1}{2}j\right) = 3 - j.$$

EXERCISE 53

Put the following products in the form $x + jy$:

(1) $(3 + 5j)(2 - j)$. (2) $(0{\cdot}5 + j)(0{\cdot}25 + 3j)$.

(3) $(2{\cdot}3 + j)(4 - 2j)$. (4) $(3 + 4j)(3 - 4j)$.

(5) $(-2 - 0{\cdot}5j)(-2 + 0{\cdot}5j)$. (6) $(3 - 2j)^2$.

(7) $(1 - 2j)^3$. (8) $(2 - j)^4$. (9) $(1 + 2j)^2 \cdot (2 + j)$.

(10) $(3 - j)(3 + j)(4 - 2j)$.

(11) $(\cos 30° + j \sin 30°) \cdot (\cos 45° + j \sin 45°)$.

(12) $(\cos 45° + j \sin 45°)(\cos 15° - j \sin 15°)$.

Evaluate the following:

(13) $\dfrac{2}{3 - 2j}$. (14) $\dfrac{2 + 3j}{4 - j}$. (15) $\dfrac{3}{4 + 6j} + \dfrac{1}{2 + 3j}$.

(16) $\dfrac{2 - j}{4 + 6j} - \dfrac{3 + j}{2 + 3j}$. (17) $\dfrac{(3 + 4j)(2 + j)}{3 - 2j}$.

(18) $\dfrac{2 + 4j}{3 + j} + \dfrac{1 - j}{1 + j}$.

7. Products in Polar Form

Let $z_1 = r_1 \,\underline{|\theta_1}, \quad z_2 = r_2 \,\underline{|\theta_2}$,

then $z_1 z_2 = r_1 (\cos \theta_1 + j \sin \theta_1) \cdot r_2 (\cos \theta_2 + j \sin \theta_2)$

$\qquad = r_1 r_2 [\cos (\theta_1 + \theta_2) + j \sin (\theta_1 + \theta_2)]$.

(See Example 3, par. 5.)

We infer from this result that the mod. of a product is the product of the mods. of the factors, whilst am. product = the sum of the ams. of the factors.

Example 1

$3 \underline{|25°} \times 2 \underline{|33°} = 6 \underline{|58°} = 6 (\cos 58° + j \sin 58°).$

Example 2

$3 \underline{|48°} \times 4 \underline{|-22°} = 12 \underline{|26°} = 12 (\cos 26° + j \sin 26°).$

Example 3

$(r \underline{|\alpha})^2 = r^2 \underline{|2\alpha} = r^2 (\cos 2\alpha + j \sin 2\alpha),$

i.e., $\qquad (r \underline{|\alpha})^2 = R \underline{|2\alpha} \text{ (where } R = r^2) \quad . \quad . \quad (1)$

This example shows us how to get the square root of a complex number when the latter is in polar form; for from (1) we see $(R \underline{|2\alpha})^{\frac{1}{2}} = \pm r \underline{|\alpha}$. But $r = \sqrt{R}$, and $\alpha = \frac{1}{2} (2\alpha)$.

Hence to get the square root of a complex number, we take the square root of the mod. of the number, halve its am., and prefix $\pm$.

Example 4

Evaluate $\sqrt{3 + 2j}$.

Mod. $(3 + 2j) = \sqrt{13} = 3 \cdot 6$, and $\sqrt{3 \cdot 6} = 1 \cdot 9$.

Am. $(3 + 2j) = \tan^{-1} \frac{2}{3} = 33° 41'$. Half of this is $16° 51'$.

Hence $\sqrt{3 + 2j} = \pm 1 \cdot 9 \underline{|16° 51'} = \pm 1 \cdot 9 (\cos 16° 51' + j \sin 16° 51')$.

8. De Moivre's Theorem

We have proved that $(\cos \theta_1 + j \sin \theta_1) \times (\cos \theta_2 + j \sin \theta_2) = [\cos (\theta_1 + \theta_2) + j \sin (\theta_1 + \theta_2)]$.

Hence, putting $\theta_1 = \theta_2 = \alpha$ we get:

$$(\cos \alpha + j \sin \alpha)^2 = (\cos 2\alpha + j \sin 2\alpha) \quad . \quad (1)$$

Multiplying both sides of (1) by $(\cos \alpha + j \sin \alpha)$ gives:

$$(\cos \alpha + j \sin \alpha)^3 = (\cos 2\alpha + j \sin 2\alpha)(\cos \alpha + j \sin \alpha)$$
$$= \cos 3\alpha + j \sin 3\alpha,$$

and continuing the process for n factors we see that:

$$(\cos \alpha + j \sin \alpha)^n = \cos n\alpha + j \sin n\alpha \quad . \quad (2)$$

(2) is De Moivre's Theorem; and it is true not only when n is a positive integer, but also when n is a negative integer or a positive or negative fraction. (See Exercise 54, nos. 29, 30.)

Example 1

$$(\cos 30^\circ + j \sin 30^\circ)^4 = \cos 120^\circ + j \sin 120^\circ = -\frac{1}{2} + \frac{j\sqrt{3}}{2}.$$

Example 2

$$(\cos 20^\circ - j \sin 20^\circ)^6 = [\cos(-20^\circ) + j \sin(-20^\circ)]^6$$
$$= \cos(-120^\circ) + j \sin(-120^\circ) = \cos 120^\circ - j \sin 120^\circ.$$

Example 3

Put $(2 + 3j)$ *in polar form, and then evaluate* $(2 + 3j)^4$.

We have:

Mod. $(2 + 3j) = \sqrt{13}$, and am. $(2 + 3j) = \tan^{-1} \frac{3}{2} = 56^\circ 19'$.

$\therefore 2 + 3j = \sqrt{13} \; \underline{|56^\circ 19'}$

$\qquad = \sqrt{13} (\cos 56^\circ 19' + j \sin 56^\circ 19').$

Hence

$$(2 + 3j)^4 = (\sqrt{13})^4 \cdot [\cos(4 \times 56^\circ 19') + j \sin(4 \times 56^\circ 19')]$$
$$= 169 (\cos 225^\circ 16' + j \sin 225^\circ 16')$$
$$= 169 (-0 \cdot 704 - 0 \cdot 71j)$$
$$= -119 - 120j.$$

Example 4

$$(\cos 60^\circ + j \sin 60^\circ)^{\frac{1}{2}} = \cos \tfrac{1}{2} \times 60^\circ + j \sin \tfrac{1}{2} \times 60^\circ$$
$$= \cos 30^\circ + j \sin 30^\circ \text{ (assuming De Moivre's Th)}.$$

Example 5

Evaluate $\sqrt{3 + 2j}$.   (See Example 4, par. 7.)

$3 + 2j = \sqrt{13}\ \underline{|33°\ 41'} = 3{\cdot}6\ (\cos 33°\ 41' + j \sin 33°\ 41')$

$\therefore\quad \sqrt{3 + 2j} = \pm\ \sqrt{3{\cdot}6}\ (\cos 33°\ 41' + j \sin 33°\ 41')^{\frac{1}{2}}$

$\qquad\qquad = \pm\ 1{\cdot}9\ \underline{|16°\ 51'}$ as before.

9. Division in Polar Form

Example 1

Consider $\dfrac{1}{\cos \theta + j \sin \theta}$.

$\dfrac{1}{\cos \theta + j \sin \theta} = \dfrac{\cos \theta - j \sin \theta}{(\cos \theta + j \sin \theta)(\cos \theta - j \sin \theta)}$

$\qquad\qquad = \dfrac{\cos \theta - j \sin \theta}{\cos^2 \theta + \sin^2 \theta} = (\cos \theta - j \sin \theta)$

$\qquad\qquad = \cos (-\theta) + j \sin (-\theta).$

Hence

$\dfrac{1}{\cos \theta + j \sin \theta} = \cos (-\theta) + j \sin (-\theta) = \cos \theta - j \sin \theta.$

i.e., $(\cos \theta + j \sin \theta)^{-1} = \cos (-1 \times \theta) + j \sin (-1 \times \theta)$,

which proves De Moivre's Th. for $n = -1$.

Example 2

Evaluate $\dfrac{r_1\ \underline{|\theta_1}}{r_2\ \underline{|\theta_2}}$.

We have:

$\dfrac{r_1\ \underline{|\theta_1}}{r_2\ \underline{|\theta_2}} = \dfrac{r_1\ (\cos \theta_1 + j \sin \theta_1)}{r_2\ (\cos \theta_2 + j \sin \theta_2)}$

$\qquad\qquad = \dfrac{r_1\ (\cos \theta_1 + j \sin \theta_1)(\cos \theta_2 - j \sin \theta_2)}{r_2\ (\cos \theta_2 + j \sin \theta_2)(\cos \theta_2 - j \sin \theta_2)}$

$\qquad\qquad = \dfrac{r_1}{r_2}\left[\cos (\theta_1 - \theta_2) + j \sin (\theta_1 - \theta_2)\right].$ [See Par. 6.]

We infer that the modulus of the quotient of two complex numbers is the quotient of their moduli; and the am. of a quotient is the difference

$$\text{am. (numerator)} - \text{am. (denominator)}.$$

Example 3

$$\frac{3 \; \lfloor 40° }{5 \; \lfloor 70° } = \frac{3}{5} \; \lfloor -30° = \frac{3}{5} (\cos 30° - j \sin 30°).$$

EXERCISE 54

Plot the following numbers on an Argand diagram, and then put them in polar form.

(1) $3 + 4j$. (2) $3 - 4j$. (3) $1{\cdot}2 + 3{\cdot}5j$.
(4) $-6 - 2j$. (5) $-0{\cdot}5 - 0{\cdot}3j$. (6) $-32 + j$.
(7) $3{\cdot}1 - 0{\cdot}5j$.

Change each of the following to the form $x + jy$:

(8) $3 \; \lfloor 30°$. (9) $2{\cdot}3 \; \lfloor 42$.
(10) $5{\cdot}2 \; \lfloor -36°$. (11) $6{\cdot}3 \; \diagdown 42°$.

Evaluate, in polar form, the following:

(12) $3 \; \lfloor 30° \times 2 \; \lfloor 15°$. (13) $2{\cdot}1 \; \lfloor 15° \times 3{\cdot}2 \; \lfloor 21°$.

(14) $2{\cdot}8 \; \lfloor 32° \times 1{\cdot}3 \; \lfloor -74°$. (15) $\dfrac{3 \; \lfloor 45}{2 \; \lfloor 15}$.

(16) $\dfrac{3 \; \lfloor 36°}{4 \; \lfloor 18°}$. (17) $\dfrac{3 \; \lfloor 72°}{2 \; \lfloor -18°}$. (18) $\dfrac{2{\cdot}3 \; \lfloor 24°}{1{\cdot}6 \; \lfloor -21°}$.

Evaluate:

(19) $\sqrt{2 + 5j}$. (20) $\sqrt{3 - 4j}$. (21) $\sqrt{2{\cdot}3 + 0{\cdot}5j}$.

(22) $\dfrac{1}{\sqrt{3 + 2j}}$. (23) $\sqrt{\overline{j}}$. (24) $\sqrt{-9j}$.

(25) $\dfrac{\sqrt{4 + 2j}}{1 - 3j}$.

(26) Evaluate in the form $a + bj$ each of the numbers $\dfrac{6 - 5j}{3 + j}$ and $\dfrac{10}{2_{30°}}$, and represent $10_{60°} - 7$ graphically, and express it in polar form.

(27) Express $\dfrac{4 - 2j}{3 + j}$ and $\dfrac{5}{2_{60°}}$ in the form $a + bj$, and show them on an Argand diagram. Find also the modulus and the principal value of the argument (or am.) of their product.

(28) If z_1 and z_2 are complex numbers, show that $|z_1 z_2| = |z_1| \times |z_2|$ and am. $(z_1 z_2) =$ am. $z_1 +$ am. z_2. Verify these relations when $z_1 = 2 + 3j$, and $z_2 = 1 - 2j$, and mark the points or vectors representing $2 + 3j$, $1 - 2j$, and $(2 + 3j)(1 - 2j)$ on an Argand diagram.

(29) If n is a positive integer, show that $\dfrac{1}{(\cos \theta + j \sin \theta)^n}$ $= \cos n\theta - j \sin n\theta$ and hence deduce De Moivre's Th. for a negative integer.

(30) Starting with $\left(\cos \dfrac{\theta}{q} + j \sin \dfrac{\theta}{q} \right)^q = \cos \theta + j \sin \theta$;

show   (1) $\cos \dfrac{\theta}{q} + j \sin \dfrac{\theta}{q} = (\cos \theta + j \sin \theta)^{\frac{1}{q}}$;

(2) $(\cos \theta + j \sin \theta)^{\frac{p}{q}} = \cos \dfrac{p\theta}{q} + j \sin \dfrac{p\theta}{q}$,

which proves De Moivre's Th. for a fraction $\dfrac{p}{q}$.

EXERCISE 55

For Revision

The one hundred examples which follow are representative of questions set in recent Final-Year examinations for the Ordinary National Certificate. Classified examples for practice follow in Exercise 56.

1. (a) Solve the equation $10 \sec^2 \theta = 3(8 - 9 \tan \theta)$ for values of θ from $0°$ to $360°$.

(b) The relation between the grid potential V volts and the anode current I milliamp of a thermionic tube for a certain constant anode potential is given by $I = a + bV + cV^2$. When $V = -5.8$, $I = 0.54$; when $V = -3.8$, $I = 1.57$; when $V = -1.8$, $I = 3.47$. Find the value of I when $V = -3$. (S.W. Essex.)

2. (a) Using the binomial approximation $(1 + x)^n = 1 + nx$ for small x, find the approximate percentage change in E when a is increased by 1%; b decreased by 2%; c increased by 1%, where

$$E = - \frac{a^3}{bc^2}.$$

(b) A straight level road runs north and south. From a point A on this road the top of a hill bears $48° 27'$ west of north and has an angle of elevation of $40° 15'$. From a point B 2500 feet north of A, the hill bears $36° 40'$ west of south. Find the height of the hill. Find also the angle of elevation of the top of the hill from the point B.

(Halifax.)

3. An endless belt passes round two pulleys without crossing. The diameters of the pulleys are 4 ft and 1 ft, their centres are x ft apart and the common tangent is inclined at an angle α radians to the line through their centres. If the total length of the belt is l ft, express x in terms of α and prove that

$$l = 3 \cot \alpha + 3\alpha + \tfrac{5}{2}\pi.$$

Calculate the length of the belt when

$$x = 3, \quad \text{taking } \pi = 3.142.$$

(N.C.T.E.C.)

4. (a) The length of a rod is 5 ft. The successive cross-sectional areas taken at equal distances apart form a geometrical progression. One end of the rod has a cross-

sectional area of $\frac{1}{4}$ in.^{2}. The area of the cross-section distant one foot from this end is $\frac{5}{16}$ in.^{2}. Calculate the area of the cross-section of the other end correct to the nearest square inch.

(b) Use a Theorem of Pappus and the formula for the volume of a sphere to find the position of the centroid the area of a semi-circular area of radius a. (E.M.E.U.)

5. (a) If $x = 1 \cdot 72$, $z_1 = 23 \cdot 4$, $z_2 = 35 \cdot 7$ evaluate:

(i) e^{2x-5} (ii) $\log_e \left(1 + \dfrac{z_1}{z_2} \right)$

(iii) $e^{2x-5} \sqrt{z_1 + z_2 + \log_e \left(1 + \dfrac{z_1}{z_2} \right)}$

giving each answer correct to three significant figures.

(b) Make x the subject of the formula

$$\log_e \frac{x+1}{x-1} = k.$$ (Nuneaton.)

6. (a) Given that $\dfrac{3x^{-3}}{(3x)^{1/2}} = \dfrac{1}{27}$ find x.

(b) Find the logarithm of $12^{-2/3}$ to the base $0 \cdot 27$.

(c) Solve the equations $pv^{1 \cdot 4} = 1230,$
$pv = 412.$

(d) Show that

$$(\sin \theta + \cos \theta)(\sin \theta - \cos \theta) = 1 - 2 \cos^2 \theta$$

and hence solve the equation

$$(\sin \theta + \cos \theta)(\sin \theta - \cos \theta) = \tfrac{1}{2}$$

for values of θ between 0 and $360°$. (Handsworth.)

7. Use the binomial theorem

(a) to evaluate the cube root of 30, correct to three significant figures;

(b) to expand $\sqrt{\dfrac{1 - 2x}{(1 - x)^2}}$ in ascending powers of x as far as the term in x^2 inclusive. (Worcester.)

8. (*a*) Given that pv^n is constant, that $p = 200$ when $v = 1 \cdot 5$ and that $p = 20$ when $v = 7$, find n.

(*b*) The efficiency E of a compressor is given by

$$E = \frac{\log_e r}{\dfrac{2n}{n-1}\left[\dfrac{n-1}{r^n-1}\right]}$$

Calculate E when $r = 7 \cdot 4$ and $n = 1 \cdot 4$.

(Shrewsbury.)

9. A corner plot of land has the dimensions shown in Fig. 146.

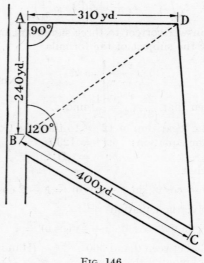

Fig. 146.

Calculate:

    (i) length of the diagonal BD;
    (ii) length of the boundary DC;
    (iii) total area of the plot in acres.

(Coventry.)

10. In the diamond pyramid hardness test the diamond indenter is an inverted square pyramid having an included angle between opposite faces of 136°. In a test the indenter is loaded with 5 kilograms. A measuring microscope gives the average of the diagonals of the impression as 0·186 mm. The hardness number is the load in kilograms divided by the pyramidal area of the impression in square mm. Calculate the hardness number. You should make a large diagram of the impression, 10 or 20 times full size.

11. The horse-power transmitted by a belt is given by the equation

$$H = \frac{2n\pi r(T_1 - T_2)}{33,000},$$

where $T_1 = T_2 e^{\mu\theta}$.

If $H = 6$, $\theta = 0\cdot8\pi$, $\mu = 0\cdot4$, $n = 960$, $r = 0\cdot75$, determine T_1 and T_2 correct to one decimal place.

(U.L.C.I.)

12. (a) Find the angles of intersection of the curves of $y = \dfrac{x^3}{10}$ and $y = \dfrac{x^2}{5}$.

(b) The slant height of a cone is 12 in. Determine the base radius and height for maximum volume.

(Worcester.)

13. (i) If $\tan \frac{1}{2}\theta = t$, prove that $\sin \theta = \dfrac{2t}{1 + t^2}$ and establish the corresponding result for $\cos \theta$.

(ii) Solve the equations

(1) $4 \cos \theta - 7 \sin \theta = 5$,

(2) $\sqrt{3} \operatorname{cosec}^2 \theta = 4 \cot \theta$,

giving all the solutions between 0° and 360°.

(West Riding.)

14. (a) Solve the equation $3^{\sin 2x} = 9^{\cos x}$ for values of x between 0° and 360°.

(b) Assuming that x is sufficiently small so that powers of

x above the second may be neglected, find the expansion of $\dfrac{(1 + 2x)^{\frac{1}{2}}}{(1 - x)^4}$ in the form $a + bx + cx^2$ where a, b and c are constants to be determined. Hence find the approximate value of $\dfrac{\sqrt{1\cdot1}}{(0\cdot95)^4}$, giving your answer to two decimal places.

(Burton-upon-Trent.)

15. A symmetrical vee groove in a truly flat plate is so proportioned that if a steel ball 0·2500 in. diam. is rested in the groove the top of the ball is flush with the face of the plate. (a) If the included angle of the groove is 75°, what are its depth, and width; (b) if the depth of the groove is 0·5 in. what is its width, and what is the included angle?

16. Expand the following in ascending powers of x as far as the term in x^3:

$$\text{(i)} \ \left(1 - \frac{x}{5}\right)^{\frac{1}{3}} \qquad \text{(ii)} \ (1 + 2x)^{-\frac{1}{3}}$$

Hence show that if x is so small that x^3 and higher powers may be neglected

$$\sqrt[3]{\frac{1 - \dfrac{x}{5}}{1 + 2x}} \simeq 1 - \frac{11x}{15} + \frac{209x^2}{225}.$$

By substituting $x = 0\cdot05$, use this formula to find $\sqrt[3]{0\cdot9}$.

(Stafford.)

17. (a) Write down the first five terms in the expansion of $(1 + x)^{-\frac{1}{2}}$ and hence find the value of $\dfrac{1}{\sqrt{1\cdot02}}$ to five decimal places.

(b) Solve the equation $e^{3x} = 4^{x+2}$.

(c) If $v = u + ft$ and $s = ut + \frac{1}{2}ft^2$, use these to obtain the formula $v^2 = u^2 + 2fs$. (E.M.E.U.)

18. For the curve $y = x^2 + x - 2$

(i) find the co-ordinates of the point where the tangent to the curve is parallel to the x-axis;

(ii) find the co-ordinates of the points where the curve cuts the x-axis, and the y-axis respectively;

(iii) without further plotting of points, sketch the curve (a freehand sketch showing clearly the position of the curve in relation to the axes will be sufficient);

(iv) find the equations of the tangent and normal to the curve at the point where x is 2.

(Coventry.)

19. (a) A triangular plate has sides AB = 8 in., BC = 6 in. and CA = 7 in.

P is a point in CA such that CP = 2 in., Q is a point in CB such that CQ = 2 in. With centre C an arc of a circle of radius 2 in. is drawn to cut CA in P and CB in Q. The sector CPQ is removed. Calculate the area of the sector CPQ and the length of the arc PQ.

(b) In the triangle DEF, DE = 13 in., EF = 7 in. and FD = 8 in. Calculate the area of the triangle DEF and find the radius of the circle which touches each of the sides DE, EF and FD. (E.M.E.U.)

20. In an experiment in which a belt passes over a pulley T_1 and T_2 are the tensions on the two ends of the belt when it is just on the point of slipping and θ is the angle of lap in radians. θ and $\frac{T_1}{T_2}$ are connected by a law of the form $\frac{T_1}{T_2} = Ae^{k\theta}$, where A and k are constants.

Corresponding values of θ and $\frac{T_1}{T_2}$ were observed as follows:

θ . .	0·90	1·64	2·00	2·64	3·30	4·40
$\frac{T_1}{T_2}$ . .	1·26	1·51	1·66	1·95	2·32	3·06

Find the values of A and k and hence state the law.

(Handsworth.)

21. Observed values of x and y are

x . . .	0·5	1·0	2·0	3·0	4·0
y . . .	1·622	1·100	0·448	0·244	0·155

and it is thought that these are connected by a relation of the form $10^{x^2y} = kx$, where k is constant. Test this, and find the probable value of k. (Sunderland.)

22. The following readings of the values of a current I and the corresponding values of the resistance R are believed to be related by an approximate equation of the form $I = \dfrac{V}{R + r}$, where V and r are constants.

I . .	2·09	1·39	1·00	0·66	0·50	0·40	0·33
R . .	10	65	130	250	360	475	600

By plotting IR with I, show that the law is approximately true and find the best values of V and r. (E.M.E.U.)

23. (i) Expand $\sqrt{(8 + x^2)}$ as a series in ascending powers of x as far as the fourth term, and state the necessary restriction on the numerical value of x so that the series may be used to approximate to $\sqrt[3]{(8 + x^2)}$.

Use your series to calculate $\sqrt[3]{(8 \cdot 32)}$ correct to four decimal places.

(ii) Solve the equation

$$3e^{2x} = 7e^x - 1,$$

giving the roots to two places of decimals.

(West Riding.)

24. (i) Four rods, AB $= 18$ in., BC $= 21$ in., CD $= 20$ in., DA $= 24$ in., are jointed together to form a plane quadrilateral ABCD.

A fifth rod joining A to C keeps the framework rigid with

$\angle$BCD $= 90°$. Determine, by calculation, the length of this fifth rod.

(ii) If $\tan \dfrac{\theta}{2} = t$ prove that $\sin \theta = \dfrac{2t}{1 + t^2}$, $\cos \theta = \dfrac{1 - t^2}{1 + t^2}$ and hence find the values of θ between $0°$ and $360°$ which satisfy the equation

$$3 \cos \theta + \sin \theta = 2.$$

(Cheltenham.)

25. Express $x = 2 \cdot 05 + 1 \cdot 65 \sin 120\pi t + 2 \cdot 25 \cos 120\pi t$ in the form $x = 2 \cdot 05 + A \sin (120\pi t + \alpha)$ giving the actual value of A to three significant figures and α in radians correct to two decimal places.

Determine also

     (i) what value of t makes x a maximum;
    (ii) the displacement when $t = 0 \cdot 2$;
   (iii) the periodic time of oscillation.

(West Riding.)

26. (a) Differentiate the following expressions with respect to x and give your answers in the simplest form.

    (i) $y = x \sin 2x$;

   (ii) $y = \dfrac{x - 4}{2x - 3}$;

  (iii) $y = \sqrt{3x^2 - 1}$.

(b) Find the values of x for which the expression,

$$2x^3 - 9x^2 - 24x + 12$$

has a maximum and a minimum value and for each determine whether the expression is a maximum or a minimum.

(Coventry.)

27. (a) Find $\dfrac{dy}{dx}$ if

    (i) $y = 6\sqrt{x} - \dfrac{8}{\sqrt{x}}$;

   (ii) $y = \log_e (1 - \cos 2x)$;

(iii) $y = \sqrt{4 - 3x^2}$;

(iv) $y = \dfrac{\sin x}{1 + \cos x}$.

(b) Find the slope of the tangent to the curve $y = \dfrac{x^2}{4} - \dfrac{2}{x}$ at the point where the curve cuts the x-axis.   (Surrey.)

28. (a) (i) Assuming the expansions for sin $(A + B)$ and cos $(A + B)$ derive an expression for tan $2A$.

(ii) Express sin $3A$ in terms of sin A.

(b) Express as the sum or difference of two sines

$$\sin 3\theta \cos 2\theta$$

(c) Find the values of θ between $0°$ and $360°$ to satisfy that the equation $\dfrac{\cos (2\theta - 35°) - 0\cdot4}{\sin 35° \sin \theta} = 2 \cos \theta$.

(Stafford.)

29. A weight hangs from one end of a spring and the other end of the spring is fixed. The weight oscillates vertically so that its displacement x in., from its mean position, at time t sec., is given by

$$x = 2 \sin 5\pi t.$$

Plot values of x against those of t for a complete period. Calculate

(i) the number of oscillations made per minute;

(ii) the velocity and acceleration when $t = 0\cdot05$;

(iii) the velocity of the weight at two successive times when it is half-way between its mean and extreme positions, and state the significance of the negative sign obtained in one case.

(West Riding.)

30. (i) Differentiate

$$\dfrac{2x}{\sin x}, \quad 5e^{x^{4/5}}, \quad 9 \cos 3x \log_e x/3.$$

(ii) If $T = 2\pi\sqrt{l/g}$, find T and $\dfrac{dT}{dl}$ when $l = 2$ and $g = 32$.

Use your results to find T when $l = 2 \cdot 12$.   (Sunderland.)

31. (a) Differentiate with respect to x

(i) $\dfrac{x}{1 + x^2}$;

(ii) $\log_e (1 + x^2)$;

(iii) $\sin^3 2x$;

(iv) $x \cos x$.

(b) If $i = \dfrac{E}{R}(1 - e^{-\frac{Rt}{L}})$, where E, L and R are constants,

verify that $L\dfrac{di}{dt} + Ri = E$.

(E.M.E.U.)

32. (a) It is thought that a law of the form $W = ae^{bt}$ gives the weight, W grams, of a substance that will dissolve in a certain liquid at a temperature $t°$ C., where a and b are constants.

Show graphically that the following values conform to this law

t . . .	15	30	45	60
W . . .	36·44	41·87	48·07	55·01

and find the values of a and b.

(b) If you were given a table, like the above, of pairs of values of the variables x and y, state as briefly as possible how you would test graphically whether x and y were connected

(i) by a law of the form $y = a + bx^2$

and   (ii) by a law of the form $y = ax + bx^2$.

(Coventry.)

33. At a height of h ft above the ground, the reading of a mercury barometer is p in.

Find the best law of the type $p = C \cdot e^{kh}$ to fit the following values of p and h, where C and k are constants.

h . .	1000	2000	3000	5000	8000	12,000	15,000
p . .	28·48	27·36	26·32	24·36	21·69	18·53	16·52

Calculate from the result the probable height of an aircraft in which the barometer reads 21·25 in.   (Dudley.)

34. The following values of H and V are thought to obey a law of the form $\log_{10}\left(\dfrac{H}{V}\right) = a + bV$:

H . .	4700	6800	11,500	16,000	22,000
V . .	13	15	18	20	22

Verify graphically that this is so, and find the values of a and b.   (Halifax.)

35. Express $1·7 \sin A - 2·5 \cos A$ in the form $r \sin (A - \alpha)$ and calculate r and α.   Use this result to

(i) find the maximum and minimum value of $y = 1·7 \sin A - 2·5 \cos A$;

(ii) solve the equation $1·7 \sin A - 2·5 \cos A = 2$ for values of A between 0° and 360°.

(West Riding.)

36. (*a*) If $\tan \theta = t$, show that $\sin 2\theta = \dfrac{2t}{1 + t^2}$ and $\cos 2\theta = \dfrac{1 - t^2}{1 + t^2}$; hence show that $\sin 4\theta = \dfrac{4(1 - t^2)t}{(1 + t^2)^2}$.

(*b*) Express $9 \cos \theta + 13 \sin \theta$ in the form $R \cos (\theta - \alpha)$, finding R and α.   Hence, or otherwise, solve the equation $9 \cos \theta + 13 \sin \theta = 5$ giving all the solutions between 0° and 360°.   (N.C.T.E.C.)

37. (a) The efficiency of a certain transformer with an input of i amp. is

$$\frac{240i}{240i + 0.72i^2 + 320}$$

Find the value of i which makes the efficiency a maximum, and hence calculate this maximum efficiency.

(b) If

$$Q = K\mu T(\cos\theta - \sin\theta)$$

find values of θ between $0°$ and $360°$ which make Q a maximum or minimum (treating K, μ, T as constants). Find the maximum and minimum values of Q.   (Halifax.)

38.

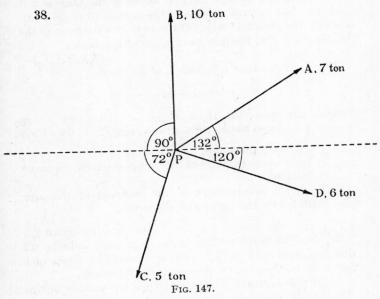

FIG. 147.

(a) Four co-planar forces A, B, C, D act on a pin in a structure in the directions shown. Find the magnitude and direction of a single force which would balance this system of forces.   Show the position of this force in relation to the given forces on a sketch diagram.

(*b*) Confirm graphically that the addition of this extra force would reduce the system to equilibrium.

(Coventry.)

39. (i) Given $y = A \cos (pt + c)$, find the first two positive values of t when turning points occur if $A = 10$, $p = \dfrac{5\pi}{3}$, and $c = \frac{1}{3}\pi$ radians.   Determine the values of y at these points.

(ii) An open tank is constructed with a rectangular base and vertical sides.   The internal width of the tank is 2 ft and the total internal volume of the tank is to be **36 cu ft**. Express the internal surface of the tank as a function of the height x and find the minimum value of this area.

(N.C.T.E.C.)

40. A curve whose equation is of the form

$$y = ax^2 + bx + c$$

crosses the y-axis at right angles at the point where $y = -8$ and also passes through the point $(2, -6)$.   Find

(i) the values of a, b and c;

(ii) the co-ordinates of the points at which the curve crosses the x-axis;

(iii) the co-ordinates of the centroid of the area bounded by the curve and the x-axis.

(Burton-upon-Trent.)

41. (*a*) The total surface area of a solid cylinder of diameter x in. is S sq in.   Obtain formulæ in terms of x and S for the height and volume of the cylinder.

(*b*) If S is constant prove that, when the volume of this cylinder is a maximum, $x = \sqrt{\dfrac{2S}{3\pi}}$ in. and that the area of its curved surface is $\dfrac{2S}{3}$ sq in.   (Halifax.)

42. The currents I_1 amp. and I_2 amp. in two branches of an electrical circuit are given by $I_1 = 3\cos\left(\omega t - \frac{\pi}{6}\right)$, $I_2 = 5\sin\left(\omega t + \frac{\pi}{3}\right)$. Obtain an expression for the total current I in the circuit in the form $R\sin(\omega t - \alpha)$ and hence find:

    (*a*) the maximum value of the current;

    (*b*) the value of t for which the current first reaches its maximum value;

    (*c*) the value of t for which the current first reaches one half its maximum value when w is taken equal to π.

(Cheltenham.)

43.

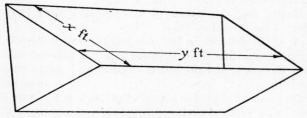

Fig. 148.

The trough shown has an open horizontal top. The ends are vertical equilateral triangles. The capacity is 3 cu ft. Show that the area of sheet metal, s sq ft., used in the construction of the trough is given by the equation

$$S = \frac{\sqrt{3}x^2}{2} + \frac{24}{\sqrt{3}x}$$

Hence determine the values of x and y for which S has a minimum value. (Coventry.)

44. (*a*) Differentiate, with respect to t,

    (i) $t^3\sqrt{\{(3 + 4t)^5\}}$;   (ii) $\dfrac{\sin 2t}{(t + 3)^2}$.

(b) if $y = ax^2 + \dfrac{b}{x}$, find the value of $x^2 \cdot \dfrac{d^2y}{dx^2}$

(i) as a function of x; (ii) as a function of y.

(N.C.T.E.C.)

45. (a) Find the maximum and minimum values of y when $y = (x + 1)^2(x - 1)$ and sketch the graph of the function.

(b) A closed rectangular container with a square base is to have a capacity of 216 cu ft. Find its dimensions in order that the least quantity of sheet metal may be used in its construction. (Halifax.)

46. (a) Write down the expansion of $\cos (A + B)$ in terms of sines and cosines of A and B, and deduce an expression for $\cos 2\theta$ in terms of $\cos \theta$.

Hence, find the values of θ between $0°$ and $180°$ for which $3 \cos 2\theta + 1 = \cos \theta$.

(b) If the distance in feet of a body from a fixed point is given by $x = 10e^{-2t} \sin 3t$ where t is the time in seconds from the start, find the initial velocity and acceleration of the body. (Surrey.)

47. (a) Find the mean value of the function $8 + 3 \sin 50\pi t$ over its first half period.

(b) Find the root mean square value of this function over a period. (S.W. Essex.)

48. Differentiate with respect to x:

(i) $\dfrac{x^3 - 2x^2 + 3}{x^3}$; (ii) $\sqrt{\left(\dfrac{2x - 1}{2x + 1}\right)}$;

(iii) $\log_e (\sin 2x)$; (iv) $x^2 \cos x$.

(West Riding.)

49. (a) A tank, with lid, as shown in Fig. 149, is in the form of a half-cylinder, the base being a semi-circle and the sides vertical. It has a capacity of 800 cu ft. Show that the total surface area, including the lid, is given by

$$A = \frac{1600}{\pi} (\pi + 2)r^{-1} + \pi r^2$$

Hence calculate its dimensions if the amount of steel plate used in its construction is to be a minimum.

Show that your answer does give a minimum and not a maximum.

(b) Evaluate the integrals

(i) $\int \left(\sin 2x + \frac{1}{x} + \frac{2}{x^2} \right) dx$

(ii) $\int_0^2 xe^x dx$

(c) Calculate the volume swept out when the area below the curve $y = x^2 + 3$ is revolved about the axis of x between the values $x = 1$ and $x = 2$.   (Coventry.)

50. Find the area enclosed by the curve $y = a + \dfrac{x^2}{4a}$, the ordinates $x = -2a$ and $x = +2a$, and the x-axis. If this area is

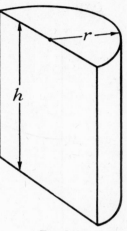

Fig. 149.

rotated about the x-axis through 2π radians, find the volume of the solid formed. Use Guldin's Theorem to deduce the position of the centroid of the area.

(Sunderland.)

51. (a) Show by integration that the area enclosed by the parabolas $y^2 = 4x$ and $x^2 = 4y$ is $\frac{16}{3}$.

(b) The work done by a gas in expanding from a volume v_1 to a volume v_2 is $\int_{v_1}^{v_2} p\,dv$, where p is the pressure. If the law connecting pressure and volume is $pv^{1\cdot2} = 500$, find the work done in expanding from a volume of 3 cu units to one of 8 cu units.   (Stafford.)

52. The area OABC (see Fig. 150) is bounded by the curve $y = x^2 + 1$, the axes of co-ordinates, and the ordinate $x = 4$.

(a) Calculate

    (i) the mean value of the ordinate of the area OABC;

    (ii) the x-co-ordinate of the centroid of the area OABC.

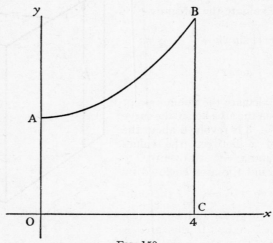

Fig. 150.

(b) The area OABC is now revolved about Ox. Write down the moment about O of a small circular disc of thickness dx, and show that the position of the centre of gravity of the solid of revolution is given by

$$x = \frac{\int_0^4 y^2 x\, dx}{\int_0^4 y^2\, dx}$$

(Coventry.)

53. (a) Evaluate the following integrals:

    (i) $\int_1^4 (15 + 32t)\, dt$ (ii) $\int_0^7 (e^x - e^{-x})\, dx$

(b) If $\dfrac{dx}{dt} = -15 \sin 3t$, find x given that $x = 0$ when $t = 0$.

(c) Differentiate $\log_e (x^2 + 1)$ and hence find the area lying between the curve $y = \dfrac{2x}{x^2 + 1}$, the axis of x and the ordinates at $x = 0$ and $x = 3.5$.   (E.M.E.U.)

54. (a) Find $\dfrac{dy}{dx}$ for each of the following functions:

(i) $y = 4x^3 - 3\sqrt{x} + \dfrac{5}{x^2}$

(ii) $y = 6 \sin 2x + 4 \cos 2x$

(iii) $y = (x^2 - 8)^8$

(iv) $y = x^4 e^{2x}$.

(b) A body is projected up a smooth incline with such a velocity that after t seconds its distance from its starting point is given by the expression

$$S = 200t - 4t^2 \text{ ft}$$

Obtain expressions for its velocity and acceleration at any time and deduce its starting velocity.

How far up the slope will it travel before it comes to rest and commences to slide back?   (Coventry.)

55. (i) Expand in full the expression $\left(\dfrac{x}{2} - \dfrac{y}{3}\right)^5$.

(ii) The frequency of oscillation, f, of an electrical circuit is given by

$$f = \dfrac{1}{2\pi\sqrt{LC}}.$$

If L is measured 1% too high, and C is 1.5% too low, find the percentage error in f.   (Sunderland.)

56. (i) Differentiate

(a) $\dfrac{x^2}{\sqrt{4 - x}}$.   (b) $\log_e (6x - 3)^2$,

expressing your result in as simple a form as possible.

(ii) If $y = x^3 e^{2x}$ show that $\dfrac{d^2y}{dx^2} - \dfrac{4dy}{dx} + 4y = \dfrac{6y}{x^2}$.

(iii) The equation to a circle is

$$x^2 + y^2 + 2x + 4y - 8 = 0.$$

Find the equation to the tangent at the point in the first quadrant where the line $x = 1$ intersects the circle.

(Halifax.)

57. Find $\dfrac{dy}{dx}$ in the following cases:

(i) $y = \sqrt{\dfrac{x}{x + 1}}$.

(ii) $y = (\sin 2x + \cos 3x)^2$.

(S.W. Essex.)

58. Show that

$$\int_1^x \frac{t + 1}{t}\, dt = x + \log_e x - 1.$$

If $\displaystyle\int_1^x \frac{t + 1}{t}\, dt = 4$, show that $\log_e x = 5 - x$, and by drawing suitable graphs from $x = 1$ to $x = 5$, find the value of x. (Sunderland.)

59. *Sketch* the curves $y = 3 \sin \theta$ and $y = \sin 3\theta$ from $\theta = 0$ to $\theta = 180°$. Hence obtain a sketch of $y = \sin 3\theta + 3 \sin \theta$, indicating clearly the turning points. Show that the differential coefficient of $\sin 3\theta + 3 \sin \theta$ can be expressed as $6 \cos 2\theta \cdot \cos \theta$, and by solving the equation $6 \cos 2\theta \cdot \cos \theta = 0$, find the values of θ at which the turning points occur; using your sketch discriminate between them.

(Handsworth.)

60. (*a*) Differentiate $\dfrac{1}{x}$ from first principles.

(*b*) Find $\dfrac{dy}{dx}$ when   (i) $y = \tan^2 x$,

(ii) $y = \dfrac{\log_e x}{x^3}$.

(c) If $y = \dfrac{\sqrt{5 + 2x}}{\sqrt[3]{1 - x}}$, by taking logs find $\dfrac{dy}{dx}$ and simplify the result as much as possible.　　　　(Handsworth.)

61. (i) Find the equation to the tangent of the curve

$$y = x^2 - 3x + 4$$

at the point on the curve where $x = 3$.　Find also the equation to the line at right angles to the tangent passing through its point of contact.

(ii) Given $\dfrac{d^2y}{dx^2} = K(L - x)$, where K and L are constants, and that $\dfrac{dy}{dx}$ and y are 0 when $x = 0$, find an expression for y in terms of x.　　　　(N.C.T.E.C.)

62. A voltage is given by the expression

$$V = 300 \sin 40\pi t + 50 \cos 40\pi t.$$

Find the maximum and minimum values of V and state for what values of t they first occur for positive values of t (i) by expressing V in the form $R \sin (40\pi t + \alpha)$, and (ii) by differentiating the original function with respect to t.

(S.W. Essex.)

63. Write down the first four terms of the expansions of $(1 + x)^n$ and $(1 - x)^{-n}$.　Expand $\sqrt[3]{1 - x^2}$ as far as the term containing x^8, and hence find the value of $\displaystyle\int_0^{0.3} (1 - x^2)^{\frac{1}{3}} \, dx$ to six significant figures.　　　　(Sunderland.)

64. (a) State the expansion for $\cos (A + B)$ and deduce expressions for $\cos 2A$ and $\cos 4A$ respectively in terms of $\sin A$.

(b) After time t seconds the current i amp. in a circuit is given by the equation $i = I \sin (\omega t + \frac{1}{3}\pi)$, where I and ω are constants.　Evaluate the R.M.S. value of i over the period $\dfrac{2\pi}{\omega}$.　　　　(N.C.T.E.C.)

65. Determine the area between the curve $y = 6x^2 - x^3$ and the x-axis. Find the co-ordinates of the centroid of the area.   (Worcester.)

66. (i) Differentiate
$$x^2e^{2x} \quad \text{and} \quad \sin(x^2).$$

(ii) Obtain

$$\int \sqrt{x}(1 + x)dx \quad \text{and} \quad \int_0^{\pi/2} \cos\left(2x - \frac{\pi}{6}\right)dx.$$

(Sunderland.)

67. (a) The area enclosed by the curve $y = e^{\frac{1}{2}x}$, the x-axis, the y-axis and the ordinate $x = 6$ is rotated through four right angles about the x-axis. Find the volume so generated. See Fig. 151.

(b)

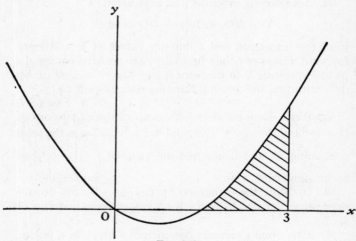

Fig. 151.

The area shaded in the figure is bounded by the curve $y = x^2 - x$, the x-axis and the ordinate $x = 3$. Find the co-ordinates of its centroid.   (Coventry.)

68. Prove by *direct integration* that the moment of inertia of a triangular plate, of mass m and height h, about an axis in its plane parallel to the base at a distance c from the opposite vertex, is

$$m(c^2 - \tfrac{4}{3}ch + \tfrac{1}{2}h^2)$$

Deduce the values of the moment of inertia when the axis (i) passes through the vertex, (ii) coincides with the base. Prove that the moment of inertia has its least value when the axis passes through the centroid of the triangle, and find this minimum value.   (Worcester.)

69. Find the co-ordinates of the centroid of the segment of area cut from the parabola $y = x(1 - 2x)$ by the x-axis. This parabolic segment lies outside a rectangle ABCD, the straight edge of the segment * coinciding with CD. AB $= \tfrac{1}{2}$ in. and BC $= 3$ in. The figure is now rotated through 2π radians about an axis in AB to form a solid wheel. By Guldin's Theorem, find the volume of the wheel.   (Sunderland.)

* It will be found that CD like AB is $\tfrac{1}{2}$ in.

70. (*a*) Evaluate the following integrals:

(i) $\displaystyle\int_0^1 \frac{dx}{x+1}$;   (ii) $\displaystyle\int (x+1)^2 dx$;   (iii) $\displaystyle\int_0^{\pi/4} \cos 3\theta \, d\theta$.

(*b*) The current i, in amperes, flowing in a circuit at a time t seconds is given by

$$i = 5(1 - e^{-20t})$$

Evaluate $\displaystyle\int_0^{0\cdot 2} i \, dt$

(*c*) The mean current I, in the primary winding of a transformer is given by

$$I = I_1 - \int_0^1 x^2(V_1 - V_2)Y \, dx$$

where I_1, V_1, V_2, and Y are constants.
Show that $I = I_1 - \tfrac{1}{3}(V_1 - V_2)Y$.   (Nuneaton.)

71. (*a*) Evaluate the following integrals, in each case correct to three significant figures:

(i) $\int_1^4 \frac{2 + \sqrt{x}}{x^2}\, dx$; (ii) $\int_1^2 \frac{dx}{5 - 2x}$; (iii) $\int_0^1 e^{4x} dx$.

(*b*) If $\frac{d^2y}{dx^2} = 6 \sin x$, for all values of x, express $\frac{dy}{dx}$ and y each in terms of x, given that when $x = 0$, $\frac{dy}{dx} = 0$ and $y = 6$.   (E.M.E.U.)

72. (i) Integrate with respect to x:

$$\frac{1}{\sqrt{(1 + 2x)}}.$$

Evaluate:

(ii) $\int_0^\pi 3 \sin^2 x\, dx$; (iii) $\int_1^3 \left(e^{2x} + \frac{2}{x} \right) dx$.

(West Riding.)

73. A bowl, 4 in. deep, is a segment of a hollow sphere, the diameter of the plane bottom being 8 in., and that of the cross section at the top being 16 in. Find the radius of the sphere and the capacity of the bowl.

(Worcester.)

74. A circular bowl has a horizontal cross-section whose radius r in. at height h in. above the base is given by

$$r = 2 + \frac{h^2}{2}.$$

(i) Derive an expression for the area of cross-section at height h in. and find the total volume of the bowl if it is 5 in. deep.

(ii) Water is entering the bowl at 12 cu in. per sec. Find the rate at which the level of the water is rising when the depth is 2 in.   (West Riding.)

75. (i) Show that the function A cos $(\theta - c)$ can be made equivalent to 3 sin θ + 4 cos θ by assigning suitable values to A (a pure number) and to c (an angle expressed in radians). Give the values of A and c. Use your result to find

$$\int (3 \sin \theta + 4 \cos \theta) d\theta.$$

(ii) If $\int_1^a x^3 . dx = 156$, find the value of a.

(iii) Given that

$$\cos 4\theta = 8 \cos^4 \theta - 4 \cos 2\theta - 3$$

find

$$\int_0^{\frac{1}{2}\pi} \cos^4 \theta \, d\theta.$$

(N.C.T.E.C.)

76. (a) The work done, W ft lb by an expanding gas is given by $W = \int P d V$. A certain gas expands in accordance with the law $PV = C$. When $V = 2$ cu ft P is 50,400 lb per sq ft. Find the work done when the gas expands from 2 cu ft to 5 cu ft.

(b) Use the theorems of Pappus to find (1) the centre of gravity of a wire bent into a semicircle and (2) the centroid of a semicircular area.   (Shrewsbury.)

77. (a) The distance S feet of a point of a moving mechanism from a fixed point O is given by

$$S = 5 \cos (2t - 1\cdot7)$$

where t is time in seconds. Find the positive value of t when the point is first 2·5 ft from O.

Find the velocity and acceleration at this time.

(b) (i) A uniform sheet is in the form of a sector of a circle of radius x. Find the position of its centre of gravity when the angle of the sector is 90°.

(ii) A uniform thin wire is bent to form a circle of radius x. One fourth of the circle is then removed. Find the position of the centre of gravity of the remainder of the wire.   (Halifax.)

78. (i) Find, by integration, the second moment of area of a rectangular lamina, having sides of lengths a in. and b in., about an axis bisecting the sides of length a in.

(ii) Calculate the second moment of area of the girder section below:

(a) about AB;

(b) about an axis through the centroid and parallel to AB.

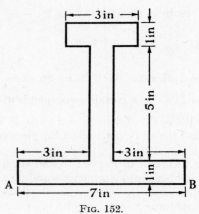

Fig. 152.

(Halifax.)

79. A straight thin uniform steel bar AB has a length of 6 ft, and a mass of 20 lb. P and Q are two points on the bar at distances 2 ft and 4 ft respectively from A. Calculate:

(a) the radius of gyration of the bar about an axis through A perpendicular to the bar;

(b) the radius of gyration of a compound body formed by the bar and a small mass of 6 lb attached to the bar at Q, about an axis through P perpendicular to the bar;

(c) the kinetic energy of the compound body when

it is rotating at 2 revolutions per second, about the axis through P.　　(Cheltenham.)

80. (*a*) Show that the radius of gyration for a circular disc, radius *r*, rotating about an axis through its centre and perpendicular to its plane, is given by $k = \dfrac{r}{\sqrt{2}}$.

(*b*) An air brake consists of four rectangular vanes ABCD rotating about an axis XX. Find the radius of gyration of the brake about the axis XX, neglecting the effect of the web connecting the vanes to the axis.

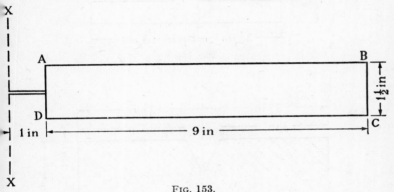

Fig. 153.

(Stafford.)

81. (i) Evaluate the following integrals:

(*a*) $\displaystyle\int_0^2 \frac{3x-1}{x+1}\,dx$;　　(*b*) $\displaystyle\int_0^1 (e^x + 1)^2\,dx$;

(*c*) $\displaystyle\int_1^e x \cdot \log x\,dx$;　　(*d*) $\displaystyle\int_0^{\pi/4} \cos^2\theta \cdot d\theta$.

(ii) For a certain curve, $\dfrac{d^2y}{dx^2} = \dfrac{1}{x^2}$. If the curve touches the line $y = 2x + 1$ at the point (1, 3), find the equation of the curve.　　(Cheltenham.)

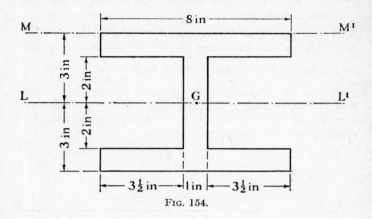

Fig. 154.

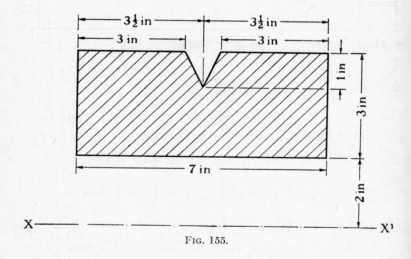

Fig. 155.

82. (*a*) Find by integration the second moment of area of a rectangle of length a, width b, about an axis through its centre and parallel to the side b.

Find the second moment of area of the H section shown, where G is the centroid of the section (Fig. 154),

(i) about LL'; (ii) about MM'.

(*b*) Find the volume of the solid swept out by the rotation of the shaded area shown in Fig. 155 about the axis XX'.

(Halifax.)

83. (*a*) Using the fact that the volume of a sphere is given by $V = \frac{4}{3}\pi R^3$, apply the rules of Guldinus to show that the position of the centroid of a semi-circular area is such that $\bar{x} = 0.424R$. See Fig. 156.

(*b*) A curved portion of coping stone may be regarded as formed by the rotation of the vertical section ABCDE about an axis XX, through a plan angle of 40°. The section is a semi-circle on one side of a rectangle. See Fig. 157.

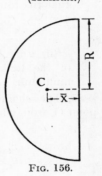

Fig. 156.

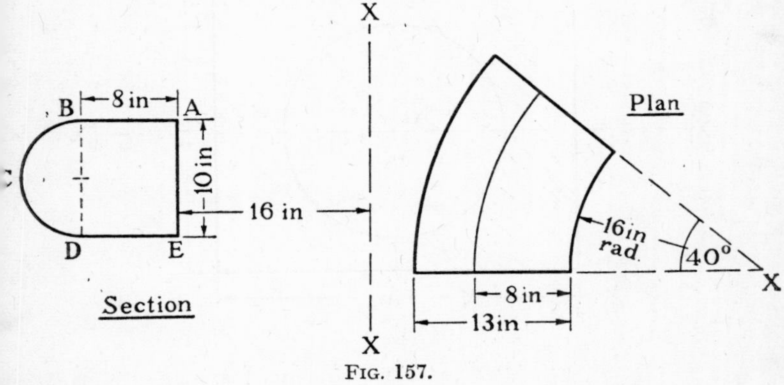

Fig. 157.

Calculate the total volume of the coping stone.

(Coventry.)

84. (*a*) Obtain the differential coefficient of

$$y = 3x^2 - 5x + 2$$

from first principles.

(*b*) A cylindrical hot-water tank is to hold 50 gallons of water.

(i) If the diameter of the tank is x feet, form an expression for the height in terms of x and hence show that the total surface area is given by

$$A = \frac{\pi x^2}{2} + \frac{32}{x} \quad (1 \text{ cu ft} = 6\tfrac{1}{4} \text{ gallons}).$$

(ii) Find, by differentiation, the diameter and height of the tank for which the surface area will be a minimum. (Coventry.)

85. The shaded figure represents a rectangle, centre point O, from which a circle, centre O, of radius 1·5 in. has

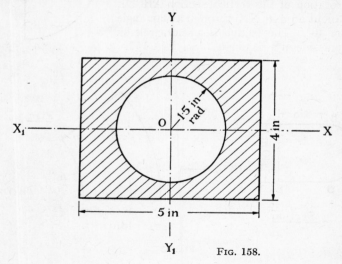

Fig. 158.

been removed. Calculate the second moment of the complete rectangle

(i) about axis XX_1;   (ii) about axis YY_1.

and deduce its second moment about an axis OZ, perpendicular to the plane of the figure.

Hence find the second moment of the shaded figure (rectangle less circle) about OZ.   (Coventry.)

86. (i) A " V " shaped groove 4 in. wide and 3 in. deep is cut round a solid cylinder of radius 6 in.

Find the volume of material removed, and the area of the surface of the groove.

(ii) A wheel is in the form of a circular cast-iron disc radius 12 in. thickness 4 in. in which there are four circular holes.

The radius of each hole is 4 in. and their centres are at a distance 6 in. from the centre of the wheel. Find the moment of inertia of the wheel about an axis through the centre perpendicular to the wheel, taking the density of iron to be 0·26 lb per cu in.   (Cheltenham.)

87. (a) Evaluate:

(i) $\int_4^{16} \dfrac{x-4}{\sqrt{x}}\,dx$;   (ii) $\int_2^6 \sqrt{2x-3}\,dx$.

(b) The area between the curve $y = 1 - \sin x$ and the axes in the first quadrant is rotated about the x-axis. Find the volume of the solid so generated.

(Burton-upon-Trent.)

88. (i) Find from first principles the moment of inertia of a thin circular disc of mass M and radius a about an axis, through its centre, and perpendicular to the plane of the disc.

(ii) A circular disc is of radius 10 ft amd mass 12 lb. Find:

(a) its moment of inertia about a tangent line to the disc;

(b) its moment of inertia about an axis perpendicular to the plane of the disc, 4 ft from the centre; and

(c) the kinetic energy of the disc when it is rotating at 120 revolutions per minute about the central axis perpendicular to its plane ($g = 32$ ft/sec^2).

(Cheltenham.)

89. (i) Perform the integrations

$$(1) \int \left(x - \frac{1}{x^2} \right) dx; \qquad (2) \int \left(\sqrt{x} + \frac{2}{\sqrt{x}} \right) dx.$$

(ii) Evaluate

$$(1) \int_0^{+5} \frac{36\pi}{49} (49 - x^2) \, dx; \qquad (2) \int_{-3}^{13} \sqrt{(5 - x)} \, dx.$$

(West Riding.)

90. Find the area enclosed by the curve $y = 2 + x - x^2$, the x-axis, and the ordinate at $x = 1$. If the area is rotated about the x-axis, calculate the volume of the solid formed, and hence apply Pappus' Theorem to find the distance above the x-axis, of the centroid of the rotating area.

(Cheltenham.)

91. (a) Integrate

$$(i) \ e^{-\frac{R}{L}t} \, dt; \qquad (ii) \ \cos \left(2\pi - \frac{x}{2} \right) dx;$$

$$(iii) \ \frac{\sqrt{x} - 1}{2x} \, dx.$$

(b) Evaluate $\displaystyle\int_0^{\pi/2} (1 - 2 \sin x)^2 \, dx.$ (Worcester.)

92. (i) Evaluate $(1) \displaystyle\int_1^4 \frac{10\sqrt{x}}{x^2} \, dx; \qquad (2) \int_0^{\pi} \sin 2x \, dx.$

(ii) If $\displaystyle\int_0^a \cos 2x \, . \, dx = \frac{1}{2}$, evaluate a.

(iii) Express $\dfrac{1}{x^2 - a^2}$ in partial fractions and hence

evaluate $\displaystyle\int_4^6 \dfrac{dx}{x^2 - 9}$.   (West Riding.)

93. (a) Integrate with respect to x

(i) $e^x + e^{-x}$;   (ii) $\dfrac{1 - 2x^2}{x}$.

(b) Evaluate $\displaystyle\int_0^{\pi/2} \cos 2x \, dx$.

Illustrate and explain your answer by reference to a sketch of the curve $y = \cos 2x$.

(c) Evaluate $\displaystyle\int_1^5 x(4 - x)^2 \, dx$.

If a force F is given in terms of the distance x by $F = x(4 - x)^2$, state the mean value of the force between $x = 1$ and $x = 5$.   (Handsworth.)

94. (b) The horizontal thrust, H, on a parabolic arch is given by

$$H = 5 \, \frac{wl^2}{8r} \cdot \int_0^{\frac{1}{2}} (x^2 - 2x^3 + x^4) \, dx.$$

Show that $H = \dfrac{wl^2}{96r}$.

(c) Find the area under the curve $y = \cos^2 x$ between the ordinates at $x = 0$ and $x = \dfrac{\pi}{4}$.   (Shrewsbury.)

95. (a) Evaluate the integrals:

(i) $\displaystyle\int 2\left(\sqrt{x} - \dfrac{1}{\sqrt{x}} \right) dx$;   (ii) $\displaystyle\int_0^{\pi/12} \sin^2 x \cdot dx$.

(b) Resolve $\dfrac{1}{x^2 - 1}$ into partial fractions and evaluate

$$\int_2^5 \frac{dx}{x^2 - 1}.$$

(c) By means of the substitution $u = 1 + x^2$, evaluate

$$\int 2x\sqrt{1 + x^2} \, . \, dx.$$

(Handsworth.)

96. If $y = \log_e (9 + x^2)$ find $\dfrac{dy}{dx}$. Use this result to

evaluate $\displaystyle\int_0^4 \dfrac{2x \, dx}{9 + x^2}$. Hence by resolving $\dfrac{36 - 2x}{(2x + 1)(9 + x^2)}$

into partial fractions evaluate $\displaystyle\int_0^4 \dfrac{36 - 2x}{(2x + 1)(9 + x^2)} \, dx$.

(Burton-upon-Trent.)

97. Evaluate:

(a) $\displaystyle\int_0^1 e^{2x-2} \, dx$;   (b) $\displaystyle\int_0^5 \dfrac{dx}{11 - 2x}$;

(c) $\displaystyle\int_1^2 \dfrac{x^4 + x^2 + 1}{x^2} \, dx$;   (d) $\displaystyle\int_0^2 \dfrac{dx}{(x + 2)^2}$.

(Halifax.)

98. (a) Simplify:

(i) $j(3 + 4j) - (5 - 2j)j^2 - 6 + j$;

(ii) $\dfrac{(9 - 3j)(2 + 7j)}{2 + 5j}$.

(b) Express $8 + 3j$ in the form of $r(\cos \theta + j \sin \theta)$ and illustrate your answer by means of an Argand Diagram.

(Shrewsbury.)

99. Express e^x as a series and use the series to calculate the value of e to four decimal places. Write down a series for e^{-x} and a series for $\frac{1}{2}(e^x + e^{-x})$.   (West Riding.)

100. (a) Express in "$a + jb$" form the square of $2 + j5$.

By converting both the original expression and your result to polar form, demonstrate that $[R \, | \, \theta \, |]^2 = R^2 \, | \, 2\theta \, |$.

(b) Reduce to its simplest form:

$$\frac{j(3 + j7)}{(4 + j5) + \dfrac{8}{(2 - j3)}}$$

(S.W. Essex.)

EXERCISE 56. Classified questions for revision

CALCULATIONS

1. (a) An ammeter read 5·72 amps. when the true reading was 5·6 amps. Express the error as a percentage of the true reading.

(b) Evaluate $\sqrt{s(s - a)(s - b)(s - c)}$, given $a = 4·2$, $b = 5·5$, $c = 6·3$ and $s = \frac{1}{2}(a + b + c)$.

2. Given $\dfrac{R}{r} = \sqrt{\dfrac{f + p}{f - p}}$, find p when $f = 3000$, $R = 3·5$ and $r = 2·5$.

3. Find, correct to three significant figures, the value of $\left(\dfrac{a^3 - b^3}{a + b}\right)^{-0·2}$, when $a = 3·23$ and $b = 2·75$.

4. If $\log_e \dfrac{1 + r}{1 - r} = 1·2$, find the value of r.

5. Evaluate $(R^{\frac{2}{3}} + r^{\frac{2}{3}})^{\frac{3}{2}}$ when $R = 8·12$, $r = 4·76$.

6. Evaluate:

(a) $\log_e \dfrac{A}{B}$ when $A = 344$ and $B = 215$.

(b) $e^{Rt/L}$ when $R = 8·6$, $L = 0·4$, $t = 0·05$.

7. Evaluate $a^{1·2}(b^{0·8} - c^{0·6})$, when $a = 5·17$, $b = 4·05$, $c = 0·91$.

8. Evaluate $e^{-Rt/L} \sin 100\pi t$, given that $e = 2·718$, $R = 6$, $L = 0·025$ and $t = 3·5 \times 10^{-3}$.

9. If $y = \dfrac{0·055n^{4·2}}{1 - 0·00035n^{2·5}}$, find y when $n = 12·4$.

10. Find the value, to three significant figures, of

(a) $\dfrac{1}{n}(a^{-n} - b^{-n})$ when $a = 4$, $b = 10$ and $n = \dfrac{3}{2}$.

(b) $\dfrac{1}{2a} \log_e \dfrac{a + x}{a - x}$ when $a = 1 + \sqrt{3}$ and $x = \sqrt{3}$.

EQUATIONS

11. Solve the following equations:

(a) $x^4 - 8 \cdot 87x^2 - 2 \cdot 28 = 0$.

(b) $54^{3x-2} = 2 \cdot 71$.

(c) $8 = x + \sqrt{x^2 - 8}$.

12. Solve:

(a) $8(5x - 3)^2 = 3(9 - 10x)$.

(b) Two quantities V and R are connected by a law of the form $V = aR + \dfrac{b}{R}$, where a and b are constants.

It is known that when $V = 2 \cdot 2$, $R = 0 \cdot 8$ and $V = 2 \cdot 3$ when $R = 1 \cdot 2$. Find a and b.

13. A law of the form $E = a\theta^2 + b\theta + c$ connects E and θ. If $E = 576$ when $\theta = 100$, $E = 1320$ when $\theta = 200$ and $E = 2072$ when $\theta = 300$, determine the values of the constants a, b, c, and hence find E when $\theta = 250$.

14. Solve:

(a) $5(2 - x)^2 = 7x - 8$.

(b) $1 \cdot 39^{2x} = 6 \cdot 31$.

(c) $\log_e (x^2 + 0 \cdot 05) = 0 \cdot 27$.

15. (a) Solve for R, $(3R - 1)^2 = (3R - 5)(3R + 5) + 2R - 6$.

(b) Solve for a and b, (i) $a + \dfrac{b}{16} = 12$, (ii) $a + \dfrac{b}{64} = 0$.

16. Find the value of r (other than zero) which satisfies the equation:

$$1 \cdot 75r^{0 \cdot 75} - 1 \cdot 87r^{0 \cdot 87} = 0.$$

17. Solve:

    (a) $3x = 2\sqrt{x} + 17$.   (b) $3 \cdot 2^{2x} = 5 \cdot 1$.

18. Solve:

    (a) $8 \cdot 756^{(4x-1)} = 4 \cdot 328^{(2x+3)}$.

    (b) $\left.\begin{array}{l} \log_5 (4x - 5) = 2 \\ \log_8 (2x + 3y) = \frac{1}{3} \end{array}\right\}$.

19. Find C, from the formulæ $C = \dfrac{Q}{E}$, $Q = \dfrac{Ktd}{2}\left(1 + \dfrac{\lambda}{2}\right)$, given that $d = 1 \cdot 3$, $K = 2 \cdot 1 \times 10^{-7}$, $t = 5 \cdot 34$, $\lambda = 0 \cdot 425$, $E = 0 \cdot 91$.

20. (a) If $y = kx^n$, find k and n, if $x = 10$ when $y = 14 \cdot 5$, and $x = 40$ when $y = 116 \cdot 0$.

    (b) Solve, $3^x \times 5^{x-1} = 6 \cdot 76$ (to two significant figures).

TRIGONOMETRY

21. N is the foot of the perpendicular from the vertex A of a triangle ABC on the horizontal plane through BC to which the plane of ABC is inclined at $40°$. Calculate the angle BAC if $\angle NBC = 70° \ 30'$ and $\angle NCB = 56° \ 30'$.

22. (a) Show how to express $a \sin \theta + b \cos \theta$ in the form $A \sin (\theta + \alpha)$, giving the values of A and α in terms of a and b.

    (b) The voltage in an electrical circuit after time t is given by $E = a \sin pt + b \cos pt$. If $a = 75$, $b = 75\pi$ and $p = 100\pi$ find the smallest positive value of t for E to have a maximum value.

23. Prove that in any triangle, $a^2 = b^2 + c^2 - 2bc \cos A$. In a force triangle ABC, $\overline{AB}$ and $\overline{BC}$ represent forces of $3 \cdot 94$ and $2 \cdot 5$ tons respectively. $\overline{AC}$ represents their resultant. If $\angle ABC = 98°$, find the magnitude and direction of this resultant.

24. (a) Simplify $\sin (A + B) - \sin (A - B)$ and deduce the formula for $\sin X - \sin Y$ as a product.

(b) Find the acute angle which satisfies the equation $\cos 2\theta = 2 \sin \theta$.

25. Express $5 \cos^2 \theta - 2 \sin^2 \theta$ in the form $a + b \cos 2\theta$, and draw the graph of the function from $\theta = 0°$ to $\theta = 180°$; also calculate the values of θ for which the function is zero.

26. Establish the formula $\tan \dfrac{B - C}{2} = \dfrac{b - c}{b + c} \cot \dfrac{A}{2}$.

From an observation post A on the shore a mine is observed at B on a bearing N. 15° E. and five minutes later it is observed at C on a bearing N. 33° E. The distances AB and AC are estimated as being 2800 ft and 2000 ft respectively. Find in m.p.h. the direction and speed of the current.

27. PQ is an arc of a circle of radius r, subtending an angle θ radians at the centre of the circle ($\theta < \pi$). Show that the area of the smaller segment cut off by the chord PQ is given by $A = \frac{1}{2}r^2(\theta - \sin \theta)$.

In a rectangle ABCD, AB = 4·33 in. and BC = 2·5 in. An arc of a circle joins the corners A and C, and DC is tangential to this arc. Find the area of that part of the rectangle bounded by the arc and the sides AB and BC.

28. Find $\sin 2\theta$ in terms of $\cos \theta$ and $\sin \theta$, and $\cos 2\theta$ in terms of $\cos \theta$; then solve $\cos 2\theta = 2 - \sqrt{3} \cos \theta$, giving the values of θ between 0° and 360°.

29. In a triangle ABC, $a = 5$ in., $b = 7$ in., $c = 8$ in. Calculate the length of the perpendicular from A to BC.

30. Prove that $\sin (A + B) = \sin A \cos B + \cos A \sin B$, and state the corresponding formula for $\cos (A + B)$.

By expanding $\cos (\theta + 153°)$ and $\sin (\theta + 243°)$ prove that $\cos (\theta + 153°) = \sin (\theta + 243°)$ for all values of θ.

31. The angles of elevation of an airplane, at a certain instant, from two stations A and B, 1500 yd apart and in the same vertical plane as the airplane, were 65° and 40° respectively. Calculate the height of the airplane.

32. In any triangle ABC, prove that $a^2 = b^2 + c^2 - 2bc \cos A$.

Two adjacent sides of a parallelogram are 3·3 ft and 4·8 ft long, and contain an angle of 65°. Calculate the lengths of the diagonals.

33. Prove $\cos \theta = \dfrac{1 - t^2}{1 + t^2}$ and $\sin \theta = \dfrac{2t}{1 + t^2}$, where $t = \tan \dfrac{\theta}{2}$.

Use the above substitutions to solve $4 \cos \theta - \sin \theta = 1$, giving the values of θ (to the nearest degree) between 0° and 360° which satisfy the equation.

34. Prove that $\dfrac{\cos (45° + \theta)}{\cos (45° - \theta)} = \dfrac{1 - \tan \theta}{1 + \tan \theta}$. Hence solve the equation

$$4 \cos (45° + \theta) = \cos (45° - \theta) \quad [0° < \theta < 360°].$$

35. ABC is a triangle in which B = 50°, AB = 7 in. and BC = 10 in. A point D is on the opposite side of AC from B, such that AD = 4 in. and CD = 5 in. Calculate the angle ADC.

36. The elevation of the top of a steeple from a place A due S. of it is 45°, and from B, 100 yd due W. of A, the elevation is 15°. Find the height of the steeple.

37. The third harmonic of a voltage wave is given as $- 0·13 \sin 3\theta + 0·11 \cos 3\theta$. Put this in the form $r \sin (3\theta + \alpha)$, and find the values of r and α.

38. (i) If $\mu = \tan \beta$, show that $\dfrac{\sin \alpha - \mu \cos \alpha}{\cos \alpha + \mu \sin \alpha} = \tan (\alpha - \beta)$.

(ii) By expressing $\sin 3\theta - \sin \theta$ as a product, or otherwise, find the values of θ between 0° and 360° which satisfy the equation $\sin 3\theta - \sin \theta = 0$.

39. OA is a crank, length 6 in.; AB a connecting rod, length 27 in. Find the length of OB when angle AOB = 100°. Find also the greatest value of the angle ABO for all positions of the rotating crank OA.

40. A ship is travelling due E. at a steady speed of 15 knots. From the ship, the bearing of a lighthouse is observed to be N. 73° E.; 10 min later the bearing is N. 42° W. How far was the ship from the lighthouse when the second bearing was taken? Find the bearing of the lighthouse from the ship when they are 3 nautical miles apart. (1 nautical mile = 6080 ft; 1 knot = 1 nautical mile per hour.)

41. Put $24 \sin \theta + 7 \cos \theta$ in the form $A \sin (\theta + \alpha)$ and find the values of A and α.

Hence find (a) when $24 \sin \theta + 7 \cos \theta$ is a maximum, (b) the values of θ which satisfy the equation $24 \sin \theta + 7 \cos \theta = 15$.

42. Establish the formula $\dfrac{a}{\sin A} = \dfrac{b}{\sin B} = \dfrac{c}{\sin C}$.

AB is a straight road, 920 yd long, running due E. from A. There is a control tower at C, which bears N. 25° E. from A, and N. 16° 15′ W. from B. Find (a) the length of a straight road from A to C, and (b) the shortest distance from C to AB.

43. A barrage balloon P is known to be vertically above a point A. Find its height above this point, given the following data:

$\angle ABC = 38°$; $\angle ACB = 69°$; $BC = 850$ ft, where A, B, C are in the horizontal plane through A and $\angle PBA = 68°$.

44. Assuming the formula for $\sin (A + B)$ and $\cos (A + B)$ (or otherwise), prove that $\tan (A + B) = \dfrac{\tan A + \tan B}{1 - \tan A \tan B}$.

PN is a vertical pole of height a, N being on the ground, and Q is a point on the pole, b above N. If O is a point on the ground c from N, and PQ subtends an angle θ at O, prove that $\tan \theta = \dfrac{(a - b)c}{ab + c^2}$.

45. If $w = 100\pi$, $R = 10$ and $L = 0.006$, express $R \sin wt - Lw \cos wt$ in the form $Z \sin (wt - \phi)$, and find the values of Z and $\cos \phi$.

CALCULUS

46. Find $\dfrac{dy}{dx}$ when (i) $y = 2x^3 - \dfrac{1}{x^3} + 1$, (ii) $y = e^x(2 - x)$,

(iii) $y = \dfrac{x}{3x + 2}$.

If $pv = 500$, find $\dfrac{dp}{dv}$ when $v = 5$.

47. If $y = 4\cdot51 \sin x + 2\cdot5 \cos x$ (x in radians), find
(a) $\dfrac{dy}{dx}$, (b) the smallest positive value of x which makes
$\dfrac{dy}{dx} = 0$, and (c) $\displaystyle\int_0^{\pi/2} y\,dx$.

48. In time t sec a body is displaced s ft in a straight path, so that $s = 25t + 16t^2$. Deduce from first principles expressions for the velocity and acceleration at time t.

(a) If $y = x^3 + \dfrac{2}{x}$, find the value of $\dfrac{d^2y}{dx^2}$ when $x = 2$.

(b) If $r = \theta \cos \theta$, find $\dfrac{dr}{d\theta}$.

49. State the conditions to be satisfied if $y = f(x)$ has a minimum value when $x = a$.

The total heat, H units generated in a circuit, is given by

$$H = 3x^2 + 4\cdot5(10 - x)^2.$$

Find the value of x for which H is least, and the value of H in this case.

50. Find $\dfrac{dy}{dx}$ when (a) $y = (3x^2 - 1)(4x + 3)$; (b) $y = \dfrac{e^x}{1 - x}$.

If $x = 10 \sin t - 3 \cos t$, show that $\dfrac{d^2x}{dt^2} = -x$, and

(c) find the value of $\dfrac{d^2x}{dt^2}$ when $x = \dfrac{2\pi}{3}$.

51. A point moves in a plane so that its co-ordinates with respect to a pair of perpendicular axes through O are, at time t, given by $x = 3 \sin t$, $y = 2 \cos t$. Find its components of velocity along the axes when $t = \dfrac{\pi}{3}$. Hence find $\dfrac{dy}{dx}$ at this time.

52. If $y = x(2 + x)$, find from first principles the value of $\dfrac{dy}{dx}$.

    (a) $y = \dfrac{8}{x} - \dfrac{x^2}{8}$, find x so that $\dfrac{d^2y}{dx^2} = 0$.

    (b) Evaluate $\dfrac{d}{d\theta}(\theta + \sin \theta \cos \theta)$ when $\theta = \dfrac{\pi}{4}$.

53. Find $\dfrac{dy}{dx}$ when (a) $y = x \log_e x$, (b) $y = \dfrac{a - x}{a + x}$ (a is constant). Show that the points $P \equiv (1, 2)$, $Q \equiv (3, 4)$ lie on the curve $10y = 1 + 22x - 3x^2$, and find to the nearest degree the angles of the triangle formed by the straight line PQ and the tangents to the curve at P and Q.

54. The motion of a lift from $t = 0$ sec, to $t = 12$ sec, is given by the formula $s = \frac{1}{240}t^5 - \frac{1}{8}t^4 + t^3$, where s ft is the distance moved. Show that the acceleration is $\frac{1}{12}t(t - 6)(t - 12)$ ft/sec², and that the maximum velocity is 27 ft/sec.

55. The rate of loss of heat from a hot body is proportional to the area of the surface exposed. Prove that the most efficient cylindrical hot-water tank, of given volume, is one whose height equals its diameter.

56. The cross-section of an open gutter made of thin material is a trapezium, with its sloping sides equal and inclined at 60° to the base. If the area of the section is $108\sqrt{3}$ sq in., find the dimensions of the section, if the gutter has a fixed length, and the amount of material used in its construction has to be a minimum.

57. The volume of a right-circular cylinder is 2 cu ft. If r is the radius in ft, prove that the total length, L ft,

of a piece of string which passes twice round the circumference, and once lengthwise round the cylinder, is given by

$$L = 4r(1 + \pi) + \frac{4}{\pi r^2}.$$

Find the value of r so that L is the shortest possible length.

58. Evaluate the following integrals:

(a) $\int_{\frac{1}{2}}^{\frac{3}{2}} \left(1 + \frac{3}{x^2}\right)dx.$ (b) $\int_{\pi/6}^{\pi/2} \cos 3\theta d\theta.$

(c) $\int_0^{0\cdot01} 30 \sin 100\pi t dt.$

59. Evaluate (a) $\int_1^5 (2x - \sqrt{x})dx$, (b) $\int_0^{\pi/12} 5 \cos 6t dt$, and (c) find the mean value of $5 \cos 6t$ between $t = 0$ and $t = \frac{\pi}{12}.$

60. If $\frac{d^2y}{dx^2} = 6x - 2$, express y as a function of x, given that $\frac{dy}{dx} = 3$, $y = -9$, when $x = 2$, and find a value of x which makes y a minimum.

61. If $\frac{dt}{dQ} = -\frac{CR}{Q}$, and $C = 0\cdot006$, $R = 80$, find t in terms of Q given that when $t = 0$, $Q = 10$.

62. Show that the mean value of $\sin x$, as x varies from 0 to π, is $\frac{1}{\pi}$. Sketch the graph of $y = 2 - \sqrt{x}$ ($\sqrt{x}$ positive only) and find the area between the graph, the x-axis, and the ordinates at $x = 0$ and $x = 4$.

63. Sketch the curve $y = 2 - \sqrt{x}$, between $x = 0$, $x = 4$, where $\sqrt{x}$ has both its positive and negative values. If the area bounded by the curve and part of the ordinate at

$x = 4$ is rotated about the x-axis, find the volume of the hollow solid generated.

64. Employ Simpson's Rule to find the area enclosed by the curve $y = \frac{1}{16}(2x^2 + 5x + 8)$, the x-axis and the ordinates at $x = -1$ and $x = 3$. Compare your result with that got by integration.

65. The deflection, y in., of a beam at x ft from one end is given by $\dfrac{d^2y}{dx^2} = \dfrac{1}{1200}(10 - x)^2$. Find y in terms of x given that both y and $\dfrac{dy}{dx}$ are zero when x is zero. Show that when $x = 10$, $y = 2\frac{1}{12}$.

66. (a) Evaluate $\displaystyle\int_0^2 \left(3\sqrt{x} - \frac{1}{3\sqrt{x}}\right)dx$ and $\displaystyle\int_0^{\pi/4} 5\sin 2\theta d\theta$, and find the mean value of the latter integral between the given limits.

(b) That part of the curve $y = 3x - x^2$ which lies above the x-axis is rotated about that axis. Find the volume generated in a complete rotation.

67. If $\dfrac{d^2y}{dx^2} = 3\sin 3x + 2\cos 2x$, show that

$y = 1 - \frac{1}{3}\sin 3x - \frac{1}{2}\cos 2x$ given that when $x = 0$, $y = \frac{1}{2}$ and $\dfrac{dy}{dx} = -1$.

Verify that y has a minimum value when $x = \dfrac{\pi}{10}$.

68. (a) Express $2\sin 2x \cos x$ as the sum of two sines and then find $\displaystyle\int_0^{\pi/3} 2\sin 2x \cos x dx$.

Evaluate (b) $\displaystyle\int_1^{6\cdot8} \frac{4}{x^{0\cdot8}}dx$, (c) $\displaystyle\int_0^{\pi/2} \sin 2\theta d\theta$.

(d) The weight of a tapering rod included between cross-sections at distances x in. and $(x + dx)$ in. from the smaller end is $\frac{1}{4}\left(1 + \dfrac{x}{60}\right)^2 dx$ lb. Find by integration the total weight of the rod, if its length is 30 in.

69. Evaluate $\int x^2(3 - 5x^2)dx$ and $\int_1^8 \frac{4}{\sqrt[3]{x}}dx$; also find the area between the curve $y = 2\cos 3x$, the x-axis, and the ordinates at $x = 0$ and $x = \frac{\pi}{18}$.

70. Evaluate (a) $\int_1^9 \frac{\sqrt{x}}{4}dx$, (b) $\int \left(x^4 + \frac{1}{x^4}\right)dx$, (c) $\int_0^\pi \sin \frac{1}{2}\theta d\theta$.

A curve $y = f(x)$ passes through the point $(0, 6)$ and $\frac{dy}{dx} = 5e^x$. Determine the form of $f(x)$.

BINOMIAL THEOREM, MOMENTS OF INERTIA, ETC.

71. If x is small show that $(1 - x)^{\frac{1}{2}}$ and $\left(1 + \frac{x}{2}\right)^{-1}$ are approx. equal (use Binomial Th.).

Write down the approx. values of $\sqrt{0\cdot994}$ and $\frac{1}{1\cdot003}$.

72. Neglecting powers of x above the second, find x from the equation:

$$\left(1 + \frac{x}{2}\right)^5 + \left(1 - \frac{x}{2}\right)^5 = 2\cdot002.$$

73. Show from first principles that the moment of inertia, I, of a triangle height h in., base b in., about an axis parallel to the base through the vertex is given by $I = \frac{1}{4}bh^3$ in.[4] units.

ABCD is a trapezium, with AB, DC parallel and 3 in. and 5 in. long respectively. Their distance apart is 4 in. The sides DA and CB are produced to meet in O. Find the distance of O from AB and use the above formula to deduce the M.I. of the trapezium about an axis XX through O and parallel to AB.

74. Expand $(1 + x)^n$ as far as the term in x^3.

If $l = (3 + a)$, and powers of a above the first may be neglected, find the approx. value of $2l^4 - 3l^3 - 5l$. Use your result to find correct to three significant figures the value of l given by the equation $2l^4 - 3l^3 - 5l = 71$, the value of l being known to differ from 3 by a small amount.

75. A plane figure is bounded by the curve $y = 3\sqrt[3]{x}$, the axis of x, and the ordinates at $x = 0$ and $x = 8$. Sketch the figure, and find its moments of inertia about the axes of x and y, using 1 in. as the unit of length along each axis.

76. Find the approx. values of $(2 + h)^6$ and $(2 + h)^3$, if powers of h above the first may be neglected.

If $R = (2 + h)$ where h is small, find the value of R given by the equation $R^6 - 7R^3 - 11R + 11 = 0$, correct to three significant figures.

77. Determine by integration the M.I. of (a) a rectangle b in. by d in., about a side of length b in., (b) a circle, diameter d in., about an axis through the centre perpendicular to its plane.

78. Find by integration the M.I. of a rod AB, about an axis through A perpendicular to the rod, given length $AB = l$ in., and m lb is its mass per in. Find also the M.I. of the rod about a parallel axis through its mid-point.

79. The co-ordinates of a point A are $x = 5$, $y = 3$, and of a point B, $x = 8$, $y = 6$. Find the length of AB and the angle which the straight line AB makes with the positive sense of OX.

80. The height of the frustum of a cone is 6 in., and the diameter of the base and top are 12 in. and 10 in., respectively. Find the height of the cone and the volume of the frustum.

81. Plot $y = 2x^2 - 7x + 5$ for values of x between 0 and 3, and from the graph determine the roots of the equation $2x^2 - 7x + 5 = 0$. Find the roots of this equation by an alternative method.

82. AB is a diameter of a circle, and AC a chord 4 in. long making 60° with AB. CD is perpendicular to AB. Calculate (a) the radius, (b) the lengths BC and CD, and (c) the area of the triangle ABC.

83. With the usual notation, prove that the area of a triangle is given by $\sqrt{s(s - a)(s - b)(s - c)}$.

Find the volume of a steel bar of length 6 ft, whose cross-section perpendicular to its length is a triangle of sides $3\frac{1}{2}$ in., $4\frac{3}{8}$ in. and $5\frac{3}{8}$ in.

84. Find the area between the parabola $y = x^2 - 3x$, the x-axis and the ordinates at $x = 1$ and $x = 3$. Find also the distance of the centroid of this area from the x-axis.

85. When x has the values $- 2, 0, + 1, + 2$, the values of the function $ax^3 + bx^2 + cx + k$, where a, b, c, k are constants, are $- 14, + 4, - 2$ and $- 2$ respectively. For what other values of x is the function equal to $+ 4$?

86. For what value of θ, between $0°$ and $180°$, is $\tan \theta + 3 \sin \theta = 0$? By putting $\sin \theta + \cos \theta$ in the form $r \sin (\theta + \alpha)$, find its maximum value. If θ is one of the remaining angles of a right-angled triangle whose perimeter is 10 in., express the length of the hypotenuse as a function of θ, and find its minimum value.

87. (a) Expand $(2 + x)^5$ in ascending powers of x.

(b) Expand $(1 - \frac{3}{2}x)^{-\frac{1}{3}}$ to four terms, and hence find the value of $\dfrac{1}{\sqrt[3]{1 - \frac{3}{2}x}}$ correct to four decimal places when $x = 0\cdot04$.

(c) Differentiate $x^{-\frac{1}{3}}$ from first principles.

88. Assuming the formula for the volume of a solid sphere of radius r, find by using Guldinus' Th. the position of the centroid of a semi-circular area of radius r.

A groove whose section is a semi-circle of diameter 1 in. is turned in a solid circular shaft of diameter 6 in. Find the volume of material removed.

89. Tabulate the values of the functions $\sin (2x + 10°)$ and $2 \cos (x + 60°)$ for values of $x = 0°, 5°, 10° \ldots$ up to $30°$. Using the same axes, draw the graphs of these two functions over the range $x = 0°$ to $x = 30°$, and read from your diagram a value of x (to the nearest degree) which satisfies the equation $\sin (2x + 10°) - 2 \cos (x + 60°) = 0$.

LOGARITHMS of numbers 100 to 549

	0	1	2	3	4	5	6	7	8	9	1	2	3	4	5	6	7	8	9
10	0000	0043	0086	0128	0170	0212	0253	0294	0334	0374	4	8	12	17	21	25	29	33	37
11	0414	0453	0492	0531	0569	0607	0645	0682	0719	0755	4	8	11	15	19	23	26	30	34
12	0792	0828	0864	0899	0934	0969	1004	1038	1072	1106	3	7	10	14	17	21	24	28	31
13	1139	1173	1206	1239	1271	1303	1335	1367	1399	1430	3	6	10	13	16	19	23	26	29
14	1461	1492	1523	1553	1584	1614	1644	1673	1703	1732	3	6	9	12	15	18	21	24	27
15	1761	1790	1818	1847	1875	1903	1931	1959	1987	2014	3	6	8	11	14	17	20	22	25
16	2041	2068	2095	2122	2148	2175	2201	2227	2253	2279	3	5	8	11	13	16	18	21	24
17	2304	2330	2355	2380	2405	2430	2455	2480	2504	2529	2	5	7	10	12	15	17	20	22
18	2553	2577	2601	2625	2648	2672	2695	2718	2742	2765	2	5	7	9	12	14	16	19	21
19	2788	2810	2833	2856	2878	2900	2923	2945	2967	2989	2	4	7	9	11	13	16	18	20
20	3010	3032	3054	3075	3096	3118	3139	3160	3181	3201	2	4	6	8	11	13	15	17	19
21	3222	3243	3263	3284	3304	3324	3345	3365	3385	3404	2	4	6	8	10	12	14	16	18
22	3424	3444	3464	3483	3502	3522	3541	3560	3579	3598	2	4	6	8	10	12	14	15	17
23	3617	3636	3655	3674	3692	3711	3729	3747	3766	3784	2	4	6	7	9	11	13	15	17
24	3802	3820	3838	3856	3874	3892	3909	3927	3945	3962	2	4	5	7	9	11	12	14	16
25	3979	3997	4014	4031	4048	4065	4082	4099	4116	4133	2	3	5	7	9	10	12	14	15
26	4150	4166	4183	4200	4216	4232	4249	4265	4281	4298	2	3	5	7	8	10	11	13	15
27	4314	4330	4346	4362	4378	4393	4409	4425	4440	4456	2	3	5	6	8	9	11	13	14
28	4472	4487	4502	4518	4533	4548	4564	4579	4594	4609	2	3	5	6	8	9	11	12	14
29	4624	4639	4654	4669	4683	4698	4713	4728	4742	4757	1	3	4	6	7	9	10	12	13
30	4771	4786	4800	4814	4829	4843	4857	4871	4886	4900	1	3	4	6	7	9	10	11	13
31	4914	4928	4942	4955	4969	4983	4997	5011	5024	5038	1	3	4	5	7	8	10	11	12
32	5051	5065	5079	5092	5105	5119	5132	5145	5159	5172	1	3	4	5	7	8	9	11	12
33	5185	5198	5211	5224	5237	5250	5263	5276	5289	5302	1	3	4	5	6	8	9	10	12
34	5315	5328	5340	5353	5366	5378	5391	5403	5416	5428	1	3	4	5	6	8	9	10	11
35	5441	5453	5465	5478	5490	5502	5514	5527	5539	5551	1	2	4	5	6	7	9	10	11
36	5563	5575	5587	5599	5611	5623	5635	5647	5658	5670	1	2	4	5	6	7	8	10	11
37	5682	5694	5705	5717	5729	5740	5752	5763	5775	5786	1	2	3	5	6	7	8	9	10
38	5798	5809	5821	5832	5843	5855	5866	5877	5888	5899	1	2	3	5	6	7	8	9	10
39	5911	5922	5933	5944	5955	5966	5977	5988	5999	6010	1	2	3	4	5	7	8	9	10
40	6021	6031	6042	6053	6064	6075	6085	6096	6107	6117	1	2	3	4	5	6	7	9	10
41	6128	6138	6149	6160	6170	6180	6191	6201	6212	6222	1	2	3	4	5	6	7	8	9
42	6232	6243	6253	6263	6274	6284	6294	6304	6314	6325	1	2	3	4	5	6	7	8	9
43	6335	6345	6355	6365	6375	6385	6395	6405	6415	6425	1	2	3	4	5	6	7	8	9
44	6435	6444	6454	6464	6474	6484	6493	6503	6513	6522	1	2	3	4	5	6	7	8	9
45	6532	6542	6551	6561	6571	6580	6590	6599	6609	6618	1	2	3	4	5	6	7	8	9
46	6628	6637	6646	6656	6665	6675	6684	6693	6702	6712	1	2	3	4	5	6	7	7	8
47	6721	6730	6739	6749	6758	6767	6776	6785	6794	6803	1	2	3	4	5	5	6	7	8
48	6812	6821	6830	6839	6848	6857	6866	6875	6884	6893	1	2	3	4	4	5	6	7	8
49	6902	6911	6920	6928	6937	6946	6955	6964	6972	6981	1	2	3	4	4	5	6	7	8
50	6990	6998	7007	7016	7024	7033	7042	7050	7059	7067	1	2	3	3	4	5	6	7	8
51	7076	7084	7093	7101	7110	7118	7126	7135	7143	7152	1	2	3	3	4	5	6	7	8
52	7160	7168	7177	7185	7193	7202	7210	7218	7226	7235	1	2	2	3	4	5	6	7	7
53	7243	7251	7259	7267	7275	7284	7292	7300	7308	7316	1	2	2	3	4	5	6	6	7
54	7324	7332	7340	7348	7356	7364	7372	7380	7388	7396	1	2	2	3	4	5	6	6	7
	0	1	2	3	4	5	6	7	8	9	1	2	3	4	5	6	7	8	9

LOGARITHMS of numbers 550 to 999

	0	1	2	3	4	5	6	7	8	9	1	2	3	4	5	6	7	8	9
55	7404	7412	7419	7427	7435	7443	7451	7459	7466	7474	1	2	2	3	4	5	5	6	7
56	7482	7490	7497	7505	7513	7520	7528	7536	7543	7551	1	2	2	3	4	5	5	6	7
57	7559	7566	7574	7582	7589	7597	7604	7612	7619	7627	1	2	2	3	4	5	5	6	7
58	7634	7642	7649	7657	7664	7672	7679	7686	7694	7701	1	1	2	3	4	4	5	6	7
59	7709	7716	7723	7731	7738	7745	7752	7760	7767	7774	1	1	2	3	4	4	5	6	7
60	7782	7789	7796	7803	7810	7818	7825	7832	7839	7846	1	1	2	3	4	4	5	6	6
61	7853	7860	7868	7875	7882	7889	7896	7903	7910	7917	1	1	2	3	4	4	5	6	6
62	7924	7931	7938	7945	7952	7959	7966	7973	7980	7987	1	1	2	3	3	4	5	6	6
63	7993	8000	8007	8014	8021	8028	8035	8041	8048	8055	1	1	2	3	3	4	5	6	6
64	8062	8069	8075	8082	8089	8096	8102	8109	8116	8122	1	1	2	3	3	4	5	5	6
65	8129	8136	8142	8149	8156	8162	8169	8176	8182	8189	1	1	2	3	3	4	5	5	6
66	8195	8202	8209	8215	8222	8228	8235	8241	8248	8254	1	1	2	3	3	4	5	5	6
67	8261	8267	8274	8280	8287	8293	8299	8306	8312	8319	1	1	2	3	3	4	4	5	6
68	8325	8331	8338	8344	8351	8357	8363	8370	8376	8382	1	1	2	3	3	4	4	5	6
69	8388	8395	8401	8407	8414	8420	8426	8432	8439	8445	1	1	2	3	3	4	4	5	6
70	8451	8457	8463	8470	8476	8482	8488	8494	8500	8506	1	1	2	2	3	4	4	5	6
71	8513	8519	8525	8531	8537	8543	8549	8555	8561	8567	1	1	2	2	3	4	4	5	5
72	8573	8579	8585	8591	8597	8603	8609	8615	8621	8627	1	1	2	2	3	4	4	5	5
73	8633	8639	8645	8651	8657	8663	8669	8675	8681	8686	1	1	2	2	3	4	4	5	5
74	8692	8698	8704	8710	8716	8722	8727	8733	8739	8745	1	1	2	2	3	4	4	5	5
75	8751	8756	8762	8768	8774	8779	8785	8791	8797	8802	1	1	2	2	3	3	4	5	5
76	8808	8814	8820	8825	8831	8837	8842	8848	8854	8859	1	1	2	2	3	3	4	5	5
77	8865	8871	8876	8882	8887	8893	8899	8904	8910	8915	1	1	2	2	3	3	4	4	5
78	8921	8927	8932	8938	8943	8949	8954	8960	8965	8971	1	1	2	2	3	3	4	4	5
79	8976	8982	8987	8993	8998	9004	9009	9015	9020	9025	1	1	2	2	3	3	4	4	5
80	9031	9036	9042	9047	9053	9058	9063	9069	9074	9079	1	1	2	2	3	3	4	4	5
81	9085	9090	9096	9101	9106	9112	9117	9122	9128	9133	1	1	2	2	3	3	4	4	5
82	9138	9143	9149	9154	9159	9165	9170	9175	9180	9186	1	1	2	2	3	3	4	4	5
83	9191	9196	9201	9206	9212	9217	9222	9227	9232	9238	1	1	2	2	3	3	4	4	5
84	9243	9248	9253	9258	9263	9269	9274	9279	9284	9289	1	1	2	2	3	3	4	4	5
85	9294	9299	9304	9309	9315	9320	9325	9330	9335	9340	1	1	2	2	3	3	4	4	5
86	9345	9350	9355	9360	9365	9370	9375	9380	9385	9390	1	1	2	2	3	3	4	4	5
87	9395	9400	9405	9410	9415	9420	9425	9430	9435	9440	0	1	1	2	2	3	3	4	4
88	9445	9450	9455	9460	9465	9469	9474	9479	9484	9489	0	1	1	2	2	3	3	4	4
89	9494	9499	9504	9509	9513	9518	9523	9528	9533	9538	0	1	1	2	2	3	3	4	4
90	9542	9547	9552	9557	9562	9566	9571	9576	9581	9586	0	1	1	2	2	3	3	4	4
91	9590	9595	9600	9605	9609	9614	9619	9624	9628	9633	0	1	1	2	2	3	3	4	4
92	9638	9643	9647	9652	9657	9661	9666	9671	9675	9680	0	1	1	2	2	3	3	4	4
93	9685	9689	9694	9699	9703	9708	9713	9717	9722	9727	0	1	1	2	2	3	3	4	4
94	9731	9736	9741	9745	9750	9754	9759	9764	9768	9773	0	1	1	2	2	3	3	4	4
95	9777	9782	9786	9791	9795	9800	9805	9809	9814	9818	0	1	1	2	2	3	3	4	4
96	9823	9827	9832	9836	9841	9845	9850	9854	9859	9863	0	1	1	2	2	3	3	4	4
97	9868	9872	9877	9881	9886	9890	9894	9899	9903	9908	0	1	1	2	2	3	3	4	4
98	9912	9917	9921	9926	9930	9934	9939	9943	9948	9952	0	1	1	2	2	3	3	4	4
99	9956	9961	9965	9969	9974	9978	9983	9987	9991	9996	0	1	1	2	2	3	3	4	4
	0	1	2	3	4	5	6	7	8	9	1	2	3	4	5	6	7	8	9

ANTI-LOGARITHMS

	0	1	2	3	4	5	6	7	8	9	1	2	3	4	5	6	7	8	9
·00	1000	1002	1005	1007	1009	1012	1014	1016	1019	1021	0	0	1	1	1	1	2	2	2
·01	1023	1026	1028	1030	1033	1035	1038	1040	1042	1045	0	0	1	1	1	1	2	2	2
·02	1047	1050	1052	1054	1057	1059	1062	1064	1067	1069	0	0	1	1	1	1	2	2	2
·03	1072	1074	1076	1079	1081	1084	1086	1089	1091	1094	0	0	1	1	1	1	2	2	2
·04	1096	1099	1102	1104	1107	1109	1112	1114	1117	1119	0	1	1	1	1	2	2	2	2
·05	1122	1125	1127	1130	1132	1135	1138	1140	1143	1146	0	1	1	1	1	2	2	2	2
·06	1148	1151	1153	1156	1159	1161	1164	1167	1169	1172	0	1	1	1	1	2	2	2	2
·07	1175	1178	1180	1183	1186	1189	1191	1194	1197	1199	0	1	1	1	1	2	2	2	2
·08	1202	1205	1208	1211	1213	1216	1219	1222	1225	1227	0	1	1	1	1	2	2	2	3
·09	1230	1233	1236	1239	1242	1245	1247	1250	1253	1256	0	1	1	1	1	2	2	2	3
·10	1259	1262	1265	1268	1271	1274	1276	1279	1282	1285	0	1	1	1	1	2	2	2	3
·11	1288	1291	1294	1297	1300	1303	1306	1309	1312	1315	0	1	1	1	2	2	2	2	3
·12	1318	1321	1324	1327	1330	1334	1337	1340	1343	1346	0	1	1	1	2	2	2	3	3
·13	1349	1352	1355	1358	1361	1365	1368	1371	1374	1377	0	1	1	1	2	2	2	3	3
·14	1380	1384	1387	1390	1393	1396	1400	1403	1406	1409	0	1	1	1	2	2	2	3	3
·15	1413	1416	1419	1422	1426	1429	1432	1435	1439	1442	0	1	1	1	2	2	2	3	3
·16	1445	1449	1452	1455	1459	1462	1466	1469	1472	1476	0	1	1	1	2	2	2	3	3
·17	1479	1483	1486	1489	1493	1496	1500	1503	1507	1510	0	1	1	1	2	2	2	3	3
·18	1514	1517	1521	1524	1528	1531	1535	1538	1542	1545	0	1	1	1	2	2	2	3	3
·19	1549	1552	1556	1560	1563	1567	1570	1574	1578	1581	0	1	1	1	2	2	3	3	3
·20	1585	1589	1592	1596	1600	1603	1607	1611	1614	1618	0	1	1	1	2	2	3	3	3
·21	1622	1626	1629	1633	1637	1641	1644	1648	1652	1656	0	1	1	2	2	2	3	3	3
·22	1660	1663	1667	1671	1675	1679	1683	1687	1690	1694	0	1	1	2	2	2	3	3	3
·23	1698	1702	1706	1710	1714	1718	1722	1726	1730	1734	0	1	1	2	2	2	3	3	4
·24	1738	1742	1746	1750	1754	1758	1762	1766	1770	1774	0	1	1	2	2	2	3	3	4
·25	1778	1782	1786	1791	1795	1799	1803	1807	1811	1816	0	1	1	2	2	3	3	3	4
·26	1820	1824	1828	1832	1837	1841	1845	1849	1854	1858	0	1	1	2	2	3	3	3	4
·27	1862	1866	1871	1875	1879	1884	1888	1892	1897	1901	0	1	1	2	2	3	3	3	4
·28	1905	1910	1914	1919	1923	1928	1932	1936	1941	1945	0	1	1	2	2	3	3	4	4
·29	1950	1954	1959	1963	1968	1972	1977	1982	1986	1991	0	1	1	2	2	3	3	4	4
·30	1995	2000	2004	2009	2014	2018	2023	2028	2032	2037	0	1	1	2	2	3	3	4	4
·31	2042	2046	2051	2056	2061	2065	2070	2075	2080	2084	0	1	1	2	2	3	3	4	4
·32	2089	2094	2099	2104	2109	2113	2118	2123	2128	2133	0	1	1	2	2	3	3	4	4
·33	2138	2143	2148	2153	2158	2163	2168	2173	2178	2183	0	1	1	2	2	3	3	4	4
·34	2188	2193	2198	2203	2208	2213	2218	2223	2228	2234	1	1	2	2	3	3	4	4	5
·35	2239	2244	2249	2254	2259	2265	2270	2275	2280	2286	1	1	2	2	3	3	4	4	5
·36	2291	2296	2301	2307	2312	2317	2323	2328	2333	2339	1	1	2	2	3	3	4	4	5
·37	2344	2350	2355	2360	2366	2371	2377	2382	2388	2393	1	1	2	2	3	3	4	4	5
·38	2399	2404	2410	2415	2421	2427	2432	2438	2443	2449	1	1	2	2	3	3	4	4	5
·39	2455	2460	2466	2472	2477	2483	2489	2495	2500	2506	1	1	2	2	3	3	4	5	5
·40	2512	2518	2523	2529	2535	2541	2547	2553	2559	2564	1	1	2	2	3	3	4	5	5
·41	2570	2576	2582	2588	2594	2600	2606	2612	2618	2624	1	1	2	2	3	4	4	5	5
·42	2630	2636	2642	2648	2655	2661	2667	2673	2679	2685	1	1	2	2	3	4	4	5	6
·43	2692	2698	2704	2710	2716	2723	2729	2735	2742	2748	1	1	2	2	3	4	4	5	6
·44	2754	2761	2767	2773	2780	2786	2793	2799	2805	2812	1	1	2	3	3	4	4	5	6
·45	2818	2825	2831	2838	2844	2851	2858	2864	2871	2877	1	1	2	3	3	4	5	5	6
·46	2884	2891	2897	2904	2911	2917	2924	2931	2938	2944	1	1	2	3	3	4	5	5	6
·47	2951	2958	2965	2972	2979	2985	2992	2999	3006	3013	1	1	2	3	3	4	5	6	6
·48	3020	3027	3034	3041	3048	3055	3062	3069	3076	3083	1	1	2	3	4	4	5	6	6
·49	3090	3097	3105	3112	3119	3126	3133	3141	3148	3155	1	1	2	3	4	4	5	6	7
	0	1	2	3	4	5	6	7	8	9	1	2	3	4	5	6	7	8	9

ANTI-LOGARITHMS

	0	1	2	3	4	5	6	7	8	9	1	2	3	4	5	6	7	8	9
·50	3162	3170	3177	3184	3192	3199	3206	3214	3221	3228	1	1	2	3	4	4	5	6	7
·51	3236	3243	3251	3258	3266	3273	3281	3289	3296	3304	1	2	2	3	4	5	5	6	7
·52	3311	3319	3327	3334	3342	3350	3357	3365	3373	3381	1	2	2	3	4	5	5	6	7
·53	3388	3396	3404	3412	3420	3428	3436	3443	3451	3459	1	2	2	3	4	5	6	6	7
·54	3467	3475	3483	3491	3499	3508	3516	3524	3532	3540	1	2	2	3	4	5	6	6	7
·55	3548	3556	3565	3573	3581	3589	3597	3606	3614	3622	1	2	2	3	4	5	6	7	7
·56	3631	3639	3648	3656	3664	3673	3681	3690	3698	3707	1	2	3	3	4	5	6	7	8
·57	3715	3724	3733	3741	3750	3758	3 767	3776	3784	3793	1	2	3	3	4	5	6	7	8
·58	3802	3811	3819	3828	3837	3846	3855	3864	3873	3882	1	2	3	4	4	5	6	7	8
·59	3890	3899	3908	3917	3926	3936	3945	3954	3963	3972	1	2	3	4	5	5	6	7	8
·60	3981	3990	3999	4009	4018	4027	4036	4046	4055	4064	1	2	3	4	5	6	7	7	8
·61	4074	4083	4093	4102	4111	4121	4130	4140	4150	4159	1	2	3	4	5	6	7	8	9
·62	4169	4178	4188	4198	4207	4217	4227	4236	4246	4256	1	2	3	4	5	6	7	8	9
·63	4266	4276	4285	4295	4305	4315	4325	4335	4345	4355	1	2	3	4	5	6	7	8	9
·64	4365	4375	4385	4395	4406	4416	4426	4436	4446	4457	1	2	3	4	5	6	7	8	9
·65	4467	4477	4487	4498	4508	4519	4529	4539	4550	4560	1	2	3	4	5	6	7	8	9
·66	4571	4581	4592	4603	4613	4624	4634	4645	4656	4667	1	2	3	4	5	6	7	8	10
·67	4677	4688	4699	4710	4721	4732	4742	4753	4764	4775	1	2	3	4	5	7	8	9	10
·68	4786	4797	4808	4819	4831	4842	4853	4864	4875	4887	1	2	3	4	6	7	8	9	10
·69	4898	4909	4920	4932	4943	4955	4966	4977	4989	5000	1	2	3	5	6	7	8	9	10
·70	5012	5023	5035	5047	5058	5070	5082	5093	5105	5117	1	2	4	5	6	7	8	9	11
·71	5129	5140	5152	5164	5176	5188	5200	5212	5224	5236	1	2	4	5	6	7	8	10	11
·72	5248	5260	5272	5284	5297	5309	5321	5333	5346	5358	1	2	4	5	6	7	9	10	11
·73	5370	5383	5395	5408	5420	5433	5445	5458	5470	5483	1	3	4	5	6	8	9	10	11
·74	5495	5508	5521	5534	5546	5559	5572	5585	5598	5610	1	3	4	5	6	8	9	10	12
·75	5623	5636	5649	5662	5675	5689	5702	5715	5728	5741	1	3	4	5	7	8	9	10	12
·76	5754	5768	5781	5794	5808	5821	5834	5848	5861	5875	1	3	4	5	7	8	9	11	12
·77	5888	5902	5916	5929	5943	5957	5970	5984	5998	6012	1	3	4	6	7	8	10	11	12
·78	6026	6039	6053	6067	6081	6095	6109	6124	6138	6152	1	3	4	6	7	8	10	11	13
·79	6166	6180	6194	6209	6223	6237	6252	6266	6281	6295	1	3	4	6	7	9	10	12	13
·80	6310	6324	6339	6353	6368	6383	6397	6412	6427	6442	1	3	4	6	7	9	10	12	13
·81	6457	6471	6486	6501	6516	6531	6546	6561	6577	6592	2	3	5	6	8	9	11	12	14
·82	6607	6622	6637	6653	6668	6683	6699	6714	6730	6745	2	3	5	6	8	9	11	12	14
·83	6761	6776	6792	6808	6823	6839	6855	6871	6887	6902	2	3	5	6	8	9	11	13	14
·84	6918	6934	6950	6966	6982	6998	7015	7031	7047	7063	2	3	5	6	8	10	11	13	14
·85	7079	7096	7112	7129	7145	7161	7178	7194	7211	7228	2	3	5	7	8	10	12	13	15
·86	7244	7261	7278	7295	7311	7328	7345	7362	7379	7396	2	3	5	7	8	10	12	14	15
·87	7413	7430	7447	7464	7482	7499	7516	7534	7551	7568	2	3	5	7	9	10	12	14	16
·88	7586	7603	7621	7638	7656	7674	7691	7709	7727	7745	2	4	5	7	9	11	12	14	16
·89	7762	7780	7798	7816	7834	7852	7870	7889	7907	7925	2	4	5	7	9	11	13	14	16
·90	7943	7962	7980	7998	8017	8035	8054	8072	8091	8110	2	4	6	7	9	11	13	15	17
·91	8128	8147	8166	8185	8204	8222	8241	8260	8279	8299	2	4	6	8	10	11	13	15	17
·92	8318	8337	8356	8375	8395	8414	8433	8453	8472	8492	2	4	6	8	10	12	14	15	17
·93	8511	8531	8551	8570	8590	8610	8630	8650	8670	8690	2	4	6	8	10	12	14	16	18
·94	8710	8730	8750	8770	8790	8810	8831	8851	8872	8892	2	4	6	8	10	12	14	16	18
·95	8913	8933	8954	8974	8995	9016	9036	9057	9078	9099	2	4	6	8	10	12	14	17	19
·96	9120	9141	9162	9183	9204	9226	9247	9268	9290	9311	2	4	6	9	11	13	15	17	19
·97	9333	9354	9376	9397	9419	9441	9462	9484	9506	9528	2	4	7	9	11	13	15	17	20
·98	9550	9572	9594	9616	9638	9661	9683	9705	9727	9750	2	4	7	9	11	13	16	18	20
·99	9772	9795	9817	9840	9863	9886	9908	9931	9954	9977	2	5	7	9	11	14	16	18	21
	0	1	2	3	4	5	6	7	8	9	1	2	3	4	5	6	7	8	9

NATURAL SINES

	0′	6′	12′	18′	24′	30′	36′	42′	48′	54′	1′	2′	3′	4′	5′
0°	0·0000	·0017	·0035	·0052	·0070	·0087	·0105	·0122	·0140	·0157	3	6	9	12	15
1	0·0175	·0192	·0209	·0227	·0244	·0262	·0279	·0297	·0314	·0332	3	6	9	12	15
2	0·0349	·0366	·0384	·0401	·0419	·0436	·0454	·0471	·0489	·0506	3	6	9	12	15
3	0·0523	·0541	·0558	·0576	·0593	·0610	·0628	·0645	·0663	·0680	3	6	9	12	15
4	0·0698	·0715	·0732	·0750	·0767	·0785	·0802	·0819	·0837	·0854	3	6	9	12	14
5	0·0872	·0889	·0906	·0924	·0941	·0958	·0976	·0993	·1011	·1028	3	6	9	12	14
6	0·1045	·1063	·1080	·1097	·1115	·1132	·1149	·1167	·1184	·1201	3	6	9	12	14
7	0·1219	·1236	·1253	·1271	·1288	·1305	·1323	·1340	·1357	·1374	3	6	9	12	14
8	0·1392	·1409	·1426	·1444	·1461	·1478	·1495	·1513	·1530	·1547	3	6	9	11	14
9	0·1564	·1582	·1599	·1616	·1633	·1650	·1668	·1685	·1702	·1719	3	6	9	11	14
10	0·1736	·1754	·1771	·1788	·1805	·1822	·1840	·1857	·1874	·1891	3	6	9	11	14
11	0·1908	·1925	·1942	·1959	·1977	·1994	·2011	·2028	·2045	·2062	3	6	9	11	14
12	0·2079	·2096	·2113	·2130	·2147	·2164	·2181	·2198	·2215	·2232	3	6	9	11	14
13	0·2250	·2267	·2284	·2300	·2317	·2334	·2351	·2368	·2385	·2402	3	6	8	11	14
14	0·2419	·2436	·2453	·2470	·2487	·2504	·2521	·2538	·2554	·2571	3	6	8	11	14
15	0·2588	·2605	·2622	·2639	·2656	·2672	·2689	·2706	·2723	·2740	3	6	8	11	14
16	0·2756	·2773	·2790	·2807	·2823	·2840	·2857	·2874	·2890	·2907	3	6	8	11	14
17	0·2924	·2940	·2957	·2974	·2990	·3007	·3024	·3040	·3057	·3074	3	6	8	11	14
18	0·3090	·3107	·3123	·3140	·3156	·3173	·3190	·3206	·3223	·3239	3	6	8	11	14
19	0·3256	·3272	·3289	·3305	·3322	·3338	·3355	·3371	·3387	·3404	3	5	8	11	14
20	0·3420	·3437	·3453	·3469	·3486	·3502	·3518	·3535	·3551	·3567	3	5	8	11	14
21	0·3584	·3600	·3616	·3633	·3649	·3665	·3681	·3697	·3714	·3730	3	5	8	11	14
22	0·3746	·3762	·3778	·3795	·3811	·3827	·3843	·3859	·3875	·3891	3	5	8	11	13
23	0·3907	·3923	·3939	·3955	·3971	·3987	·4003	·4019	·4035	·4051	3	5	8	11	13
24	0·4067	·4083	·4099	·4115	·4131	·4147	·4163	·4179	·4195	·4210	3	5	8	11	13
25	0·4226	·4242	·4258	·4274	·4289	·4305	·4321	·4337	·4352	·4368	3	5	8	11	13
26	0·4384	·4399	·4415	·4431	·4446	·4462	·4478	·4493	·4509	·4524	3	5	8	10	13
27	0·4540	·4555	·4571	·4586	·4602	·4617	·4633	·4648	·4664	·4679	3	5	8	10	13
28	0·4695	·4710	·4726	·4741	·4756	·4772	·4787	·4802	·4818	·4833	3	5	8	10	13
29	0·4848	·4863	·4879	·4894	·4909	·4924	·4939	·4955	·4970	·4985	3	5	8	10	13
30	0·5000	·5015	·5030	·5045	·5060	·5075	·5090	·5105	·5120	·5135	2	5	8	10	12
31	0·5150	·5165	·5180	·5195	·5210	·5225	·5240	·5255	·5270	·5284	2	5	7	10	12
32	0·5299	·5314	·5329	·5344	·5358	·5373	·5388	·5402	·5417	·5432	2	5	7	10	12
33	0·5446	·5461	·5476	·5490	·5505	·5519	·5534	·5548	·5563	·5577	2	5	7	10	12
34	0·5592	·5606	·5621	·5635	·5650	·5664	·5678	·5693	·5707	·5721	2	5	7	10	12
35	0·5736	·5750	·5764	·5779	·5793	·5807	·5821	·5835	·5850	·5864	2	5	7	9	12
36	0·5878	·5892	·5906	·5920	·5934	·5948	·5962	·5976	·5990	·6004	2	5	7	9	12
37	0·6018	·6032	·6046	·6060	·6074	·6088	·6101	·6115	·6129	·6143	2	5	7	9	12
38	0·6157	·6170	·6184	·6198	·6211	·6225	·6239	·6252	·6266	·6280	2	5	7	9	11
39	0·6293	·6307	·6320	·6334	·6347	·6361	·6374	·6388	·6401	·6414	2	4	7	9	11
40	0·6428	·6441	·6455	·6468	·6481	·6494	·6508	·6521	·6534	·6547	2	4	7	9	11
41	0·6561	·6574	·6587	·6600	·6613	·6626	·6639	·6652	·6665	·6678	2	4	6	9	11
42	0·6691	·6704	·6717	·6730	·6743	·6756	·6769	·6782	·6794	·6807	2	4	6	9	11
43	0·6820	·6833	·6845	·6858	·6871	·6884	·6896	·6909	·6921	·6934	2	4	6	8	11
44	0·6947	·6959	·6972	·6984	·6997	·7009	·7022	·7034	·7046	·7059	2	4	6	8	10
	0′	6′	12′	18′	24′	30′	36′	42′	48′	54′	1′	2′	3′	4′	5′

NATURAL SINES

Proportional Parts

	0′	6′	12′	18′	24′	30′	36′	42′	48′	54′	1′	2′	3′	4′	5′
45°	0·7071	·7083	·7096	·7108	·7120	·7133	·7145	·7157	·7169	·7181	2	4	6	8	10
46	0·7193	·7206	·7218	·7230	·7242	·7254	·7266	·7278	·7290	·7302	2	4	6	8	10
47	0·7314	·7325	·7337	·7349	·7361	·7373	·7385	·7396	·7408	·7420	2	4	6	8	10
48	0·7431	·7443	·7455	·7466	·7478	·7490	·7501	·7513	·7524	·7536	2	4	6	8	10
49	0·7547	·7559	·7570	·7581	·7593	·7604	·7615	·7627	·7638	·7649	2	4	6	8	9
50	0·7660	·7672	·7683	·7694	·7705	·7716	·7727	·7738	·7749	·7760	2	4	6	7	9
51	0·7771	·7782	·7793	·7804	·7815	·7826	·7837	·7848	·7859	·7869	2	4	5	7	9
52	0·7880	·7891	·7902	·7912	·7923	·7934	·7944	·7955	·7965	·7976	2	4	5	7	9
53	0·7986	·7997	·8007	·8018	·8028	·8039	·8049	·8059	·8070	·8080	2	3	5	7	9
54	0·8090	·8100	·8111	·8121	·8131	·8141	·8151	·8161	·8171	·8181	2	3	5	7	8
55	0·8192	·8202	·8211	·8221	·8231	·8241	·8251	·8261	·8271	·8281	2	3	5	7	8
56	0·8290	·8300	·8310	·8320	·8329	·8339	·8348	·8358	·8368	·8377	2	3	5	6	8
57	0·8387	·8396	·8406	·8415	·8425	·8434	·8443	·8453	·8462	·8471	2	3	5	6	8
58	0·8480	·8490	·8499	·8508	·8517	·8526	·8536	·8545	·8554	·8563	2	3	5	6	8
59	0·8572	·8581	·8590	·8599	·8607	·8616	·8625	·8634	·8643	·8652	1	3	4	6	7
60	0·8660	·8669	·8678	·8686	·8695	·8704	·8712	·8721	·8729	·8738	1	3	4	6	7
61	0·8746	·8755	·8763	·8771	·8780	·8788	·8796	·8805	·8813	·8821	1	3	4	6	7
62	0·8829	·8838	·8846	·8854	·8862	·8870	·8878	·8886	·8894	·8902	1	3	4	5	7
63	0·8910	·8918	·8926	·8934	·8942	·8949	·8957	·8965	·8973	·8980	1	3	4	5	6
64	0·8988	·8996	·9003	·9011	·9018	·9026	·9033	·9041	·9048	·9056	1	2	4	5	6
65	0·9063	·9070	·9078	·9085	·9092	·9100	·9107	·9114	·9121	·9128	1	2	4	5	6
66	0·9135	·9143	·9150	·9157	·9164	·9171	·9178	·9184	·9191	·9198	1	2	3	5	6
67	0·9205	·9212	·9219	·9225	·9232	·9239	·9245	·9252	·9259	·9265	1	2	3	4	6
68	0·9272	·9278	·9285	·9291	·9298	·9304	·9311	·9317	·9323	·9330	1	2	3	4	5
69	0·9336	·9342	·9348	·9354	·9361	·9367	·9373	·9379	·9385	·9391	1	2	3	4	5
70	0·9397	·9403	·9409	·9415	·9421	·9426	·9432	·9438	·9444	·9449	1	2	3	4	5
71	0·9455	·9461	·9466	·9472	·9478	·9483	·9489	·9494	·9500	·9505	1	2	3	4	5
72	0·9511	·9516	·9521	·9527	·9532	·9537	·9542	·9548	·9553	·9558	1	2	3	3	4
73	0·9563	·9568	·9573	·9578	·9583	·9588	·9593	·9598	·9603	·9608	1	2	2	3	4
74	0·9613	·9617	·9622	·9627	·9632	·9636	·9641	·9646	·9650	·9655	1	2	2	3	4
75	0·9659	·9664	·9668	·9673	·9677	·9681	·9686	·9690	·9694	·9699	1	1	2	3	4
76	0·9703	·9707	·9711	·9715	·9720	·9724	·9728	·9732	·9736	·9740	1	1	2	3	3
77	0·9744	·9748	·9751	·9755	·9759	·9763	·9767	·9770	·9774	·9778	1	1	2	2	3
78	0·9781	·9785	·9789	·9792	·9796	·9799	·9803	·9806	·9810	·9813	1	1	2	2	3
79	0·9816	·9820	·9823	·9826	·9829	·9833	·9836	·9839	·9842	·9845	1	1	2	2	3
80	0·9848	·9851	·9854	·9857	·9860	·9863	·9866	·9869	·9871	·9874	0	1	1	2	2
81	0·9877	·9880	·9882	·9885	·9888	·9890	·9893	·9895	·9898	·9900	0	1	1	2	2
82	0·9903	·9905	·9907	·9910	·9912	·9914	·9917	·9919	·9921	·9923	0	1	1	1	2
83	0·9925	·9928	·9930	·9932	·9934	·9936	·9938	·9940	·9942	·9943	0	1	1	1	2
84	0·9945	·9947	·9949	·9951	·9952	·9954	·9956	·9957	·9959	·9960	0	1	1	1	1
85	0·9962	·9963	·9965	·9966	·9968	·9969	·9971	·9972	·9973	·9974	0	0	1	1	1
86	0·9976	·9977	·9978	·9979	·9980	·9981	·9982	·9983	·9984	·9985	0	0	0	1	1
87	0·9986	·9987	·9988	·9989	·9990	·9990	·9991	·9992	·9993	·9993	0	0	0	1	1
88	0·9994	·9995	·9995	·9996	·9996	·9997	·9997	·9997	·9998	·9998	0	0	0	0	0
89	0·9998	·9999	·9999	·9999	0·9999	1·0000	·0000	·0000	·0000	·0000	0	0	0	0	0
	0′	6′	12′	18′	24′	30′	36′	42′	48′	54′	1′	2′	3′	4′	5′

NATURAL COSINES

	0′	6′	12′	18′	24′	30′	36′	42′	48′	54′	1′	2′	3′	4′	5′
0°	1·0000	·0000	·0000	·0000	·0000	1·0000	0·9999	·9999	·9999	·9999	0	0	0	0	0
1	0·9998	·9998	·9998	·9997	·9997	·9997	·9996	·9996	·9995	·9995	0	0	0	0	0
2	0·9994	·9993	·9993	·9992	·9991	·9990	·9990	·9989	·9988	·9987	0	0	0	0	1
3	0·9986	·9985	·9984	·9983	·9982	·9981	·9980	·9979	·9978	·9977	0	0	0	1	1
4	0·9976	·9974	·9973	·9972	·9971	·9969	·9968	·9966	·9965	·9963	0	0	1	1	1
5	0·9962	·9960	·9959	·9957	·9956	·9954	·9952	·9951	·9949	·9947	0	1	1	1	1
6	0·9945	·9943	·9942	·9940	·9938	·9936	·9934	·9932	·9930	·9928	0	1	1	1	2
7	0·9925	·9923	·9921	·9919	·9917	·9914	·9912	·9910	·9907	·9905	0	1	1	1	2
8	0·9903	·9900	·9898	·9895	·9893	·9890	·9888	·9885	·9882	·9880	0	1	1	2	2
9	0·9877	·9874	·9871	·9869	·9866	·9863	·9860	·9857	·9854	·9851	0	1	1	2	2
10	0·9848	·9845	·9842	·9839	·9836	·9833	·9829	·9826	·9823	·9820	1	1	2	2	3
11	0·9816	·9813	·9810	·9806	·9803	·9799	·9796	·9792	·9789	·9785	1	1	2	2	3
12	0·9781	·9778	·9774	·9770	·9767	·9763	·9759	·9755	·9751	·9748	1	1	2	2	3
13	0·9744	·9740	·9736	·9732	·9728	·9724	·9720	·9715	·9711	·9707	1	1	2	3	3
14	0·9703	·9699	·9694	·9690	·9686	·9681	·9677	·9673	·9668	·9664	1	1	2	3	4
15	0·9659	·9655	·9650	·9646	·9641	·9636	·9632	·9627	·9622	·9617	1	2	2	3	4
16	0·9613	·9608	·9603	·9598	·9593	·9588	·9583	·9578	·9573	·9568	1	2	2	3	4
17	0·9563	·9558	·9553	·9548	·9542	·9537	·9532	·9527	·9521	·9516	1	2	3	3	4
18	0·9511	·9505	·9500	·9494	·9489	·9483	·9478	·9472	·9466	·9461	1	2	3	4	5
19	0·9455	·9449	·9444	·9438	·9432	·9426	·9421	·9415	·9409	·9403	1	2	3	4	5
20	0·9397	·9391	·9385	·9379	·9373	·9367	·9361	·9354	·9348	·9342	1	2	3	4	5
21	0·9336	·9330	·9323	·9317	·9311	·9304	·9298	·9291	·9285	·9278	1	2	3	4	5
22	0·9272	·9265	·9259	·9252	·9245	·9239	·9232	·9225	·9219	·9212	1	2	3	4	6
23	0·9205	·9198	·9191	·9184	·9178	·9171	·9164	·9157	·9150	·9143	1	2	3	5	6
24	0·9135	·9128	·9121	·9114	·9107	·9100	·9092	·9085	·9078	·9070	1	2	4	5	6
25	0·9063	·9056	·9048	·9041	·9033	·9026	·9018	·9011	·9003	·8996	1	2	4	5	6
26	0·8988	·8980	·8973	·8965	·8957	·8949	·8942	·8934	·8926	·8918	1	3	4	5	6
27	0·8910	·8902	·8894	·8886	·8878	·8870	·8862	·8854	·8846	·8838	1	3	4	5	7
28	0·8829	·8821	·8813	·8805	·8796	·8788	·8780	·8771	·8763	·8755	1	3	4	6	7
29	0·8746	·8738	·8729	·8721	·8712	·8704	·8695	·8686	·8678	·8669	1	3	4	6	7
30	0·8660	·8652	·8643	·8634	·8625	·8616	·8607	·8599	·8590	·8581	1	3	4	6	7
31	0·8572	·8563	·8554	·8545	·8536	·8526	·8517	·8508	·8499	·8490	2	3	5	6	8
32	0·8480	·8471	·8462	·8453	·8443	·8434	·8425	·8415	·8406	·8396	2	3	5	6	8
33	0·8387	·8377	·8368	·8358	·8348	·8339	·8329	·8320	·8310	·8300	2	3	5	6	8
34	0·8290	·8281	·8271	·8261	·8251	·8241	·8231	·8221	·8211	·8202	2	3	5	7	8
35	0·8192	·8181	·8171	·8161	·8151	·8141	·8131	·8121	·8111	·8100	2	3	5	7	8
36	0·8090	·8080	·8070	·8059	·8049	·8039	·8028	·8018	·8007	·7997	2	3	5	7	9
37	0·7986	·7976	·7965	·7955	·7944	·7934	·7923	·7912	·7902	·7891	2	4	5	7	9
38	0·7880	·7869	·7859	·7848	·7837	·7826	·7815	·7804	·7793	·7782	2	4	5	7	9
39	0·7771	·7760	·7749	·7738	·7727	·7716	·7705	·7694	·7683	·7672	2	4	6	7	9
40	0·7660	·7649	·7638	·7627	·7615	·7604	·7593	·7581	·7570	·7559	2	4	6	8	9
41	0·7547	·7536	·7524	·7513	·7501	·7490	·7478	·7466	·7455	·7443	2	4	6	8	10
42	0·7431	·7420	·7408	·7396	·7385	·7373	·7361	·7349	·7337	·7325	2	4	6	8	10
43	0·7314	·7302	·7290	·7278	·7266	·7254	·7242	·7230	·7218	·7206	2	4	6	8	10
44	0·7193	·7181	·7169	·7157	·7145	·7133	·7120	·7108	·7096	·7083	2	4	6	8	10
	0′	6′	12′	18′	24′	30′	36′	42′	48′	54′	1′	2′	3′	4′	5′

NATURAL COSINES

	0′	6′	12′	18′	24′	30′	36′	42′	48′	54′	1′	2′	3′	4′	5′
45°	0·7071	·7059	·7046	·7034	·7022	·7009	·6997	·6984	·6972	·6959	2	4	6	8	10
46	0·6947	·6934	·6921	·6909	·6896	·6884	·6871	·6858	·6845	·6833	2	4	6	8	11
47	0·6820	·6807	·6794	·6782	·6769	·6756	·6743	·6730	·6717	·6704	2	4	6	9	11
48	0·6691	·6678	·6665	·6652	·6639	·6626	·6613	·6600	·6587	·6574	2	4	6	9	11
49	0·6561	·6547	·6534	·6521	·6508	·6494	·6481	·6468	·6455	·6441	2	4	7	9	11
50	0·6428	·6414	·6401	·6388	·6374	·6361	·6347	·6334	·6320	·6307	2	4	7	9	11
51	0·6293	·6280	·6266	·6252	·6239	·6225	·6211	·6198	·6184	·6170	2	5	7	9	11
52	0·6157	·6143	·6129	·6115	·6101	·6088	·6074	·6060	·6046	·6032	2	5	7	9	12
53	0·6018	·6004	·5990	·5976	·5962	·5948	·5934	·5920	·5906	·5892	2	5	7	9	12
54	0·5878	·5864	·5850	·5835	·5821	·5807	·5793	·5779	·5764	·5750	2	5	7	9	12
55	0·5736	·5721	·5707	·5693	·5678	·5664	·5650	·5635	·5621	·5606	2	5	7	10	12
56	0·5592	·5577	·5563	·5548	·5534	·5519	·5505	·5490	·5476	·5461	2	5	7	10	12
57	0·5446	·5432	·5417	·5402	·5388	·5373	·5358	·5344	·5329	·5314	2	5	7	10	12
58	0·5299	·5284	·5270	·5255	·5240	·5225	·5210	·5195	·5180	·5165	2	5	7	10	12
59	0·5150	·5135	·5120	·5105	·5090	·5075	·5060	·5045	·5030	·5015	2	5	8	10	12
60	0·5000	·4985	·4970	·4955	·4939	·4924	·4909	·4894	·4879	·4863	3	5	8	10	13
61	0·4848	·4833	·4818	·4802	·4787	·4772	·4756	·4741	·4726	·4710	3	5	8	10	13
62	0·4695	·4679	·4664	·4648	·4633	·4617	·4602	·4586	·4571	·4555	3	5	8	10	13
63	0·4540	·4524	·4509	·4493	·4478	·4462	·4446	·4431	·4415	·4399	3	5	8	10	13
64	0·4384	·4368	·4352	·4337	·4321	·4305	·4289	·4274	·4258	·4242	3	5	8′	11	13
65	0·4226	·4210	·4195	·4179	·4163	·4147	·4131	·4115	·4099	·4083	3	5	8	11	13
66	0·4067	·4051	·4035	·4019	·4003	·3987	·3971	·3955	·3939	·3923	3	5	8	11	13
67	0·3907	·3891	·3875	·3859	·3843	·3827	·3811	·3795	·3778	·3762	3	5	8	11	13
68	0·3746	·3730	·3714	·3697	·3681	·3665	·3649	·3633	·3616	·3600	3	5	8	11	14
69	0·3584	·3567	·3551	·3535	·3518	·3502	·3486	·3469	·3453	·3437	3	5	8	11	14
70	0·3420	·3404	·3387	·3371	·3355	·3338	·3322	·3305	·3289	·3272	3	5	8	11	14
71	0·3256	·3239	·3223	·3206	·3190	·3173	·3156	·3140	·3123	·3107	3	6	8	11	14
72	0·3090	·3074	·3057	·3040	·3024	·3007	·2990	·2974	·2957	·2940	3	6	8	11	14
73	0·2924	·2907	·2890	·2874	·2857	·2840	·2823	·2807	·2790	·2773	3	6	8	11	14
74	0·2756	·2740	·2723	·2706	·2689	·2672	·2656	·2639	·2622	·2605	3	6	8	11	14
75	0·2588	·2571	·2554	·2538	·2521	·2504	·2487	·2470	·2453	·2436	3	6	8	11	14
76	0·2419	·2402	·2385	·2368	·2351	·2334	·2317	·2300	·2284	·2267	3	6	8	11	14
77	0·2250	·2232	·2215	·2198	·2181	·2164	·2147	·2130	·2113	·2096	3	6	9	11	14
78	0·2079	·2062	·2045	·2028	·2011	·1994	·1977	·1959	·1942	·1925	3	6	9	11	14
79	0·1908	·1891	·1874	·1857	·1840	·1822	·1805	·1788	·1771	·1754	3	6	9	11	14
80	0·1736	·1719	·1702	·1685	·1668	·1650	·1633	·1616	·1599	·1582	3	6	9	11	14
81	0·1564	·1547	·1530	·1513	·1495	·1478	·1461	·1444	·1426	·1409	3	6	9	11	14
82	0·1392	·1374	·1357	·1340	·1323	·1305	·1288	·1271	·1253	·1236	3	6	9	12	14
83	0·1219	·1201	·1184	·1167	·1149	·1132	·1115	·1097	·1080	·1063	3	6	9	12	14
84	0·1045	·1028	·1011	·0993	·0976	·0958	·0941	·0924	·0906	·0889	3	6	9	12	14
85	0·0872	·0854	·0837	·0819	·0802	·0785	·0767	·0750	·0732	·0715	3	6	9	12	14
86	0·0698	·0680	·0663	·0645	·0628	·0610	·0593	·0576	·0558	·0541	3	6	9	12	15
87	0·0523	·0506	·0489	·0471	·0454	·0436	·0419	·0401	·0384	·0366	3	6	9	12	15
88	0·0349	·0332	·0314	·0297	·0279	·0262	·0244	·0227	·0209	·0192	3	6	9	12	15
89	0·0175	·0157	·0140	·0122	·0105	·0087	·0070	·0052	·0035	·0017	3	6	9	12	15
	0′	6′	12′	18′	24′	30′	36′	42′	48′	54′	1′	2′	3′	4′	5′

NATURAL TANGENTS

	0′	6′	12′	18′	24′	30′	36′	42′	48′	54′	1′	2′	3′	4′	5′
0°	0·0000	·0017	·0035	·0052	·0070	·0087	·0105	·0122	·0140	·0157	3	6	9	12	15
1	0·0175	·0192	·0209	·0227	·0244	·0262	·0279	·0297	·0314	·0332	3	6	9	12	15
2	0·0349	·0367	·0384	·0402	·0419	·0437	·0454	·0472	·0489	·0507	3	6	9	12	15
3	0·0524	·0542	·0559	·0577	·0594	·0612	·0629	·0647	·0664	·0682	3	6	9	12	15
4	0·0699	·0717	·0734	·0752	·0769	·0787	·0805	·0822	·0840	·0857	3	6	9	12	15
5	0·0875	·0892	·0910	·0928	·0945	·0963	·0981	·0998	·1016	·1033	3	6	9	12	15
6	0·1051	·1069	·1086	·1104	·1122	·1139	·1157	·1175	·1192	·1210	3	6	9	12	15
7	0·1228	·1246	·1263	·1281	·1299	·1317	·1334	·1352	·1370	·1388	3	6	9	12	15
8	0·1405	·1423	·1441	·1459	·1477	·1495	·1512	·1530	·1548	·1566	3	6	9	12	15
9	0·1584	·1602	·1620	·1638	·1655	·1673	·1691	·1709	·1727	·1745	3	6	9	12	15
10	0·1763	·1781	·1799	·1817	·1835	·1853	·1871	·1890	·1908	·1926	3	6	9	12	15
11	0·1944	·1962	·1980	·1998	·2016	·2035	·2053	·2071	·2089	·2107	3	6	9	12	15
12	0·2126	·2144	·2162	·2180	·2199	·2217	·2235	·2254	·2272	·2290	3	6	9	12	15
13	0·2309	·2327	·2345	·2364	·2382	·2401	·2419	·2438	·2456	·2475	3	6	9	12	15
14	0·2493	·2512	·2530	·2549	·2568	·2586	·2605	·2623	·2642	·2661	3	6	9	12	16
15	0·2679	·2698	·2717	·2736	·2754	·2773	·2792	·2811	·2830	·2849	3	6	9	13	16
16	0·2867	·2886	·2905	·2924	·2943	·2962	·2981	·3000	·3019	·3038	3	6	9	13	16
17	0·3057	·3076	·3096	·3115	·3134	·3153	·3172	·3191	·3211	·3230	3	6	9	13	16
18	0·3249	·3269	·3288	·3307	·3327	·3346	·3365	·3385	·3404	·3424	3	6	10	13	16
19	0·3443	·3463	·3482	·3502	·3522	·3541	·3561	·3581	·3600	·3620	3	6	10	13	16
20	0·3640	·3659	·3679	·3699	·3719	·3739	·3759	·3779	·3799	·3819	3	6	10	13	17
21	0·3839	·3859	·3879	·3899	·3919	·3939	·3959	·3979	·4000	·4020	3	7	10	13	17
22	0·4040	·4061	·4081	·4101	·4122	·4142	·4163	·4183	·4204	·4224	3	7	10	14	17
23	0·4245	·4265	·4286	·4307	·4327	·4348	·4369	·4390	·4411	·4431	3	7	10	14	17
24	0·4452	·4473	·4494	·4515	·4536	·4557	·4578	·4599	·4621	·4642	4	7	11	14	18
25	0·4663	·4684	·4706	·4727	·4748	·4770	·4791	·4813	·4834	·4856	4	7	11	14	18
26	0·4877	·4899	·4921	·4942	·4964	·4986	·5008	·5029	·5051	·5073	4	7	11	15	18
27	0·5095	·5117	·5139	·5161	·5184	·5206	·5228	·5250	·5272	·5295	4	7	11	15	18
28	0·5317	·5339	·5362	·5384	·5407	·5430	·5452	·5475	·5498	·5520	4	8	11	15	19
29	0·5543	·5566	·5589	·5612	·5635	·5658	·5681	·5704	·5727	·5750	4	8	12	15	19
30	0·5774	·5797	·5820	·5844	·5867	·5891	·5914	·5938	·5961	·5985	4	8	12	16	20
31	0·6009	·6032	·6056	·6080	·6104	·6128	·6152	·6176	·6200	·6224	4	8	12	16	20
32	0·6249	·6273	·6297	·6322	·6346	·6371	·6395	·6420	·6445	·6469	4	8	12	16	20
33	0·6494	·6519	·6544	·6569	·6594	·6619	·6644	·6669	·6694	·6720	4	8	13	17	21
34	0·6745	·6771	·6796	·6822	·6847	·6873	·6899	·6924	·6950	·6976	4	9	13	17	21
35	0·7002	·7028	·7054	·7080	·7107	·7133	·7159	·7186	·7212	·7239	4	9	13	18	22
36	0·7265	·7292	·7319	·7346	·7373	·7400	·7427	·7454	·7481	·7508	5	9	14	18	23
37	0·7536	·7563	·7590	·7618	·7646	·7673	·7701	·7729	·7757	·7785	5	9	14	18	23
38	0·7813	·7841	·7869	·7898	·7926	·7954	·7983	·8012	·8040	·8069	5	10	14	19	24
39	0·8098	·8127	·8156	·8185	·8214	·8243	·8273	·8302	·8332	·8361	5	10	15	20	24
40	0·8391	·8421	·8451	·8481	·8511	·8541	·8571	·8601	·8632	·8662	5	10	15	20	25
41	0·8693	·8724	·8754	·8785	·8816	·8847	·8878	·8910	·8941	·8972	5	10	16	21	26
42	0·9004	·9036	·9067	·9099	·9131	·9163	·9195	·9228	·9260	·9293	5	11	16	21	26
43	0·9325	·9358	·9391	·9424	·9457	·9490	·9523	·9556	·9590	·9623	6	11	17	22	28
44	0·9657	·9691	·9725	·9759	·9793	·9827	·9861	·9896	·9930	·9965	6	11	17	23	29
	0′	6′	12′	18′	24′	30′	36′	42′	48′	54′	1′	2′	3′	4′	5′

NATURAL TANGENTS

	0′	6′	12′	18′	24′	30′	36′	42′	48′	54′	1′	2′	3′	4′	5′
45°	1·0000	·0035	·0070	·0105	·0141	·0176	·0212	·0247	·0283	·0319	6	12	18	24	30
46	1·0355	·0392	·0428	·0464	·0501	·0538	·0575	·0612	·0649	·0686	6	12	18	25	31
47	1·0724	·0761	·0799	·0837	·0875	·0913	·0951	·0990	·1028	·1067	6	13	19	25	32
48	1·1106	·1145	·1184	·1224	·1263	·1303	·1343	·1383	·1423	·1463	7	13	20	27	33
49	1·1504	·1544	·1585	·1626	·1667	·1708	·1750	·1792	·1833	·1875	7	14	21	28	34
50	1·1918	·1960	·2002	·2045	·2088	·2131	·2174	·2218	·2261	·2305	7	14	22	29	36
51	1·2349	·2393	·2437	·2482	·2527	·2572	·2617	·2662	·2708	·2753	8	15	23	30	38
52	1·2799	·2846	·2892	·2938	·2985	·3032	·3079	·3127	·3175	·3222	8	16	24	31	39
53	1·3270	·3319	·3367	·3416	·3465	·3514	·3564	·3613	·3663	·3713	8	16	25	33	41
54	1·3764	·3814	·3865	·3916	·3968	·4019	·4071	·4124	·4176	·4229	9	17	26	34	43
55	1·4281	·4335	·4388	·4442	·4496	·4550	·4605	·4659	·4715	·4770	9	18	27	36	45
56	1·4826	·4882	·4938	·4994	·5051	·5108	·5166	·5224	·5282	·5340	10	19	29	38	48
57	1·5399	·5458	·5517	·5577	·5637	·5697	·5757	·5818	·5880	·5941	10	20	30	40	50
58	1·6003	·6066	·6128	·6191	·6255	·6319	·6383	·6447	·6512	·6577	11	21	32	43	53
59	1·6643	·6709	·6775	·6842	·6909	·6977	·7045	·7113	·7182	·7251	11	23	34	45	57
60	1·7321	·7391	·7461	·7532	·7603	·7675	·7747	·7820	·7893	·7966	12	24	36	48	60
61	1·8040	·8115	·8190	·8265	·8341	·8418	·8495	·8572	·8650	·8728	13	26	38	51	64
62	1·8807	·8887	·8967	·9047	·9128	·9210	·9292	·9375	·9458	·9542	14	27	41	55	68
63	1·9626	·9711	·9797	·9883	1·9970	2·0057	·0145	·0233	·0323	·0413	15	29	44	58	73
64	2·0503	·0594	·0686	·0778	·0872	·0965	·1060	·1155	·1251	·1348	16	31	47	63	78
65	2·145	·154	·164	·174	·184	·194	·204	·215	·225	·236	2	3	5	7	8
66	2·246	·257	·267	·278	·289	·300	·311	·322	·333	·344	2	4	5	7	9
67	2·356	·367	·379	·391	·402	·414	·426	·438	·450	·463	2	4	6	8	10
68	2·475	·488	·500	·513	·526	·539	·552	·565	·578	·592	2	4	6	9	11
69	2·605	·619	·633	·646	·660	·675	·689	·703	·718	·733	2	5	7	9	12
70	2·747	·762	·778	·793	·808	·824	·840	·856	·872	·888	3	5	8	10	13
71	2·904	·921	·937	·954	·971	2·989	3·006	·024	·042	·060	3	6	9	12	14
72	3·078	·096	·115	·133	·152	·172	·191	·211	·230	·251	3	6	10	13	16
73	3·271	·291	·312	·333	·354	·376	·398	·420	·442	·465	4	7	11	14	18
74	3·487	·511	·534	·558	·582	·606	·630	·655	·681	·706	4	8	12	16	20
75	3·732	·758	·785	·812	·839	·867	·895	·923	·952	·981	5	9	14	19	23
76	4·011	·041	·071	·102	·134	·165	·198	·230	·264	·297	5	11	16	21	27
77	4·331	·366	·402	·437	·474	·511	·548	·586	·625	·665	6	12	19	25	31
78	4·705	·745	·787	·829	·872	·915	4·959	5·005	·050	·097	7	15	22	29	37
79	5·145	·193	·242	·292	·343	·396	·449	·503	·558	·614	9	18	26	35	44
80	5·671	·730	·789	·850	·912	5·976	6·041	·107	·174	·243	11	21	32	43	54
81	6·314	·386	·460	·535	·612	·691	·772	·855	6·940	7·026	13	27	40	54	67
82	7·115	·207	·300	·396	·495	·596	·700	·806	7·916	8·028	17	34	51	69	86
83	8·144	·264	·386	·513	·643	·777	8·915	9·058	·205	·357	23	46	68	91	114
84	9·514	9·677	9·845	10·019	10·199	10·385	10·579	10·780	10·988	11·205					
85	11·43	11·66	11·91	12·16	12·43	12·71	13·00	13·30	13·62	13·95	p.p. cease				
86	14·30	14·67	15·06	15·46	15·89	16·35	16·83	17·34	17·89	18·46	to be				
87	19·08	19·74	20·45	21·20	22·02	22·90	23·86	24·90	26·03	27·27	sufficiently				
88	28·64	30·14	31·82	33·69	35·80	38·19	40·92	44·07	47·74	52·08	accurate				
89	57·29	63·66	71·62	81·85	95·49	114·6	143·2	191·0	286·5	573·0					
	0′	6′	12′	18′	24′	30′	36′	42′	48′	54′	1′	2′	3′	4′	5′

LOGARITHMIC SINES

Proportional Parts

	0′	6′	12′	18′	24′	30′	36′	42′	48′	54′	1′	2′	3′	4′	5′
0°	− ∞	3̄·2419	·5429	·7190	·8439	3̄·9408	2̄·0200	·0870	·1450	·1961					
1	2̄·2419	·2832	·3210	·3558	·3880	·4179	·4459	·4723	·4971	·5206		p.p. cease			
2	2̄·5428	·5640	·5842	·6035	·6220	·6397	·6567	·6731	·6889	·7041			to be		
3	2̄·7188	·7330	·7468	·7602	·7731	·7857	·7979	·8098	·8213	·8326		sufficiently			
4	2̄·8436	·8543	·8647	·8749	·8849	·8946	·9042	·9135	·9226	·9315			accurate		
5	2̄·9403	·9489	·9573	·9655	·9736	·9816	·9894	2̄·9970	1̄·0046	·0120	13	26	39	53	66
6	1̄·0192	·0264	·0334	·0403	·0472	·0539	·0605	·0670	·0734	·0797	11	22	33	44	56
7	1̄·0859	·0920	·0981	·1040	·1099	·1157	·1214	·1271	·1326	·1381	10	19	29	38	48
8	1̄·1436	·1489	·1542	·1594	·1646	·1697	·1747	·1797	·1847	·1895	8	17	25	34	42
9	1̄·1943	·1991	·2038	·2085	·2131	·2176	·2221	·2266	·2310	·2353	8	15	23	30	38
10	1̄·2397	·2439	·2482	·2524	·2565	·2606	·2647	·2687	·2727	·2767	7	14	20	27	34
11	1̄·2806	·2845	·2883	·2921	·2959	·2997	·3034	·3070	·3107	·3143	6	12	19	25	31
12	1̄·3179	·3214	·3250	·3284	·3319	·3353	·3387	·3421	·3455	·3488	6	11	17	23	28
13	1̄·3521	·3554	·3586	·3618	·3650	·3682	·3713	·3745	·3775	·3806	5	11	16	21	26
14	1̄·3837	·3867	·3897	·3927	·3957	·3986	·4015	·4044	·4073	·4102	5	10	15	20	24
15	1̄·4130	·4158	·4186	·4214	·4242	·4269	·4296	·4323	·4350	·4377	5	9	14	18	23
16	1̄·4403	·4430	·4456	·4482	·4508	·4533	·4559	·4584	·4609	·4634	4	9	13	17	21
17	1̄·4659	·4684	·4709	·4733	·4757	·4781	·4805	·4829	·4853	·4876	4	8	12	16	20
18	1̄·4900	·4923	·4946	·4969	·4992	·5015	·5037	·5060	·5082	·5104	4	8	11	15	19
19	1̄·5126	·5148	·5170	·5192	·5213	·5235	·5256	·5278	·5299	·5320	4	7	11	14	18
20	1̄·5341	·5361	·5382	·5402	·5423	·5443	·5463	·5484	·5504	·5523	3	7	10	13	17
21	1̄·5543	·5563	·5583	·5602	·5621	·5641	·5660	·5679	·5698	·5717	3	6	10	13	16
22	1̄·5736	·5754	·5773	·5792	·5810	·5828	·5847	·5865	·5883	·5901	3	6	9	12	15
23	1̄·5919	·5937	·5954	·5972	·5990	·6007	·6024	·6042	·6059	·6076	3	6	9	12	14
24	1̄·6093	·6110	·6127	·6144	·6161	·6177	·6194	·6210	·6227	·6243	3	6	8	11	14
25	1̄·6259	·6276	·6292	·6308	·6324	·6340	·6356	·6371	·6387	·6403	3	5	8	11	13
26	1̄·6418	·6434	·6449	·6465	·6480	·6495	·6510	·6526	·6541	·6556	3	5	8	10	13
27	1̄·6570	·6585	·6600	·6615	·6629	·6644	·6659	·6673	·6687	·6702	2	5	7	10	12
28	1̄·6716	·6730	·6744	·6759	·6773	·6787	·6801	·6814	·6828	·6842	2	5	7	9	12
29	1̄·6856	·6869	·6883	·6896	·6910	·6923	·6937	·6950	·6963	·6977	2	4	7	9	11
30	1̄·6990	·7003	·7016	·7029	·7042	·7055	·7068	·7080	·7093	·7106	2	4	6	9	11
31	1̄·7118	·7131	·7144	·7156	·7168	·7181	·7193	·7205	·7218	·7230	2	4	6	8	10
32	1̄·7242	·7254	·7266	·7278	·7290	·7302	·7314	·7326	·7338	·7349	2	4	6	8	10
33	1̄·7361	·7373	·7384	·7396	·7407	·7419	·7430	·7442	·7453	·7464	2	4	6	8	10
34	1̄·7476	·7487	·7498	·7509	·7520	·7531	·7542	·7553	·7564	·7575	2	4	6	7	9
35	1̄·7586	·7597	·7607	·7618	·7629	·7640	·7650	·7661	·7671	·7682	2	4	5	7	9
36	1̄·7692	·7703	·7713	·7723	·7734	·7744	·7754	·7764	·7774	·7785	2	3	5	7	9
37	1̄·7795	·7805	·7815	·7825	·7835	·7844	·7854	·7864	·7874	·7884	2	3	5	7	8
38	1̄·7893	·7903	·7913	·7922	·7932	·7941	·7951	·7960	·7970	·7979	2	3	5	6	8
39	1̄·7989	·7998	·8007	·8017	·8026	·8035	·8044	·8053	·8063	·8072	2	3	5	6	8
40	1̄·8081	·8090	·8099	·8108	·8117	·8125	·8134	·8143	·8152	·8161	1	3	4	6	7
41	1̄·8169	·8178	·8187	·8195	·8204	·8213	·8221	·8230	·8238	·8247	1	3	4	6	7
42	1̄·8255	·8264	·8272	·8280	·8289	·8297	·8305	·8313	·8322	·8330	1	3	4	6	7
43	1̄·8338	·8436	·8354	·8362	·8370	·8378	·8386	·8394	·8402	·8410	1	3	4	5	7
44	1̄·8418	·8426	·8433	·8441	·8449	·8457	·8464	·8472	·8480	·8487	1	3	4	5	6
	0′	6′	12′	18′	24′	30′	36′	42′	48′	54′	1′	2′	3′	4′	5′

LOGARITHMIC SINES

	0′	6′	12′	18′	24′	30′	36′	42′	48′	54′	1′	2′	3′	4′	5′
45°	1̄·8495	·8502	·8510	·8517	·8525	·8532	·8540	·8547	·8555	·8562	1	2	4	5	6
46	1̄·8569	·8577	·8584	·8591	·8598	·8606	·8613	·8620	·8627	·8634	1	2	4	5	6
47	1̄·8641	·8648	·8655	·8662	·8669	·8676	·8683	·8690	·8697	·8704	1	2	4	5	6
48	1̄·8711	·8718	·8724	·8731	·8738	·8745	·8751	·8758	·8765	·8771	1	2	3	4	6
49	1̄·8778	·8784	·8791	·8797	·8804	·8810	·8817	·8823	·8830	·8836	1	2	3	4	5
50	1̄·8843	·8849	·8855	·8862	·8868	·8874	·8880	·8887	·8893	·8899	1	2	3	4	5
51	1̄·8905	·8911	·8917	·8923	·8929	·8935	·8941	·8947	·8953	·8959	1	2	3	4	5
52	1̄·8965	·8971	·8977	·8983	·8989	·8995	·9000	·9006	·9012	·9018	1	2	3	4	5
53	1̄·9023	·9029	·9035	·9041	·9046	·9052	·9057	·9063	·9069	·9074	1	2	3	4	5
54	1̄·9080	·9085	·9091	·9096	·9101	·9107	·9112	·9118	·9123	·9128	1	2	3	4	5
55	1̄·9134	·9139	·9144	·9149	·9155	·9160	·9165	·9170	·9175	·9181	1	2	3	3	4
56	1̄·9186	·9191	·9196	·9201	·9206	·9211	·9216	·9221	·9226	·9231	1	2	3	3	4
57	1̄·9236	·9241	·9246	·9251	·9255	·9260	·9265	·9270	·9275	·9279	1	2	2	3	4
58	1̄·9284	·9289	·9294	·9298	·9303	·9308	·9312	·9317	·9322	·9326	1	2	2	3	4
59	1̄·9331	·9335	·9340	·9344	·9349	·9353	·9358	·9362	·9367	·9371	1	1	2	3	4
60	1̄·9375	·9380	·9384	·9388	·9393	·9397	·9401	·9406	·9410	·9414	1	1	2	3	4
61	1̄·9418	·9422	·9427	·9431	·9435	·9439	·9443	·9447	·9451	·9455	1	1	2	3	3
62	1̄·9459	·9463	·9467	·9471	·9475	·9479	·9483	·9487	·9491	·9495	1	1	2	3	3
63	1̄·9499	·9503	·9506	·9510	·9514	·9518	·9522	·9525	·9529	·9533	1	1	2	3	3
64	1̄·9537	·9540	·9544	·9548	·9551	·9555	·9558	·9562	·9566	·9569	1	1	2	2	3
65	1̄·9573	·9576	·9580	·9583	·9587	·9590	·9594	·9597	·9601	·9604	1	1	2	2	3
66	1̄·9607	·9611	·9614	·9617	·9621	·9624	·9627	·9631	·9634	·9637	1	1	2	2	3
67	1̄·9640	·9643	·9647	·9650	·9653	·9656	·9659	·9662	·9665	·9669	1	1	2	2	3
68	1̄·9672	·9675	·9678	·9681	·9684	·9687	·9690	·9693	·9696	·9699	1	1	2	2	2
69	1̄·9702	·9704	·9707	·9710	·9713	·9716	·9719	·9722	·9724	·9727	0	1	1	2	2
70	1̄·9730	·9733	·9735	·9738	·9741	·9743	·9746	·9749	·9751	·9754	0	1	1	2	2
71	1̄·9757	·9759	·9762	·9764	·9767	·9770	·9772	·9775	·9777	·9780	0	1	1	2	2
72	1̄·9782	·9785	·9787	·9789	·9792	·9794	·9797	·9799	·9801	·9804	0	1	1	2	2
73	1̄·9806	·9808	·9811	·9813	·9815	·9817	·9820	·9822	·9824	·9826	0	1	1	1	2
74	1̄·9828	·9831	·9833	·9835	·9837	·9839	·9841	·9843	·9845	·9847	0	1	1	1	2
75	1̄·9849	·9851	·9853	·9855	·9857	·9859	·9861	·9863	·9865	·9867	0	1	1	1	2
76	1̄·9869	·9871	·9873	·9875	·9876	·9878	·9880	·9882	·9884	·9885	0	1	1	1	2
77	1̄·9887	·9889	·9891	·9892	·9894	·9896	·9897	·9899	·9901	·9902	0	1	1	1	1
78	1̄·9904	·9906	·9907	·9909	·9910	·9912	·9913	·9915	·9916	·9918	0	1	1	1	1
79	1̄·9919	·9921	·9922	·9924	·9925	·9927	·9928	·9929	·9931	·9932	0	0	1	1	1
80	1̄·9934	·9935	·9936	·9937	·9939	·9940	·9941	·9943	·9944	·9945	0	0	1	1	1
81	1̄·9946	·9947	·9949	·9950	·9951	·9952	·9953	·9954	·9955	·9956	0	0	1	1	1
82	1̄·9958	·9959	·9960	·9961	·9962	·9963	·9964	·9965	·9966	·9967	0	0	0	1	1
83	1̄·9968	·9968	·9969	·9970	·9971	·9972	·9973	·9974	·9975	·9975	0	0	0	1	1
84	1̄·9976	·9977	·9978	·9978	·9979	·9980	·9981	·9981	·9982	·9983	0	0	0	0	1
85	1̄·9983	·9984	·9985	·9985	·9986	·9987	·9987	·9988	·9988	·9989	0	0	0	0	0
86	1̄·9989	·9990	·9990	·9991	·9991	·9992	·9992	·9993	·9993	·9994	0	0	0	0	0
87	1̄·9994	·9994	·9995	·9995	·9996	·9996	·9996	·9996	·9997	·9997	0	0	0	0	0
88	1̄·9997	·9998	·9998	·9998	·9998	·9999	·9999	·9999	·9999	·9999	0	0	0	0	0
89	1̄·9999	1̄·9999	0·0000	·0000	·0000	·0000	·0000	·0000	·0000	·0000	0	0	0	0	0
	0′	6′	12′	18′	24′	30′	36′	42′	48′	54′	1′	2′	3′	4′	5′

LOGARITHMIC COSINES

	0′	6′	12′	18′	24′	30′	36′	42′	48′	54′	1′	2′	3′	4′	
0°	0·0000	·0000	·0000	·0000	·0000	·0000	·0000	·0000	0·0000	T̄·9999	0	0	0	0	
1	T̄·9999	·9999	·9999	·9999	·9999	·9999	·9998	·9998	·9998	·9998	0	0	0	0	
2	T̄·9997	·9997	·9997	·9996	·9996	·9996	·9996	·9995	·9995	·9994	0	0	0	0	
3	T̄·9994	·9994	·9993	·9993	·9992	·9992	·9991	·9991	·9990	·9990	0	0	0	0	
4	T̄·9989	·9989	·9988	·9988	·9987	·9987	·9986	·9985	·9985	·9984	0	0	0	0	
5	T̄·9983	·9983	·9982	·9981	·9981	9980	·9979	·9978	·9978	·9977	0	0	0	0	
6	T̄·9976	·9975	·9975	·9974	·9973	·9972	·9971	·9970	·9969	·9968	0	0	0	1	
7	T̄·9968	·9967	·9966	·9965	·9964	·9963	·9962	·9961	·9960	·9959	0	0	0	1	
8	T̄·9958	·9956	·9955	·9954	·9953	·9952	·9951	·9950	·9949	·9947	0	0	1	1	
9	T̄·9946	·9945	·9944	·9943	·9941	·9940	·9939	·9937	·9936	·9935	0	0	1	1	
10	T̄·9934	·9932	·9931	·9929	·9928	·9927	·9925	·9924	·9922	·9921	0	0	1	1	
11	T̄·9919	·9918	·9916	·9915	·9913	·9912	·9910	·9909	·9907	·9906	0	1	1	1	
12	T̄·9904	·9902	·9901	·9899	·9897	·9896	·9894	·9892	·9891	·9889	0	1	1	1	
13	T̄·9887	·9885	·9884	·9882	·9880	·9878	·9876	·9875	·9873	·9871	0	1	1	1	
14	T̄·9869	·9867	·9865	·9863	·9861	·9859	·9857	·9855	·9853	·9851	0	1	1	1	
15	T̄·9849	·9847	·9845	·9843	·9841	·9839	·9837	·9835	·9833	·9831	0	1	1	1	
16	T̄·9828	·9826	·9824	·9822	·9820	·9817	·9815	·9813	·9811	·9808	0	1	1	1	
17	T̄·9806	·9804	·9801	·9799	·9797	·9794	·9792	·9789	·9787	·9785	0	1	1	2	
18	T̄·9782	·9780	·9777	·9775	·9772	·9770	·9767	·9764	·9762	·9759	0	1	1	2	
19	T̄·9757	·9754	·9751	·9749	·9746	·9743	·9741	·9738	·9735	·9733	0	1	1	2	
20	T̄·9730	·9727	·9724	·9722	·9719	·9716	·9713	·9710	·9707	·9704	0	1	1	2	
21	T̄·9702	·9699	·9696	·9693	·9690	·9687	·9684	·9681	·9678	·9675	1	1	2	2	
22	T̄·9672	·9669	·9665	·9662	·9659	·9656	·9653	·9650	·9647	·9643	1	1	2	2	
23	T̄·9640	·9637	·9634	·9631	·9627	·9624	·9621	·9617	·9614	·9611	1	1	2	2	
24	T̄·9607	·9604	·9601	·9597	·9594	·9590	·9587	·9583	·9580	·9576	1	1	2	2	
25	T̄·9573	·9569	·9566	·9562	·9558	·9555	·9551	·9548	·9544	·9540	1	1	2	2	
26	T̄·9537	·9533	·9529	·9525	·9522	·9518	·9514	·9510	·9506	·9503	1	1	2	3	
27	T̄·9499	·9495	·9491	·9487	·9483	·9479	·9475	·9471	·9467	·9463	1	1	2	3	
28	T̄·9459	·9455	·9451	·9447	·9443	·9439	·9435	·9431	·9427	·9422	1	1	2	3	
29	T̄·9418	·9414	·9410	·9406	·9401	·9397	·9393	·9388	·9384	·9380	1	1	2	3	
30	T̄·9375	·9371	·9367	·9362	·9358	·9353	·9349	·9344	·9340	·9335	1	1	2	3	
31	T̄·9331	·9326	·9322	·9317	·9312	·9308	·9303	·9298	·9294	·9289	1	2	2	3	
32	T̄·9284	·9279	·9275	·9270	·9265	·9260	·9255	·9251	·9246	·9241	1	2	2	3	
33	T̄·9236	·9231	·9226	·9221	·9216	·9211	·9206	·9201	·9196	·9191	1	2	3	3	
34	T̄·9186	·9181	·9175	·9170	·9165	·9160	·9155	·9149	·9144	·9139	1	2	3	3	
35	T̄·9134	·9128	·9123	·9118	·9112	·9107	·9101	·9096	·9091	·9085	1	2	3	4	5
36	T̄·9080	·9074	·9069	·9063	·9057	·9052	·9046	·9041	·9035	·9029	1	2	3	4	5
37	T̄·9023	·9018	·9012	·9006	·9000	·8995	·8989	·8983	·8977	·8971	1	2	3	4	5
38	T̄·8965	·8959	·8953	·8947	·8941	·8935	·8929	·8923	·8917	·8911	1	2	3	4	5
39	T̄·8905	·8899	·8893	·8887	·8880	·8874	·8868	·8862	·8855	·8849	1	2	3	4	5
40	T̄·8843	·8836	·8830	·8823	·8817	·8810	·8804	·8797	·8791	·8784	1	2	3	4	5
41	T̄·8778	·8771	·8765	·8758	·8751	·8745	·8738	·8731	·8724	·8718	1	2	3	4	6
42	T̄·8711	·8704	·8697	·8690	·8683	·8676	·8669	·8662	·8655	·8648	1	2	4	5	6
43	T̄·8641	·8634	·8627	·8620	·8613	·8606	·8598	·8591	·8584	·8577	1	2	4	5	6
44	T̄·8569	·8562	·8555	·8547	·8540	·8532	·8525	·8517	·8510	·8502	1	2	4	5	6
	0′	6′	12′	18′	24′	30′	36′	42′	48′	54′	1′	2′	3′	4′	5

LOGARITHMIC COSINES

	0'	6'	12'	18'	24'	30'	36'	42'	48'	54'	1'	2'	3'	4'	5'
45°	Ī·8495	·8487	·8480	·8472	·8464	·8457	·8449	·8441	·8433	·8426	1	3	4	5	6
46	Ī·8418	·8410	·8402	·8394	·8386	·8378	·8370	·8362	·8354	·8346	1	3	4	5	7
47	Ī·8338	·8330	·8322	·8313	·8305	·8297	·8289	·8280	·8272	·8264	1	3	4	6	7
48	Ī·8255	·8247	·8238	·8230	·8221	·8213	·8204	·8195	·8187	·8178	1	3	4	6	7
49	Ī·8169	·8161	·8152	·8143	·8134	·8125	·8117	·8108	·8099	·8090	1	3	4	6	7
50	Ī·8081	·8072	·8063	·8053	·8044	·8035	·8026	·8017	·8007	·7998	2	3	5	6	8
51	Ī·7989	·7979	·7970	·7960	·7951	·7941	·7932	·7922	·7913	·7903	2	3	5	6	8
52	Ī·7893	·7884	·7874	·7864	·7854	·7844	·7835	·7825	·7815	·7805	2	3	5	7	8
53	Ī·7795	·7785	·7774	·7764	·7754	·7744	·7734	·7723	·7713	·7703	2	3	5	7	9
54	Ī·7692	·7682	·7671	·7661	·7650	·7640	·7629	·7618	·7607	·7597	2	4	5	7	9
55	Ī·7586	·7575	·7564	·7553	·7542	·7531	·7520	·7509	·7498	·7487	2	4	6	7	9
56	Ī·7476	·7464	·7453	·7442	·7430	·7419	·7407	·7396	·7384	·7373	2	4	6	8	10
57	Ī·7361	·7349	·7338	·7326	·7314	·7302	·7290	·7278	·7266	·7254	2	4	6	8	10
58	Ī·7242	·7230	·7218	·7205	·7193	·7181	·7168	·7156	·7144	·7131	2	4	6	8	10
59	Ī·7118	·7106	·7093	·7080	·7068	·7055	·7042	·7029	·7016	·7003	2	4	6	9	11
60	Ī·6990	·6977	·6963	·6950	·6937	·6923	·6910	·6896	·6883	·6869	2	4	7	9	11
61	Ī·6856	·6842	·6828	·6814	·6801	·6787	·6773	·6759	·6744	·6730	2	5	7	9	12
62	Ī·6716	·6702	·6687	·6673	·6659	·6644	·6629	·6615	·6600	·6585	2	5	7	10	12
63	Ī·6570	·6556	·6541	·6526	·6510	·6495	·6480	·6465	·6449	·6434	3	5	8	10	13
64	Ī·6418	·6403	·6387	·6371	·6356	·6340	·6324	·6308	·6292	·6276	3	5	8	11	13
65	Ī·6259	·6243	·6227	·6210	·6194	·6177	·6161	·6144	·6127	·6110	3	6	8	11	14
66	Ī·6093	·6076	·6059	·6042	·6024	·6007	·5990	·5972	·5954	·5937	3	6	9	12	14
67	Ī·5919	·5901	·5883	·5865	·5847	·5828	·5810	·5792	·5773	·5754	3	6	9	12	15
68	Ī·5736	·5717	·5698	·5679	·5660	·5641	·5621	·5602	·5583	·5563	3	6	10	13	16
69	Ī·5543	·5523	·5504	·5484	·5463	·5443	·5423	·5402	·5382	·5361	3	7	10	13	17
70	Ī·5341	·5320	·5299	·5278	·5256	·5235	·5213	·5192	·5170	·5148	4	7	11	14	18
71	Ī·5126	·5104	·5082	·5060	·5037	·5015	·4992	·4969	·4946	·4923	4	8	11	15	19
72	Ī·4900	·4876	·4853	·4829	·4805	·4781	·4757	·4733	·4709	·4684	4	8	12	16	20
73	Ī·4659	·4634	·4609	·4584	·4559	·4533	·4508	·4482	·4456	·4430	4	9	13	17	21
74	Ī·4403	·4377	·4350	·4323	·4296	·4269	·4242	·4214	·4186	·4158	5	9	14	18	23
75	Ī·4130	·4102	·4073	·4044	·4015	·3986	·3957	·3927	·3897	·3867	5	10	15	20	24
76	Ī·3837	·3806	·3775	·3745	·3713	·3682	·3650	·3618	·3586	·3554	5	11	16	21	26
77	Ī·3521	·3488	·3455	·3421	·3387	·3353	·3319	·3284	·3250	·3214	6	11	17	23	28
78	Ī·3179	·3143	·3107	·3070	·3034	·2997	·2959	·2921	·2883	·2845	6	12	19	25	31
79	Ī·2806	·2767	·2727	·2687	·2647	·2606	·2565	·2524	·2482	·2439	7	14	20	27	34
80	Ī·2397	·2353	·2310	·2266	·2221	·2176	·2131	·2085	·2038	·1991	8	15	23	30	38
81	Ī·1943	·1895	·1847	·1797	·1747	·1697	·1646	·1594	·1542	·1489	8	17	25	34	42
82	Ī·1436	·1381	·1326	·1271	·1214	·1157	·1099	·1040	·0981	·0920	10	19	29	38	48
83	Ī·0859	·0797	·0734	·0670	·0605	·0539	·0472	·0403	·0334	·0264	11	22	33	44	56
84	Ī·0192	·0120	Ī·0046	2·9970	·9894	·9816	·9736	·9655	·9573	·9489	13	26	39	53	66
85	2̄·9403	·9315	·9226	·9135	·9042	·8946	·8849	·8749	·8647	·8543	p.p. cease				
86	2̄·8436	·8326	·8213	·8098	·7979	·7857	·7731	·7602	·7468	·7330	to be				
87	2̄·7188	·7041	·6889	·6731	·6567	·6397	·6220	·6035	·5842	·5640	sufficiently				
88	2̄·5428	·5206	·4971	·4723	·4459	·4179	·3880	·3558	·3210	·2832	accurate				
89	2̄·2419	·1961	·1450	·0870	2̄·0200	3̄·9408	·8439	·7190	·5429	·2419					
	0'	6'	12'	18'	24'	30'	36'	42'	48'	54'	1'	2'	3'	4'	5'

LOGARITHMIC TANGENTS

Proportional Parts

	0′	6′	12′	18′	24′	30′	36′	42′	48′	54′	1′	2′	3′	4′	5
0°	− ∞	3̄·2419	·5429	·7190	·8439	3̄·9409	2̄·0200	·0870	·1450	·1962					
1	2̄·2419	·2833	·3211	·3559	·3881	·4181	·4461	·4725	·4973	·5208			p.p. cease		
2	2̄·5431	·5643	·5845	·6038	·6223	·6401	·6571	·6736	·6894	·7046			to be		
3	2̄·7194	·7337	·7475	·7609	·7739	·7865	·7988	·8107	·8223	·8336			sufficiently		
4	2̄·8446	·8554	·8659	·8762	·8862	·8960	·9056	·9150	·9241	·9331			accurate		
5	2̄·9420	·9506	·9591	·9674	·9756	·9836	·9915	2̄·9992	1̄·0068	·0143	13	27	40	53	66
6	1̄·0216	·0289	·0360	·0430	·0499	·0567	·0633	·0699	·0764	·0828	11	22	34	45	56
7	1̄·0891	·0954	·1015	·1076	·1135	·1194	·1252	·1310	·1367	·1423	10	20	29	39	49
8	1̄·1478	·1533	·1587	·1640	·1693	·1745	·1797	·1848	·1898	·1948	9	17	26	35	43
9	1̄·1997	·2046	·2094	·2142	·2189	·2236	·2282	·2328	·2374	·2419	8	16	23	31	39
10	1̄·2463	·2507	·2551	·2594	·2637	·2680	·2722	·2764	·2805	·2846	7	14	21	28	35
11	1̄·2887	·2927	·2967	·3006	·3046	·3085	·3123	·3162	·3200	·3237	6	13	19	26	32
12	1̄·3275	·3312	·3349	·3385	·3422	·3458	·3493	·3529	·3564	·3599	6	12	18	24	30
13	1̄·3634	·3668	·3702	·3736	·3770	·3804	·3837	·3870	·3903	·3935	6	11	17	22	28
14	1̄·3968	·4000	·4032	·4064	·4095	·4127	·4158	·4189	·4220	·4250	5	10	16	21	26
15	1̄·4281	·4311	·4341	·4371	·4400	·4430	·4459	·4488	·4517	·4546	5	10	15	20	24
16	1̄·4575	·4603	·4632	·4660	·4688	·4716	·4744	·4771	·4799	·4826	5	9	14	19	23
17	1̄·4853	·4880	·4907	·4934	·4961	·4987	·5014	·5040	·5066	·5092	4	9	13	18	22
18	1̄·5118	·5143	·5169	·5195	·5220	·5245	·5270	·5295	·5320	·5345	4	8	13	17	21
19	1̄·5370	·5394	·5419	·5443	·5467	·5491	·5516	·5539	·5563	·5587	4	8	12	16	20
20	1̄·5611	·5634	·5658	·5681	·5704	·5727	·5750	·5773	·5796	·5819	4	8	12	15	19
21	1̄·5842	·5864	·5887	·5909	·5932	·5954	·5976	·5998	·6020	·6042	4	7	11	15	18
22	1̄·6064	·6086	·6108	·6129	·6151	·6172	·6194	·6215	·6236	·6257	4	7	11	14	18
23	1̄·6279	·6300	·6321	·6341	·6362	·6383	·6404	·6424	·6445	·6465	3	7	10	14	17
24	1̄·6486	·6506	·6527	·6547	·6567	·6587	·6607	·6627	·6647	·6667	3	7	10	13	17
25	1̄·6687	·6706	·6726	·6746	·6765	·6785	·6804	·6824	·6843	·6863	3	6	10	13	16
26	1̄·6882	·6901	·6920	·6939	·6958	·6977	·6996	·7015	·7034	·7053	3	6	10	13	16
27	1̄·7072	·7090	·7109	·7128	·7146	·7165	·7183	·7202	·7220	·7238	3	6	9	12	15
28	1̄·7257	·7275	·7293	·7311	·7330	·7348	·7366	·7384	·7402	·7420	3	6	9	12	15
29	1̄·7438	·7455	·7473	·7491	·7509	·7526	·7544	·7562	·7579	·7597	3	6	9	12	15
30	1̄·7614	·7632	·7649	·7667	·7684	·7701	·7719	·7736	·7753	·7771	3	6	9	12	15
31	1̄·7788	·7805	·7822	·7839	·7856	·7873	·7890	·7907	·7924	·7941	3	6	9	11	14
32	1̄·7958	·7975	·7992	·8008	·8025	·8042	·8059	·8075	·8092	·8109	3	6	8	11	14
33	1̄·8125	·8142	·8158	·8175	·8191	·8208	·8224	·8241	·8257	·8274	3	6	8	11	14
34	1̄·8290	·8306	·8323	·8339	·8355	·8371	·8388	·8404	·8420	·8436	3	5	8	11	13
35	1̄·8452	·8468	·8484	·8501	·8517	·8533	·8549	·8565	·8581	·8597	3	5	8	11	13
36	1̄·8613	·8629	·8644	·8660	·8676	·8692	·8708	·8724	·8740	·8755	3	5	8	11	13
37	1̄·8771	·8787	·8803	·8818	·8834	·8850	·8865	·8881	·8897	·8912	3	5	8	10	13
38	1̄·8928	·8944	·8959	·8975	·8990	·9006	·9022	·9037	·9053	·9068	3	5	8	10	13
39	1̄·9084	·9099	·9115	·9130	·9146	·9161	·9176	·9192	·9207	·9223	3	5	8	10	13
40	1̄·9238	·9254	·9269	·9284	·9300	·9315	·9330	·9346	·9361	·9376	3	5	8	10	13
41	1̄·9392	·9407	·9422	·9438	·9453	·9468	·9483	·9499	·9514	·9529	3	5	8	10	13
42	1̄·9544	·9560	·9575	·9590	·9605	·9621	·9636	·9651	·9666	·9681	3	5	8	10	13
43	1̄·9697	·9712	·9727	·9742	·9757	·9772	·9788	·9803	·9818	·9833	3	5	8	10	13
44	1̄·9848	·9864	·9879	·9894	·9909	·9924	·9939	·9955	·9970	·9985	3	5	8	10	13
	0′	6′	12′	18′	24′	30′	36′	42′	48′	54′	1′	2′	3′	4′	5′

LOGARITHMIC TANGENTS

	0′	6′	12′	18′	24′	30′	36′	42′	48′	54′	1′	2′	3′	4′	5′
45°	0·0000	·0015	·0030	·0045	·0061	·0076	·0091	·0106	·0121	·0136	3	5	8	10	13
46	0·0152	·0167	·0182	·0197	·0212	·0228	·0243	·0258	·0273	·0288	3	5	8	10	13
47	0·0303	·0319	·0334	·0349	·0364	·0379	·0395	·0410	·0425	·0440	3	5	8	10	13
48	0·0456	·0471	·0486	·0501	·0517	·0532	·0547	·0562	·0578	·0593	3	5	8	10	13
49	0·0608	·0624	·0639	·0654	·0670	·0685	·0700	·0716	·0731	·0746	3	5	8	10	13
50	0·0762	·0777	·0793	·0808	·0824	·0839	·0854	·0870	·0885	·0901	3	5	8	10	13
51	0·0916	·0932	·0947	·0963	·0978	·0994	·1010	·1025	·1041	·1056	3	5	8	10	13
52	0·1072	·1088	·1103	·1119	·1135	·1150	·1166	·1182	·1197	·1213	3	5	8	10	13
53	0·1229	·1245	·1260	·1276	·1292	·1308	·1324	·1340	·1356	·1371	3	5	8	11	13
54	0·1387	·1403	·1419	·1435	·1451	·1467	·1483	·1499	·1516	·1532	3	5	8	11	13
55	0·1548	·1564	·1580	·1596	·1612	·1629	·1645	·1661	·1677	·1694	3	5	8	11	13
56	0·1710	·1726	·1743	·1759	·1776	·1792	·1809	·1825	·1842	·1858	3	6	8	11	14
57	0·1875	·1891	·1908	·1925	·1941	·1958	·1975	·1992	·2008	·2025	3	6	8	11	14
58	0·2042	·2059	·2076	·2093	·2110	·2127	·2144	·2161	·2178	·2195	3	6	9	11	14
59	0·2212	·2229	·2247	·2264	·2281	·2299	·2316	·2333	·2351	·2368	3	6	9	12	15
60	0·2386	·2403	·2421	·2438	·2456	·2474	·2491	·2509	·2527	·2545	3	6	9	12	15
61	0·2562	·2580	·2598	·2616	·2634	·2652	·2670	·2689	·2707	·2725	3	6	9	12	15
62	0·2743	·2762	·2780	·2798	·2817	·2835	·2854	·2872	·2891	·2910	3	6	9	12	15
63	0·2928	·2947	·2966	·2985	·3004	·3023	·3042	·3061	·3080	·3099	3	6	10	13	16
64	0·3118	·3137	·3157	·3176	·3196	·3215	·3235	·3254	·3274	·3294	3	6	10	13	16
65	0·3313	·3333	·3353	·3373	·3393	·3413	·3433	·3453	·3473	·3494	3	7	10	13	17
66	0·3514	·3535	·3555	·3576	·3596	·3617	·3638	·3659	·3679	·3700	3	7	10	14	17
67	0·3721	·3743	·3764	·3785	·3806	·3828	·3849	·3871	·3892	·3914	4	7	11	14	18
68	0·3936	·3958	·3980	·4002	·4024	·4046	·4068	·4091	·4113	·4136	4	7	11	15	18
69	0·4158	·4181	·4202	·4227	·4250	·4273	·4296	·4319	·4342	·4366	4	8	12	15	19
70	0·4389	·4413	·4437	·4461	·4484	·4509	·4533	·4557	·4581	·4606	4	8	12	16	20
71	0·4630	·4655	·4680	·4705	·4730	·4755	·4780	·4805	·4831	·4857	4	8	13	17	21
72	0·4882	·4908	·4934	·4960	·4986	·5013	·5039	·5066	·5093	·5120	4	9	13	18	22
73	0·5147	·5174	·5201	·5229	·5256	·5284	·5312	·5340	·5368	·5397	5	9	14	19	23
74	0·5425	·5454	·5483	·5512	·5541	·5570	·5600	·5629	·5659	·5689	5	10	15	20	24
75	0·5719	·5750	·5780	·5811	·5842	·5873	·5905	·5936	·5968	·6000	5	10	16	21	26
76	0·6032	·6065	·6097	·6130	·6163	·6196	·6230	·6264	·6298	·6332	6	11	17	22	28
77	0·6366	·6401	·6436	·6471	·6507	·6542	·6578	·6615	·6651	·6688	6	12	18	24	30
78	0·6725	·6763	·6800	·6838	·6877	·6915	·6954	·6994	·7033	·7073	6	13	19	26	32
79	0·7113	·7154	·7195	·7236	·7278	·7320	·7363	·7406	·7449	·7493	7	14	21	28	35
80	0·7537	·7581	·7626	·7672	·7718	·7764	·7811	·7858	·7906	·7954	8	16	23	31	39
81	0·8003	·8052	·8102	·8152	·8203	·8255	·8307	·8360	·8413	·8467	9	17	26	35	43
82	0·8522	·8577	·8633	·8690	·8748	·8806	·8865	·8924	·8985	·9046	10	20	29	39	49
83	0·9109	·9172	·9236	·9301	·9367	·9433	·9501	·9570	·9640	·9711	11	22	34	45	56
84	0·9784	·9857	0·9932	1·0008	·0085	·0164	·0244	·0326	·0409	·0494	13	27	40	53	66
85	1·0580	·0669	·0759	·0850	·0944	·1040	·1138	·1238	·1341	·1446			p.p. cease		
86	1·1554	·1664	·1777	·1893	·2012	·2135	·2261	·2391	·2525	·2663			to be		
87	1·2806	·2954	·3106	·3264	·3429	·3599	·3777	·3962	·4155	·4357			sufficiently		
88	1·4569	·4792	·5027	·5275	·5539	·5819	·6119	·6441	·6789	·7167			accurate		
89	1·7581	·8038	·8550	·9130	1·9800	2·0591	·1561	·2810	·4571	·7581					
	0′	6′	12′	18′	24′	30′	36′	42′	48′	54′	1′	2′	3′	4′	5′

CONSTANTS

Constant.	Number.	Log.
π	3·1416	0·4972
$\dfrac{\pi}{4}$	0·7854	$\bar{1}$·8951
$\dfrac{1}{\pi}$	0·3183	$\bar{1}$·5028
π^2	9·8696	0·9944
$\sqrt{\pi}$	1·7725	0·2486
$\frac{4}{3}\pi$	4·1888	0·6221
$\dfrac{180}{\pi}$	57·2958	1·7581
$\dfrac{\pi}{180}$	0·01745	$\bar{2}$·2419
e	2·71828	0·4343
$\mathrm{Log}_e\,10$	2·3026	0·3622

CONVERSION FACTORS

To convert	Multiply by	Log.
Metres to inches . . .	39·37	1·5952
Inches to centimetres . .	2·5400	0·4048
Kilometres to miles . . .	0·6214	$\bar{1}$·7934
Kilograms to lb . . .	2·20462	0·3434
Lb to kilograms . . .	0·45359	$\bar{1}$·6567
Gallons to cubic inches . .	277·45	2·4431
Radians to degrees . . .	57·2958	1·7581
Miles per hour to feet per second	1·4666	0·1663

G. (at Greenwich) $\quad= \quad$ 32·191 ft per sec.^{2}
$\qquad\qquad\qquad\qquad = \quad$ 981·18 cm per sec.^{2}
Weight of 1 cu ft of water $=$ 62·42 lb (at 4° C.)

ANSWERS

EXERCISE 1

p. 14.

1. $x = \frac{1}{3}$; $\frac{3}{4}$.

2. (a) $(x - 5)(x + 4)$; (b) $\pi(R - 2r)(R + 2r)$;
(c) $R(R + 4r)(R + 2r)$; (b) $94 \cdot 2$; (c) $= 877 \cdot 5$.

3. $d = D\sqrt{\dfrac{f - p}{f + p}}$. $d = 5 \cdot 6$. **4.** $x = 162 \cdot 8$ or $136 \cdot 2$.

5. 4 in. and $1 \cdot 6$ in. **6.** $(3a - b)$; $60 \cdot 3$.

7. (a) real; (b) complex; (c) equal; (d) real.

8. $A = x\left(\dfrac{P}{2} - x\right)$; $7 \cdot 37$ and $1 \cdot 63$.

9. $2 \cdot 13$ or $-5 \cdot 63$. **10.** 87 sec.

EXERCISE 2

p. 18.

1. $x = \mp\sqrt{2}$; $\pm\sqrt{3}$.

2. $\dfrac{1}{y^2} = -3$ or 2; real value of y is $\pm\sqrt{\dfrac{2}{2}}$. **3.** $x = \dfrac{1}{81}$.

4. $x = 1 \pm \sqrt{2}$; or $1 \pm \sqrt{17}$. **5.** $z = 28$.

6. $\sin \theta = \frac{3}{4}$ or $\frac{1}{3}$. **7.** $\tan \theta = \frac{1}{4}$ or -5.

8. $\sin \theta = \frac{2}{3}$ or $\frac{1}{2}$. **9.** $\tan \theta = -\frac{2}{3}$ or 4.

10. $x = 1$ or 2. **11.** $x = \pm 2$. **12.** $\cos \theta = 0 \cdot 129$.

13. (i) $x = 0$ or $0 \cdot 1761$;

(ii) $\sin x = \pm \dfrac{1}{\sqrt{2}}$ i.e. $x \mp 0 \cdot 78$ radians.

EXERCISE 3

p. 20.

1. $9 \cdot 667$. **2.** 22. **3.** ± 5.

4. $= 2 \cdot 25$. **5.** $-0 \cdot 29$. **6.** $y = 4$ or $2 \cdot 86$.

7. $z = 3$. **8.** $x = 1$. **9.** $x = 4$ or 11.

10. $p = 2 \cdot 727$.

EXERCISE 4

p. 27.

1. $x = -1, y = 0.$ **2.** $x = 7, y = 4.$

3. $x = 3$ or $2, y = 2$ or $3.$ **4.** $z = 8, w = 2.$

5. $x = \pm 1, y : \pm 2.$ **6.** $x = 1$ or $\frac{1}{9}, y = 2$ or $\frac{22}{9}.$

7. $x = \pm 7\sqrt{2}, y = \pm \sqrt{2}.$
$x = \pm \sqrt{2}, y = \pm 7\sqrt{2}.$ **8.** $\frac{1}{x} = 4; \frac{1}{y} = 3.$

9. $x = y = \pm 1.$ **10.** $y = \frac{13}{25}, x = \frac{52}{25}.$

11. $x = 100, y = 173 \cdot 2.$

12. $a = 1 \cdot 6, b = 0 \cdot 4, c = -1 \cdot 5, S = 102 \cdot 8.$

13. $A = 2, B = \frac{1}{2}, C = \frac{1}{4}.$

EXERCISE 5

p. 29.

1. $a = 1 \cdot 37, b = 1 \cdot 86, n = 1 \cdot 46.$ **2.** $p = 24 \cdot 23, T = 328 \cdot 3.$

3. $x = 1 \cdot 525.$ **4.** $x = 3$ or $-1.$

5. $x = -\frac{5}{3}, y = \frac{7}{3}.$ **6.** $x = 5$ or $-1.$

7. $x = -\frac{28}{3}, y = -4.$

8. $a = 2 \cdot 36, b = 0 \cdot 84, c = 1 \cdot 43; y = 43 \cdot 1.$

9. (a) $30\left(1 - \frac{2}{\pi}\right)$ cm; (b) $104 \cdot 6$ in.^{2}.

10. (a) $0 \cdot 59$; (b) $x = 1 \cdot 318$; (c) $x = 3, y = 4, z = -2.$

11. (i) $17 \cdot 6 \times 10^4$;   **12.** (i) $83 \cdot 57$;
(ii) $-0 \cdot 58.$ (ii) (a) $x = -\frac{13}{5}$ or 2;
                                       (b) $x = 0 \cdot 509.$

EXERCISE 6

p. 44.

1. (a) $y - 3 = \frac{1}{\sqrt{3}}(x - 2)$;   (b) $y + \sqrt{3x} + \sqrt{3} - 1 = 0$;

    (c) $y + 2 = 0 \cdot 7536(x + 3)$;   (d) $3x - 7y + 27 = 0$;

    (e) $x + 6y + 2 = 0.$ **2.** $0 \cdot 6$ too small.

3. $a = 684, b = 39 \cdot 5.$ **4.** $n = 5 \cdot 7, m = 20 \cdot 1.$

5. $a = 0 \cdot 182, b = 9 \cdot 81.$ **6.** $a = 5 \cdot 5, b = 0 \cdot 25.$

EXERCISE 8

p. 56.

1. $x = 3 \cdot 2$ or $2.$ **2.** $x = 4 \cdot 1$ or $2 \cdot 3.$

3. $x = 1 \cdot 78$ or $-0 \cdot 28.$ **4.** $x = 2 \cdot 77.$

5. $x = 1 \cdot 27$ and $3 \cdot 82.$ Turning points $(3, 5 \cdot 4)$; $(2, 1).$

EXERCISE 8A

(Miscellaneous)

p. 57.

1. $a = 29 \cdot 2$, $n = 1 \cdot 84$, $220 \cdot 8$ lb wt.

2. $c = 565$, $n = 1 \cdot 05$, $25 \cdot 7$ lb/in.^{2}.

3. $a = 99 \cdot 6$, $n = 2 \cdot 49$, $34{,}900$ lb/min.

4. $a = 0 \cdot 4$, $n = 1 \cdot 5$.

5. (i) $x = 1$, $y = 2$, $z = 3$;
(ii) (a) $x = -3$, $y = -4$; or $x = 2$, $y = 1$.
(b) $2 \cdot 245$ or $-1 \cdot 245$.

6. (a) $13 \cdot 19$; (b) $18 \cdot 06°$ C.

7. (i) $x = \frac{1}{5}$, $y = \frac{1}{5}$, $z = \frac{1}{4}$; (ii) $x = 3 \cdot 281$; (iii) $60°$, $300°$, $138° \, 35'$, $221° \, 24'$.

8. (a) (i) $800 \, (\frac{19}{20})^n$, (ii) £$558 \cdot 4$; (b) 14 years; (c) $x : 1 \cdot 49$.

9. (i) $3 \cdot 64$, (ii) $x = 1 \cdot 132$.   **10.** $y = 1 \cdot 412$, $c = 50 \cdot 58$.

11. (i) 5th amplitude $= 0 \cdot 480$.   Total distance $= 5 \cdot 546$ in.

12. $a = 30$, $k = -2 \cdot 05 \times 10^{-5}$.

13. (b) Lift $= 0 \cdot 4$ in., Rotation $= 53° \, 8'$.

14. (b) $x = -2 \cdot 4$, $-0 \cdot 75$, $+3 \cdot 4$.

15. (a) $43° \, 37'$, $316° \, 23'$; and (b) tan A $= 11 \cdot 55$;
(c) $3 \cdot 9 \sin(x + 0 \cdot 3945)$.

16. Height $= 8(6 - 5 \cos \theta)$.
(a) $4 \cdot 78$ ft/sec; (b) $-2 \cdot 97$ ft/sec.

17. (a) (a) $4 \cdot 99$ radians; (b) $T_1 = 765$, $T_2 = 1510$;
(b) $y = x^3 - 3x^2 + 2x + 5$.

18. (b) $11° \, 46'$, $65° \, 21'$.

19. (a) $x = \frac{1}{5}$; (b) $x = 2 \cdot 161$; (c) $x = \pm 3$, $+\frac{3}{2}$.

20. (a) $10° \, 9'$; (b) $0 \cdot 007$ ft/sec.

21. (a) $t = -\dfrac{L}{R} \log_e \left(1 - \dfrac{Ri}{E}\right)$, $t = 0 \cdot 2618$ sec;
(b) $x = -0 \cdot 08825$.

22. $n = 0 \cdot 785$, $a = 10 \cdot 5$.

23. (a) £345, after 21 years; (b) $4 \cdot 8$ ft.

24. £$35 \cdot 8$, at end of 6 years.   **25.** (ii) $0 \cdot 115$ in.^{2}.

EXERCISE 9

p. 68.

1. (a) 210; (b) 1680; (c) 720.   **2.** (a) $\dfrac{\lfloor 6}{\lfloor 4}$; (b) $\lfloor 5$; (c) $\dfrac{\lfloor 8}{\lfloor 6}$.

4. 504.   **5.** 36.   **6.** 30.   **7.** 60, 125.   **8.** $2 \times \lfloor 7 = 10{,}080$.

EXERCISE 10

p. 71.

1. (a) 35; (b) 28; (c) 10; (d) 1.

2. (a) $\dfrac{\lfloor 7}{\lfloor 4 \ \lfloor 3}$; (b) $\dfrac{\lfloor 8}{\lfloor 2 \ \lfloor 6}$; (c) $\dfrac{\lfloor 10}{\lfloor 9}$; (d) $\dfrac{\lfloor 5}{\lfloor 5}$.

4. 560.   **5.** (a) 28; (b) 56.   **6.** $^{8}C_3 \times {}^{6}C_4 = 840.$

7. $^{17}C_7$ or $^{17}C_{10}$.   **8.** $r = 5$ or 7.

EXERCISE 11

p. 80.

1. (a) $1 + \dfrac{z}{2} - \dfrac{z^2}{8} + \dfrac{z^3}{16}$;   (b) $1 + h + h^2 + h^3$;

(c) $1 + \dfrac{3y}{2} + \dfrac{3y^2}{8} - \dfrac{y^3}{16}$;   (d) $1 + \dfrac{5x}{4} + \dfrac{45x^2}{32} + \dfrac{195x^3}{128}$;

(e) $1 - x + x^2 - x^3$;   (f) $1 + \dfrac{x}{2} + \dfrac{3x^2}{8} + \dfrac{5x^3}{16}$;

(g) $1 - \dfrac{x}{4} + \dfrac{5x^2}{32} - \dfrac{5x^3}{128}$;   (h) $1 - 3x + 6x^2 - 10x^2$;

(k) $\dfrac{1}{a^2} - \dfrac{2x}{a^3} + \dfrac{3x^2}{a^4} - \dfrac{4x^3}{a^5}$;   (l) $a^{\frac{1}{2}}\left(1 + \dfrac{h}{a} - \dfrac{h^2}{2a^2} + \dfrac{h^3}{2a^3}\right)$;

(m) $\dfrac{1}{2^4}\left(1 + 6x + \dfrac{45x^2}{2} + \dfrac{135x^3}{2}\right)$.

2. (a) 1·104;   (b) 0·988;   (c) 1·003;
(d) 1·004;   (e) 0·332;   (f) 1·007.

3. $8x^7, \ \dfrac{1}{2\sqrt{x}}$.   **4.** $1 + x - \dfrac{x^2}{2} + \dfrac{x^3}{2} - \dfrac{5x^4}{8}$.

6. $1 - \dfrac{5x}{6} + \dfrac{19x^2}{2}$.   **7.** $\dfrac{5 \times 2^5}{7^3 \times 3^5}$.

8. $1 - 27x + 324x^2 - 2268x^3 + 10,206x^4$,
4th 0·489888, 5th 0·13226976.

9. $^{12}C_6 . a^{12}$.

10. $x^{\frac{1}{2}}\left(1 - \dfrac{y}{2x} - \dfrac{y^2}{8x^2} - \dfrac{y^2}{16x^3}\right)$, 1·732, 0·02885 − 0·0002406.

11. 4th term $-{}^{14}C_3 \left(\dfrac{3}{4}\right)^3 \left(\dfrac{x^2}{2}\right)^{11}$.   **12.** $\dfrac{4lm}{d^3}$.

EXERCISE 12

p. 84.

1. (a) 4; (b) 2; (c) 44; (d) $\frac{1}{4}$. **2.** (a) 4; (b) 5·364; (c) 6·062.
3. (a) 53; (b) 70. **4.** (a) $8x + 6$; (b) $h(2h + 4x - 1)$.
5. $6t + 11$.

EXERCISE 13

p. 88.

1. 5. **2.** 5. **3.** 7. **4.** 3. **5.** $\frac{11}{8}$. **6.** $\frac{3}{5}$. **7.** $\frac{17}{11}$.

EXERCISE 14

p. 93.

1. 9. **2.** (a) 7; (b) 1; (c) $2 + h$.
3. $2, y - 2x + 1 = 0$. **4.** $y - 16x + 16 = 0$.
5. $y - 9x + 7 = 0$.

EXERCISE 15

p. 97.

1. (a) $2x$; (b) $6x + 1$; (c) $3x^2$. **2.** $8t, 4z$.
3. $y - 8x - 1 = 0, \dfrac{dy}{dx} = 6x + 2$. **4.** 5.

EXERCISE 16

p. 101.

1. (i) $7x^6$; (ii) $-\dfrac{8}{x^5}$; (iii) $-\dfrac{6}{x^3}$; (iv) $-\dfrac{15}{x^4}$.

2. $-\dfrac{10}{t^6}, \dfrac{-5}{2\sqrt{y^3}}, \dfrac{-2}{\sqrt[3]{z^5}}$.

3. (a) $-\dfrac{4}{x^2}$; (b) $\dfrac{-50}{3\sqrt[3]{y^{13}}}$; (c) $\dfrac{66\sqrt[5]{x^6}}{5}$.

4. (i) $-\frac{3}{2}x^{-\frac{5}{2}}$; (ii) $\dfrac{15}{4}\theta^{-\frac{1}{4}}$; (iii) $-8z^{-5}$; (iv) $\dfrac{55t^{\frac{7}{4}}}{4}$.

5. (i) $6\cdot4x^{2\cdot2}$; (ii) $0\cdot13x^{-0\cdot87}$; (iii) $-10\cdot70x^{-3\cdot14}$;
   (iv) $-\dfrac{1\cdot5}{3\sqrt{2}}x^{-1\cdot5}$; (v) $\dfrac{-5}{2\sqrt{x^3}}$.

EXERCISE 17

p. 102.

1. $6x^2 - 6x + 4$, $2 \cdot 6t^{0 \cdot 3} + 8t^{-3} - 3t^{-2}$.

2. (i) $-x^{-2} + 4x^{-3} - 12x^{-5}$; (ii) $4 \cdot 8t^{0 \cdot 6} + 2 \cdot 8t^{-1 \cdot 7} - 2t^{-2}$; (iii) $2x - 1$; (iv) $6(3x + 1)$.

3. (a) $2^3 \cdot 9x^8$; (b) $\dfrac{2}{3x^3}$; (c) $0 \cdot 5x^{-0 \cdot 5}(1 + 12x^{-2})$; (d) $\frac{3}{2}x^2 + \frac{1}{2}x^{-2}$; (e) $2x^3(2 - x)(4 - 3x)$.

4. (i) $-\dfrac{2^{13}}{x^3}$; (ii) $8x(x - 2^5)(x + 2^5)$; (iii) $\frac{3}{5}x^{-\frac{8}{5}}$; (iv) $-\dfrac{2^9}{10}x^{-0 \cdot 6}$; (v) $6x^5 + 3x^{-4}$, for $x = 2^5$. (i) $-\frac{1}{4}$; (ii) 0; (iii) $\frac{3}{20}$; (iv) $\frac{32}{5}$.

5. $\dfrac{2}{\sqrt[3]{x}} - \dfrac{3}{x^{2 \cdot 5}} + \dfrac{15}{x^4}$.

6. (a) $3x^2 + 4x$; (b) $19 \cdot 2x^{2 \cdot 2} + \dfrac{2}{x^2}$; (c) $4x^3 - 12x^2 + 6x - 12$.

7. (a) $6x + 2$; (b) $-\frac{25}{27}$.

8. (a) (i) $8x + 1$, (ii) $3 - \dfrac{12}{x^2}$;

(b) (i) $x = \dfrac{\sqrt{38}}{3}$, $y = 26\sqrt{38} + 20$

and $x = -\dfrac{\sqrt{38}}{3}$, $y = -26\sqrt{38} + 20$,

(ii) $x = 2$, $y = -28$; and $x = -2$, $y = 68$.

9. $2x + 2$, (i) $20 \cdot 3x^{-0 \cdot 3}$, (ii) $\dfrac{6 - 3x^2}{x^4}$.

10. $K = \frac{3}{2}$, gradient $= \frac{1}{8}$.

11. $\dfrac{dy}{dx} = x^2 - 6x + 5$; (i) $y = -\frac{13}{3}$ when $x = 5$, $y = \frac{19}{3}$ when $x = 1$; (ii) $y = 1 - \dfrac{7\sqrt{5}}{3}$ when $x = 3 + \sqrt{5}$, $y = 1 + \dfrac{7\sqrt{5}}{3}$ when $x = 3 - \sqrt{5}$.

12. $a = 36$, $b = \frac{1}{2}$. **13.** $6x$; (a) $-\dfrac{1}{x^2}$; (b) $-2Ax$.

EXERCISE 18

p. 105.

1. $12x^3 - 12x + 2$, $36x^2 - 12$. **2.** $6\left(1 - \dfrac{1}{t^3}\right)$. **3.** 6.

4. (a) $\dfrac{d^5y}{dx^5}$; (b) $\dfrac{d^4v}{dx^4}$.   **5.** $y = -\dfrac{1262}{243}$, $x = \dfrac{4}{9}$.

EXERCISE 19

p. 109.

1. $3(x^2 + x)^2(2x + 1)$.   **2.** $4(3x^2 - 5x + 6)^3(6x - 5)$.

3. $5(x^2 + 3)^4(2x)$.   **4.** $\dfrac{-(2x + 3)}{(x^2 + 3x + 4)^2}$.

5. $\dfrac{-1}{(x + 3)^2}$.   **6.** $\dfrac{-4x}{(x^2 + 3)^3}$.   **7.** $\dfrac{-16(3x^2 - 3)}{(x^3 + 3x + 4)^2}$.

8. $3(x^2 - 1 \cdot 3x + 4)^2(2x - 1 \cdot 3)$.   **9.** $\dfrac{-x}{\sqrt{(x^2 + 3)^3}}$.

10. $\dfrac{-4(4x + 1)}{3\sqrt[3]{(2x^2 + x + 1)^4}}$.

EXERCISE 20

p. 111.

1. $4x^3 + 9x^2 + 12x$.   **2.** $\frac{7}{2}x^{\frac{5}{2}} + \frac{25}{2}x^{\frac{3}{2}} - 3x^{\frac{1}{2}}$.

3. (i) $2x(x^2 + 3x + 6)^2 + 2x^2(x^2 + 3x + 6)(2x + 3)$;
(ii) $5x^4(x - 1)^4 + 4x^5(x - 1)^3$.

4. (i) $-9x^{-4}(x^2 + 2)^4 + 12x^{-3}(x^2 + 2)^3 \cdot 2x$;
(ii) $-\frac{1}{2}t^{-\frac{3}{2}}(t + 3)^3 + 3t^{-\frac{1}{2}}(t + 3)^2$.

5. (i) $4x^3(x^2 + 3)^{-2} - 2x^4(x^2 + 3)^{-3} \cdot 2x$;
(ii) $4x(1 - x^2)^{-2} + 8x^3(1 - x^2)^{-3}$;
(iii) $3(2 - x)^{-4} + 12x(2 - x)^{-5}$.

6. (i) $(x + 2)^{-2} - 2x(x + 2)^{-3}$;
(ii) $6x(1 - x)^{-1} + 3x^2(1 - x)^{-2}$;
(iii) $-2x^{-3}(x + 3)^{-1} - x^{-2}(x + 3)^{-2}$;
(iv) $(2x + 1)(x + 1)^{-2} - 2(x^2 + x + 2)(x + 1)^{-3}$;
(v) $2t(1 + t + t^2)^{-2} - 2(t^2 + 3)(1 + t + t^2)^{-3}(1 + 2t)$.

EXERCISE 21

p. 113.

1. $\dfrac{a}{(x + a)^2}$.   **2.** $\dfrac{4a^2x}{(x^2 + a^2)^2}$.

3. $\dfrac{x(x + 2)}{(x + 1)^2}$.   **4.** $\dfrac{2 - x}{2\sqrt{x}(x + 2)^2}$.

5. $\dfrac{3x(x+4)}{(x+2)^2}.$

6. $\dfrac{10x(1-x)(1+x)}{(x^2+1)^3}.$

7. $\dfrac{1}{(1-x)^{\frac{3}{2}}(1+x)^{\frac{1}{2}}}.$

8. $\dfrac{5x^2+20x+3}{3(x+2)^{\frac{2}{3}}(5x^2+3)^{\frac{2}{3}}}.$

EXERCISE 22

p. 115.

1. $3 \cdot 6x^{0 \cdot 2} - \dfrac{2}{\sqrt{x}} - \dfrac{9}{x^4}.$　　**2.** $6(2x-3)^2.$

3. $\dfrac{1}{2\sqrt{x-4}}.$　　**4.** $\dfrac{-2}{(x+a)^3}.$　　**5.** $\dfrac{-10}{\sqrt{(4x-2)^3}}.$

6. $\dfrac{-3}{\sqrt{(5-6x)}}.$　　**7.** $-8x(3-x^2)^3.$

8. $8(3x-1)(3x^2-2x+2)^3.$　　**9.** $\dfrac{(3x+2a)}{2\sqrt{x+a}}.$

10. $3x^2(x+a)^2(2x+a).$

11. $2x^4(x^2+2x+3)(9x^2+14x+15).$

12. $\dfrac{3x}{24\sqrt[4]{x^2-a^2}}.$　　**13.** $\dfrac{-(2x+1)}{3\sqrt[3]{(x^2+x+1)^4}}.$

14. $\dfrac{3(x^2+4x+1)}{(x+2)^2}.$　　**15.** $\dfrac{x^2(5x+6)}{2\sqrt{(x+1)^3}}.$

16. $\dfrac{14x}{(x^2+3)^2}.$　　**17.** $\dfrac{-5}{2\sqrt{(2+x)^3(3-x)}}.$　　**18.** $5, 11.$

19. $\frac{8}{9}, \frac{3}{4}.$　　**20.** $-\dfrac{x}{y}.$　　**21.** $-\dfrac{(2x+3y)}{3x}.$　　**22.** $-\dfrac{(2x+3)}{2(y+2)}.$

EXERCISE 23

p. 127.

(The constant of integration is omitted 1–23.)

1. $\dfrac{x^5}{5}.$　　**2.** $\dfrac{2x^{\frac{3}{2}}}{3}.$　　**3.** $\dfrac{-2}{\sqrt{x}}.$　　**4.** $\dfrac{-x^{-4}}{4}.$　　**5.** $\dfrac{x^6}{2}.$

6. $\dfrac{8x^{\frac{7}{4}}}{7}.$　　**7.** $\dfrac{20}{3}x^{\frac{3}{4}}.$　　**8.** $\dfrac{-4x^{-3}}{3}.$　　**9.** $\dfrac{x^{1 \cdot 6}}{0 \cdot 8}.$　　**10.** $\dfrac{3 \cdot 2x^{2 \cdot 3}}{2 \cdot 3}.$

11. $0 \cdot 525x^4.$　　**12.** $-x^{-0 \cdot 1}.$　　**13.** $\dfrac{x^3}{3} + \dfrac{3x^2}{2}.$

14. $\dfrac{x^{2 \cdot 3}}{2 \cdot 3} - \dfrac{x^{1 \cdot 4}}{1 \cdot 4} - \dfrac{1}{2x}.$ **15.** $x^3 - x^{-2} - \dfrac{1}{3x^3}.$

16. $\dfrac{x^{1 \cdot 2}}{0 \cdot 4} + \dfrac{2 \cdot 1 x^{2 \cdot 3}}{2 \cdot 3}.$ **17.** $y = \dfrac{3}{5} x^5 + \dfrac{17}{5}.$ **18.** $t^3 - 4.$

19. $\dfrac{2t^3}{3} + 5t - 31.$

20. $(a) -\dfrac{1}{4x^2};$ $(b)\ \sqrt{2x} - \dfrac{x^{1 \cdot 25}}{0 \cdot 3125};$ $(c)\ \dfrac{x^3}{3} + \dfrac{2}{x^2} - \dfrac{1}{5x^5}.$

21. $(a)\ \dfrac{24}{7} x^{\frac{7}{4}};$ $(b)\ 3x - \dfrac{x^{0 \cdot 8}}{0 \cdot 4};$ $(c)\ \dfrac{x^7}{7} - \dfrac{x^6}{3} + \dfrac{x^5}{5};$ $(d)\ \dfrac{x^3}{3} + \dfrac{1}{x}.$

22. $(a) -\dfrac{1}{\sqrt{2x}};$ $(b)\ \pi x - 10\sqrt{x};$ $(c)\ x - \dfrac{x^3}{9} - \sqrt{x};$

      $(d)\ x(3x^{\frac{5}{3}} + 8x + 6x^{\frac{1}{3}}).$ **23.** $(a)\ \dfrac{t^2}{2};$ $(b)\ 12\sqrt{x} + 2x.$

EXERCISE 24

p. 131.

(The constant of integration is omitted 1–16.)

1. $\dfrac{x^2}{2} + 3x.$ **2.** $\dfrac{x^3}{3} + 4x^2 + 16x.$ **3.** $\dfrac{-(5+x)^{-3}}{3}.$

4. $\dfrac{-1}{(x+3)}.$ **5.** $\dfrac{(x^2+3)^2}{2}.$ **6.** $\dfrac{(x^2+3)^2}{4}.$

7. $\dfrac{(x^2-1)^4}{8}.$ **8.** $\dfrac{(x^3-1)^3}{6}.$ **9.** $\dfrac{(x^3+3)^4}{12}.$

10. $\dfrac{-1}{2(x^2+5)^2}.$ **11.** $\dfrac{-1}{6(x^2+5)^3}.$ **12.** $\dfrac{-1}{(x^3-2)}.$

13. $2\sqrt{x^2+3}.$ **14.** $\tfrac{3}{4}(x^2+a^2)^{\frac{2}{3}}.$ **15.** $\dfrac{-1}{(x^2+x+3)}.$

16. $\dfrac{-1}{2(x^3+x^2+1)^2}.$

EXERCISE 25

p. 136.

1. 2 ft; 35 ft/sec; $\frac{1}{6}$ sec; 6 ft/sec²; 23 ft/sec.

2. 73; $\frac{28}{15}.$

3. $(a)\ 108 - 3t^2;$ $(b)\ -6t;$ $(c)\ t = 6$ sec; $s = 440$ ft from $t = 0.$ **4.** 19 ft/sec².

5. 168: 136; 104; 72; 40: 8 ft/sec − 32 ft/sec².

EXERCISE 26

p. 150.

1. (i) Max. $(-1, \frac{31}{6})$, min. $(2, \frac{2}{3})$;
    (ii) Max. $(0, 12)$, min. $(4, -20)$;
    (iii) Max. $(-1, 5)$, min. $(\frac{1}{3}, \frac{103}{27})$.
2. $2 \cdot 41$ ft³.   3. 206 in.³.   4. V $= 31$; E $= 108,000$.
5. 2 ft³.   6. $5 \cdot 64$ in. from one end.
8. $x = 1 \cdot 5$; $\frac{dy}{dx} = -2$; $x = -2$, $\frac{dy}{dx} = -9$;
   Min. $= \frac{3}{4}$, $x = 2 \cdot 5$.
9. (i) $a = 36$, $b = \frac{1}{2}$; (ii) Min. $16 \cdot 35$.
10. Length $= 3 \cdot 40$ in. Side of triangle $= 5 \cdot 88$ in.
11. (i) $x = \frac{1}{2}$; (ii) $x = 0$, $x = \frac{8}{5}$.
12. $a = \frac{3}{16}$; $b = \frac{43}{16}$; $y = 2$; 1; 4.
13. $x = 0$; $x = -1$.   14. $4 \cdot 46 \times 8 \cdot 95$ in.
15. (a) $x = \frac{3}{2}$ min.; (b) H $= \frac{9}{2}$.
16. Radius $= 69 \cdot 4$ ft. Height $= 66 \cdot 1$ ft.

EXERCISE 27

p. 155.

1. $\pm 0 \cdot 173$ sq in.   2. $\pm 0 \cdot 4$ sq in.
3. $\pm 8\pi/100$ sq in.   4. $\frac{3}{20}$ too long.
5. (1) $19\frac{6}{7}$; (2) $20\frac{1}{35}$; (3) $13 \cdot 86$.
6. 1% increase.   7. $\frac{1}{50}$.   9. $0 \cdot 028$ in.

EXERCISE 28

p. 159.

1. $14 \cdot 4\pi$ cu in./sec.   2. 22.   3. $24\pi/5$ cu in./sec.
5. $0 \cdot 087$ ft/sec towards 0.   6. $\dfrac{1}{h \tan 20°}$, $h =$ ht. at time t.
7. 6 ft/sec.   8. $0 \cdot 754$ cu ft/sec.

EXERCISE 28A

p. 160.

1. (i) $1 + 2x - 8x^2 + 40x^3$; (ii) $1 + 2x - 8x^2 + 32x^3$, $\frac{217}{200}$.
2. (i) $3x^2$;
   (ii) (1) $\frac{2}{7}x^{-\frac{5}{7}}$,   (2) $-2 \sin \frac{x}{2}$,   (3) $\cos^2 \theta - \sin^2 \theta = \cos 2\theta$,
       (4) $-45x \sin(3x + 2) \cos^2 (3x + 2)$;
   (iii) $\sec^2 x$.
3. (a) (i) $\dfrac{1}{(2x - 1)^3}$, (ii) $\dfrac{-3x}{\sqrt{1 - 3x^2}}$; (b) $x = \dfrac{\pi}{3\sqrt{3}}$, max.

4. (b) 3·83 ft.

5. (a) $1 + \dfrac{x}{2} - \dfrac{x^2}{8} + \dfrac{x^3}{16}$, x 0·252;

(b) A = $\frac{1}{4}$, B = $\frac{19}{48}$, C = $\frac{293}{2304}$.

6. (i) $\dfrac{-2}{x^3}$;

(ii) (a) $2x \sin (3x + 1) + 3x^2 \cos (3x + 1)$,

(b) $7x^6\left[\dfrac{2}{(x^7 + 1)^2}\right] = \dfrac{14x^6}{(x^7 + 1)^2}$,

(c) $140x^3(7x^4 - 1)^4$.

7. (a) $v = \dfrac{fu}{u - f}$; (b) $-0·014$; (c) $\frac{49}{1720}$ in./sec.

8. (b) $\dfrac{125\pi}{4}$ $\dfrac{dS}{dV} = \dfrac{5\pi^{\frac{1}{3}}}{6V^{\frac{1}{3}}(\frac{1}{4})^{\frac{1}{3}}}$, $\frac{5}{3}\pi^{\frac{1}{3}}$, $v = 2$.

9. (a) $\frac{7}{8}$ in. down; (b) $v = bp$ accn. $= -ap^2$.

10. (i) Max. 12, min. -15; (ii) $r = 2·65$ in., $h = 2·64$ in.

11. (a) (i) $1 - 15x + 90x^2 - 270x^3 + 405x^4 - 243x^5$;
(ii) 0·98509;

(b) A = 45·2°.

12. (a) (i) $\dfrac{2x^2 - 4x - 3}{(x - 1)^2}$; (ii) $\dfrac{2x - 3}{2(x^2 - 3x + 4)^{\frac{1}{2}}}$;

(b) $v = e^{-3t}(-3 \sin t + \cos t)$ $f = e^{-3t}(8 \sin t - 6 \cos t)$.

13. Max. $(\frac{1}{2}, \frac{19}{4})$; min. $(2, -2)$.

14. (a) (i) 221 yd, (ii) 63·4°; (b) 3·45 ft³.

15. (i) (1) $\dfrac{3x - 2}{\sqrt{2x + 1}}$; (2) $\dfrac{2x^3 - 3x^2 - 2}{(x - 1)^2}$; (3) $x \cos x$.

(ii) $t = \frac{120}{41}$ secs.

16. (a) $x = 1·98$; (b) $y = \frac{1}{2} + \frac{13}{12}x - \frac{5}{12}x^2$.

17. $\dfrac{2x \cos x + 2x^2 \sin x}{\cos^3 x}$, $e^x\left[\log \dfrac{x}{2} + \dfrac{1}{x}\right]$, $\dfrac{3\pi}{4} - 2$,

$\dfrac{x^3}{3} - \dfrac{x^2}{2} - 6x + C$.

18. $a = 10·42$, $b = 16·2$, $c = 1·56$. (i) 7·2; (ii) 73·1.

19. (a) (i) $+1$, (ii) $3 + 2 \log_e 2$, (iii) $\dfrac{e^2 + 2e - 3}{2}$; (b) 0.

20. A = 65, $b = 0·00263$, $\dfrac{dt}{dx} = -0·160$.

21. (a) 1·9878;

(b) $g' = \dfrac{g}{1 + 2(h/r)} = \dfrac{rg}{r + 2h}$ % decrease $= 0·25$.

22. (a) $x^4 + 4x^2 + 6 + \dfrac{4}{x^2} + \dfrac{1}{24}$;

    (b) $1 + 2x + 4x^2 + 8x^3$, $x < \frac{1}{2}$;

    (c) $1 + \dfrac{x}{2} - \dfrac{x^2}{8}$, $1 - \dfrac{x}{2} - \dfrac{x^2}{8}$, $1 \cdot 005$, $0 \cdot 9875$;

    (d) 9% decrease.

23. (a) (i) $\log_e 2 - 6$, (ii) $\dfrac{e}{4} + \dfrac{1}{4e}$;   (b) $\frac{8}{3}$.

24. (a) $x^2 = \dfrac{1}{K^2} \log \dfrac{K}{y\sqrt{\pi}}$;   (b) $a = 12$, $b = -1 \cdot 5$, $c = 0 \cdot 1$;

    (c) $x = 2 \cdot 79$ or $-1 \cdot 79$.

25. $\sqrt{2}$.

26. (i) $1 + nx + \dfrac{n(n-1)}{21}x^2 + \dfrac{n(n-1)(n-3)}{31}x^3$;

    (ii) (1) $0 \cdot 998498875$, (2) $0 \cdot 9806$; (iii) $-0 \cdot 25\%$.

27. (i) $\frac{31}{32}$; (ii) $\frac{1983}{2048}$.

28. $\left(-\frac{1}{3}, \frac{11}{9}\right)$, $\left(\frac{1}{3}, \frac{7}{9}\right)$, $x = 0 \cdot 86$, $z = -1 \cdot 86$.

29. (a) (i) $-\dfrac{\cos x}{3}\left(3x - \dfrac{\pi}{2}\right) + C$,

    (ii) $\frac{1}{3}(x^2 + 25)^{\frac{3}{2}} + C$, (iii) $x + 2\log x - \dfrac{1}{x}$;

    (b) $a = \frac{10}{3}$.

30. (a) $\eta = 0 \cdot 87$; (b) $99 \cdot 3$ ft/min.

31. (a)   (i) $\dfrac{15}{2}\sqrt{x} + \dfrac{3}{\sqrt{x}} - \dfrac{3}{x^2}$,

    (ii) $3x \tan^2 4x + 8x^3 \tan 4x \sec^2 4x$, (iii) $\dfrac{2}{1 - x^2}$;

    (b) -2.

32. (a)   (i) $\dfrac{4}{2x - 3}$, (ii) $18x^2 - \dfrac{6}{x^3} - \dfrac{1}{4x^{\frac{3}{2}}}$,

    (iii) $2e^{2x}(\sin 6x + 3\cos 6x)$.

33. (a) $a = 6 \cdot 5$; (b) $(1 \cdot 97, -4)$.

34. (ii) $x = \frac{1}{3}$ $\left(\frac{4}{3}, \frac{50}{27}$ max. $2, -2$ min.$\right)$.

35. (a) $a = 4 \cdot 3$, $b = 2 \cdot 7$, $c = 3$; (b) $x = \frac{11}{10}$ ft; (c) BP $= 15$ ft.

36. (a) (i) $\frac{46}{15}$, (ii) $\frac{1}{4}\tan 4x - \dfrac{e^{2x}}{2}$, (iii) $\dfrac{\log(4x^2 - 8x + 3)}{8}$;

    (b) $\frac{55}{8}$ ft.

37. (a) (i) $\dfrac{(3x - 7)^6}{18} + C$, (ii) $-\dfrac{\cos(5x - 7)}{5} + C$; (b) $= \frac{21}{23}$.

38. (a) Max. 25, min. -2; (b) $x = \dfrac{l}{2}$, max. M $= \dfrac{Wl^2}{8}$.

39. $x = \dfrac{10}{\sqrt{3}}$ in.

40. (a) $1 + x + x^2 + x^3 + x^4$,

$\qquad \log (1 - x) = - \left(x + \dfrac{x^2}{2} + \dfrac{x^3}{3} + \dfrac{x^4}{4} + \dfrac{x^5}{5} \cdots \right),$

$\qquad \log 0 \cdot 9 = \bar{1} \cdot 89464;$

(b) $24 + 26h + 9h^2 + h^3,\ x = 1 \cdot 92.$

41. (a) $\dfrac{2x - x^4}{(1 + x^3)^2},\ x = 0$ or $\sqrt[3]{2};$ (c) $6t.$

42. (a) (i) $\dfrac{3x^2 - 2}{(2x^3 - 4x)^{\frac{1}{2}}};$ (ii) $\dfrac{x(2 + x)}{(1 + x)^2};$ (iii) $4e^{4x-11}.$

43. (a) $\dfrac{2}{\sqrt{x}} - \dfrac{8}{\sqrt[3]{x^5}} + 4\sqrt[3]{x};$ (b) $6 \cos 2\theta - 2 \sin \tfrac{1}{2}\theta + \tan \theta;$

(c) $\dfrac{-41}{(2 + 5x)^2};$ (d) $\mathrm{K} = \tfrac{3}{2},\ y' = \tfrac{1}{8};$ (e) $f''(t) = \dfrac{4}{t^3} - \dfrac{18}{t^4}.$

44. (a) $\tfrac{1}{169}$ ohms. **45.** (ii) $-6 \cdot 5\%.$

46. (a) $\dfrac{5 - h^2}{h};$ (b) $\dfrac{20}{3} \sqrt{\dfrac{5}{3}}$ ft³; (c) $\dfrac{125}{6\sqrt{3}}$ ft³.

47. (a) $2x;$ (b) (i) $2xe^{2x}(1 + x),$ (ii) $\dfrac{-1}{2x},$ (iii) $\dfrac{-2x^3}{\sqrt{4 - x^4}};$

(c) $t = 4 \cdot 78.$

48. $r = 5 \cdot 23$ ft.

49. (i) $f'(x) = 0,\ f''(x)$ is negative when $x = a;$ (ii) $t = 4$ sec,
$t = 4$ sec, -208 ft/sec.

EXERCISE 29

p. 188.

1. (i) $0 \cdot 829;$ (ii) $-0 \cdot 6428;$ (iii) $0 \cdot 8391;$ (iv) $-4 \cdot 809;$
(v) $2 \cdot 923;$ (vi) $0 \cdot 866;$ (vii) $0 \cdot 9749;$ (viii) $-0 \cdot 4142.$

2. $\dfrac{2\sqrt{5}}{3}\quad \dfrac{\sqrt{5}}{3}.$ **3.** Sin A $= \dfrac{3\sqrt{10}}{10}$ cos A $\dfrac{\sqrt{10}}{10}.$

4. Sin $\theta = \dfrac{2\sqrt{2}}{3}$ tan $\theta = 2\sqrt{2}.$

6. $\dfrac{\pi}{6},\ \dfrac{\pi}{4},\ \dfrac{\pi}{3},\ \dfrac{2\pi}{3},\ \dfrac{57\pi}{45}.$

7. $36°,\ 67° \ 30',\ 25\tfrac{5}{7}°,\ \dfrac{60\theta}{\pi},\ \dfrac{120}{\pi}.$ **10.** $5860.$

EXERCISE 30

p. 194.

1. 2π, 2π, π.   **2.** π.

3. (i) $\dfrac{2\pi}{3}$; (ii) $\dfrac{\pi}{2}$; (iii) $\dfrac{\pi}{3}$; (iv) $\dfrac{2\pi}{5}$; (v) $\dfrac{2\pi}{a}$; (vi) 2π; (vii) 2π.

4. Sin $90 + A = \cos A$, $\cos 90 + A = -\sin A$,
tan $90 + A = -\cot A$.

5. (i) $15°$, $75°$;   (ii) $10°$, $110°$;
(iii) $22\frac{1}{2}°$, $112\frac{1}{2}°$;   (iv) $4° 15'$, $31° 45'$;
 (v) $21° 9'$, $81° 9'$;   (vi) $x = 20°$ or $100°$.

6. $48° 12'$, $311° 48'$ $(0°, 360°)$.

7. $120°$, $240°$, $70° 32'$, $289° 28'$.

8. $14° 29'$, $165° 31'$, $41° 48'$, $138° 12'$.

9. (i) $\dfrac{2\pi}{3}$; (ii) $\dfrac{2\pi}{5}$; (iii) π; (iv) $\dfrac{\pi}{4}$; (v) $\dfrac{2\pi}{a}$.

10. $-\sin 20°$, $\cos 60°$, $-\tan 42°$, $\sec 130°$.

EXERCISE 31

p. 203.

1. $7\cdot93$, $3\cdot17$ miles.   **2.** (1) $3\cdot607$; (2) $5\cdot405$.   AC $= 6\cdot498$ in.

3. (i) $r = \sqrt{5}$, $\alpha = 26° 34'$; (ii) $r = \sqrt{34}$, $\alpha = 30° 58'$.
$\sqrt{5} \sin (x + 26° 34')$ $\sqrt{34} \cos (x + 30° 58')$.

4. $10° 28'$, $17° 4'$.   **5.** (b) $\dfrac{\sqrt{2}}{4}(\sqrt{3} + 1)$; $\dfrac{(\sqrt{3} - 1)^2}{2}$.

8. $3\cdot61$.   **9.** $3 \cos 4t - 2 \cos\left(4t + \dfrac{\pi}{6}\right)$; $1\cdot62$ ft; $t = 0\cdot167$ sec.

11. A $= 45\cdot6$, $\alpha = 64°$,
(1) $\theta = 26°$, (2) $\theta = 206°$,
(3) $\theta = -64°$, (4) $\theta = 8° 6'$ or $43° 54'$.

12. A $= \sqrt{5}$, $\alpha = 26° 34'$.

EXERCISE 32

p. 213.

1. tan $\theta = 0\cdot618$ or $-1\cdot618$.   **2.** $6 = \frac{1}{3}$ or $-\frac{5}{4}$, A $= 34°$.

3. $\theta = 60°$, $300°$, $36° 52'$, $323° 8'$.

4. $4 \sin A(1 - \sin A)(1 + \sin A)$; $1\cdot225$.   **5.** tan B $= 0\cdot21$.

6. (i) $\frac{1}{2}(\sin 50° + \sin 14°)$; (ii) $\frac{1}{2}(\sin 90° - \sin 16°)$;
(iii) $(\cos 82° + \cos 6°)$;   (iv) $(\cos 4° - \cos 80°)$;
 (v) $(\cos 2\alpha - \cos 4\theta)$.

7. (i) $2 \sin \dfrac{5x}{2} \cos \dfrac{x}{2}$;   (ii) $2 \sin 42° \cos 6°$;

(iii) $2 \cos 40° \cos 11°$;   (iv) $-2 \sin \left(x + \dfrac{h}{2} \right) \sin \dfrac{h}{2}$.

9. $\cos^3 \theta = \frac{1}{4} (\cos 3\theta + 3 \cos \theta)$. $\sin^3 \theta = \frac{1}{4}(\beta \sin \theta - \sin 3\theta)$.
10. $\theta = 77°$, $283°$.

EXERCISE 33
p. 234.
1. $49°$; $59°$.   **2.** 500 ft.   **3.** $1·998$ in.
4. $6·14$ ft; $57° 54'$; $122° 6'$. **5.** $36° 52'$; $81° 12'$; $61° 56'$.
6. $58°$.   **7.** 19 ft; $19·8$ ft; $56° 29'$.
8. 48 yd.   **9.** $70°$; $2·1$ in.   **10.** $29·8$ in.
11. $654·2$ ft.   **12.** $446·1$ ft.   **13.** 2564 ft.
14. $H = 0·214$ in; $h = 0·142$ in., $r = 0·0305$ in.; $1·858$ in.
15. $l = 0·261$ in. **17.** $r = 2·30$ in. **18.** $d = 0·1990$ in., $f = 0·2$.

EXERCISE 34
p. 245.
1. $B = 65° 15'$, $C = 56° 21'$.   **2.** 1515 ft².
3. $30·43$ ft; $92° 51'$; $49° 5'$.   **4.** $90° 14'$.
5. $70° 20'$, $107° 40'$, and $36·45$ in.².

EXERCISE 35
p. 250.

1. $\cos t$.   **2.** $4 \cos 4t$.   **3.** $\dfrac{1}{3} \cos \dfrac{t}{3}$.

4. $\pi \cos \pi t$.   **5.** $n \cos nt$.   **6.** $6 \cos 2t$.

7. $\dfrac{1}{6} \cos \dfrac{t}{3}$.   **8.** $2 \cos \pi t$.   **9.** $ab \cos bt$.

10. $5 \cos (\theta + \alpha)$.   **11.** $3 \cos (\theta + \pi)$.   **12.** $a \cos \left(\theta - \dfrac{\pi}{3} \right)$.

13. $15 \cos \left(3\theta - \dfrac{\pi}{5} \right)$. **14.** $\dfrac{1}{4} \cos \left(\dfrac{\theta}{2} + \dfrac{\pi}{3} \right)$. **15.** $2af \cos (2ft + n\pi)$.

16. $-3 \sin 3x$.   **17.** $-\dfrac{1}{5} \sin \dfrac{x}{5}$.   **18.** $-\pi \sin \pi x$.

19. $-15 \sin 3\theta$.   **20.** $-15 \sin (5\theta + \alpha)$.

21. $-12 \sin \left(3\theta + \dfrac{\pi}{4} \right).$ **22.** $-\dfrac{K}{2} \sin (K\theta + \alpha).$

23. $-2na \sin (2nx + k\pi).$

EXERCISE 36

p. 253.

1. $\sec^2 \theta.$ **2.** $\sec x \tan x.$ **3.** $-\operatorname{cosec} z \cot z.$

4. $-\operatorname{cosec}^2 y.$ **5.** $3 \sec^2 3\theta.$ **6.** $\dfrac{1}{2} \sec \dfrac{\theta}{2} \tan \dfrac{\theta}{2}.$

7. $-3 \operatorname{cosec} 3x \cot 3x.$ **8.** $-12 \operatorname{cosec}^2 4\theta.$

9. $10 \sec \left(2\theta + \dfrac{\pi}{2} \right) \tan \left(2\theta + \dfrac{\pi}{2} \right) = 10 \operatorname{cosec} 2\theta . \cot 2\theta.$

10. $3 \sec^2 \theta.$ **11.** $\dfrac{\pi}{60} \cos 3x°.$

12. $-\dfrac{\pi}{120} \sin \dfrac{x°}{2}.$ **13.** $\dfrac{\pi}{90} \sec^2 x°.$

EXERCISE 37

p. 255.

1. $2x \sin x + x^2 \cos x.$ **2.** $6x^2 \sin x + 2x^3 \cos x.$

3. $4x^3 \sin 2x + 2x^4 \cos 2x.$ **4.** $12x^5 \cos 3x - 6x^6 \sin 3x.$

5. $2x^{-3} (x \cos 2x - \sin 2x).$

6. $-12x^{-5} \cos 4x - 12x^{-4} \sin 4x.$

7. $\cos \theta . \cos 2\theta - 2 \sin \theta \sin 2\theta.$

8. $6 \cos 2\theta \cos 4\theta - 12 \sin 2\theta \sin 4\theta.$

9. $\dfrac{\cos 2\theta \cos \theta + 2 \sin 2\theta \sin \theta}{\cos^2 2\theta}.$

10. $12 \cos 3\theta . \cos 4\theta - 16 \sin 3\theta \sin 4\theta.$

11. $2\pi \cos 2\pi t . \cos \pi t - \pi \sin 2\pi t \sin \pi t.$

12. $\sin 2x.$ **13.** $9 \sin^2 x \cos x.$ **14.** $-3 \cos^2 \theta \sin \theta.$

15. $-30 \cos 3\theta \sin 3\theta = -15 \sin 6\theta.$

16. $24 \sin^2 4x \cos 4x.$ **17.** $-2 \cos x - \dfrac{\cos^3 x}{\sin^2 x}.$

18. $-6 \cos^2 x \sin x - 12 \sin 2x \cos 2x.$

EXERCISE 38

p. 265.

1. (a) $0·49975$; (b) $1·0006$; (c) $0·49975$.

2. $0·056$ ft.   **3.** $K \sec^2 \theta . d\theta$, $1·75\%$.   **4.** $0·71$ ft.

5. (1) $\left(\text{Max. } \dfrac{\pi}{4}, \dfrac{9\pi}{4}\right)$, where $\theta = \dfrac{\pi}{4}, \dfrac{5\pi}{4}$, etc.

   (2) where $x = 36° 22', 143° 38', 237° 27', 302° 33'$,
   Max. at $x = 36° 22', 237° 27'$.

   (3) where $x = \dfrac{\pi}{2}, \dfrac{3\pi}{2}, 14° 29', 165° 31'$,
   Max. where $x = 14° 29'$ and $165° 31'$.

   (4) where $\theta = 0, \dfrac{\pi}{2}, \dfrac{3\pi}{2}$,
   Max where $\theta = \dfrac{\pi}{2}$.

7. 3·83 lb/lb.   **8.** 0·37 sec.
9. 1·10 tons at end of stroke, 0·775 tons, crank at 45°.
10. 115 vibrations/min.
11. 0·185 ft/sec, 0·347 ft/sec², max. displacement 4·717 in.

EXERCISE 39

p. 268.

The constant has been omitted in the answers

1. $\sin \theta$.   **2.** $-\cos \theta$.   **3.** $-\frac{1}{3}\cos 3\theta$.   **4.** $-\frac{3}{2}\cos 2\theta$.

5. $\frac{1}{2}\sin 4\theta$.   **6.** $2 \sin \frac{1}{2}\theta$.   **7.** $-\dfrac{9}{8}\cos \dfrac{2\theta}{8}$.

8. $-\frac{3}{2}\cos 2\theta - \frac{4}{5}\sin 5\theta$.   **9.** $-\cos (\theta + \alpha)$.

10. $\dfrac{1}{3}\sin\left(3\theta + \dfrac{\pi}{7}\right)$.   **11.** $2 \cos\left(\dfrac{\pi}{5} - \theta\right)$.   **12.** $-6 \sin\left(\alpha - \dfrac{\theta}{2}\right)$.

EXERCISE 39A
Miscellaneous

p. 269.

1. (a)   (i) $-\frac{1}{4}x^{-\frac{3}{2}} - 6x^{-4}$,
         (ii) $6x^2 \cos (3x + 2) + 4x \sin (3x + 2)$, (iii) $\cot x$;
   (b) depth = 9 in., breadth = 3 in.   **2.** 4.

3. (a)   (i) $\frac{1}{5}\log_e (5x^3 - 1) + C$,
         (ii) $\dfrac{x^3}{3} - \dfrac{3x^2}{2} + 2x - \frac{1}{2}\log_e (x - \frac{1}{2}) + C$,
         (iii) $3 \log_e (x - 2) - 2 \log_e (x + 4) + C$.
   (b) $y = 3x + 2 - \frac{1}{4}\sin 4x - \frac{1}{2}\cos 2x$.

4. (a) $\dfrac{dy}{dx} = -\frac{1}{16}$.
   (b) Vel. $= -0·207. = e^{-t}\cos t - e^{-t}\sin t$.

5. (a) 14·45 sq units; (b) 88 in.

6. (b) $\dfrac{3}{2}\left[\sin\dfrac{5wt}{2} - \sin - \dfrac{3wt}{2}\right]$.

   (c) $\theta = 48° 12'$, $\theta = 0°$, $\theta = 311° 48'$, $\theta = 360°$.

7. (a) $5\cdot4$ in.^{2}.   **8.** $l = 2$, $h = 6$, £10 : 10s.

9. (a) (i) $-\frac{1}{2}x^{-\frac{3}{2}} - \frac{5}{3}x^{-\frac{2}{3}} - \frac{5}{6}x^{-\frac{7}{6}}$;

      (ii) $e^{3x}(3 \sin 2x + 2 \cos 2x)$;

      (iii) $\dfrac{2}{x^3}(1 - \log_e x^2) + 14$;

      (iv) $-x(x^2 - 1)^{-\frac{3}{2}} + 2 \sec^2 2x$.

10. (a) (i) $x(x^2 + 16)^{-\frac{1}{2}}$,

      (ii) $3 \cos 3x \cos 5x - 5 \sin 3x \sin 5x$,

      (iii) $\dfrac{16 - 2x}{2y + 12}$.

   (b) (iv) $\dfrac{81x^5}{5} + 189x^4 + 882x^3 + 2058x^2 + 2401x + c$,

      (v) $\dfrac{7}{5\pi} \sin 50\pi t + c$.

11. (a) $1\cdot89$; (b) 81 ft/sec.

12. (a) $a = 1$, $b = -2$, $c = 3$; (b) $x = 2\cdot69$.

13. $X = £1765$.   **14.** (b) $\theta = 81° 21'$.

15. $x = -0\cdot8$; $-\sqrt{8 + 6x} + 2\sqrt{1 + x} = -2\sqrt{1 - x}$.

16. (a) $\dfrac{3}{x - 1} - \dfrac{x}{(x - 1)^2}$; (b) $r = 4$ in., $l = 4$.

17. (a) $h = 45 + 40 \sin \theta$, $0\cdot092$ ft; (b) $3\cdot78$ ft/sec.

18. Index cutter 6° from diameter, cutter feed $0\cdot00825$ in. from surface.

19. (a) $x = \left(\dfrac{Rn}{r}\right)^{\frac{1}{2}}$;

   (b) velocity $= -\frac{39}{16}$ in./sec, acceleration $= \frac{29}{128}$ ft/sec^2.

20. (a) (i) $-e^{-2x}(3 \sin 3x + 2 \cos 3x)$, (ii) $\dfrac{4x}{(1 + 2x^2)}$,

      (iii) $\dfrac{2(x + 1)(x - 1)}{(x^2 + 1)^2}$, (iv) $6 \sin 6x \sin^2 3x$;

   (b) $0\cdot6$ radians/hour.

21. $BC = 4\cdot84$ ft, $BE = 12\cdot3$ ft, $CE = 10\cdot7$ ft, $CD = 5\cdot05$ ft.

22. (a) $u = 31\cdot4$; (b) $u = 47\cdot6$; (c) $x = -0\cdot958$.

23. (b) Rectangle $5\cdot61$ ft $\times 2\cdot795$ ft with semicircle a diameter of $5\cdot61$ ft.

24. $T_0 = 347$, $K = 0\cdot316$, $T = 98\cdot1°$ C.

25. (a) (i) $\frac{1}{3}x^3 + 6x - \dfrac{9}{x} + c$, (ii) $-\dfrac{\cot^2 x}{2} + c$; (b) $\dfrac{2}{\pi}$.

26. (a) $\theta = 0, \dfrac{2\pi}{3}, \dfrac{4\pi}{3}$; (b) $r = 6{\cdot}4031$, $\alpha = 51° \, 21'$, $\theta = 18° \, 13'$
and $59° \, 05'$; (c) $\frac{1}{12}\sin 3x + \frac{3}{4}\sin x + c$.

27. $2{\cdot}51$.   **28.** $OA = (3a^2 - 4aVt + V^2t^2)^{\frac{1}{2}}$.

29. (a) $48° \, 19'$; (b) Resultant of $34{\cdot}1$ lb at $26{\cdot}7°$ to 23 lb force.

31. (a) (i) $-20(1 - 2x)^9$; (ii) $\dfrac{10x}{(1 + x^2)^2}$; (iii) $6\sin^2 2x \cos 2x$;
(iv) $\dfrac{-1}{1 - x^2}$.

32. $73{\cdot}5$ in².

33. (i) £1 15s. 10d.; (ii) (a) $1 - x - \dfrac{x^2}{2} - \dfrac{x^3}{2}$.
(b) $1 - x + x^3 - x^4 + x^6 - x^7 - x^9 + x^{10} + 0{\cdot}8065$.

34. (a) $a^n + nc_1a^{n-1}x + nc_2a^{n-2}x^2 + nc_3a^{n-3}x^3$; (b) $0{\cdot}9899$.

35. Length $= (20 - x) + (36 + x^2)^{\frac{1}{2}}$, increase $= 0{\cdot}132$ in.,
decreasing by $0{\cdot}143$ ft/sec.

36. (i) $t = 13{\cdot}52$; (ii) $\dfrac{T_2}{T_1} (1) = \left(\dfrac{V_1}{V_2}\right)^{\gamma - 1}$, (2) $\left(\dfrac{P_1}{P_2}\right)^{\frac{1 - \gamma}{\gamma}}$.

37. (a) $25\sin (x + 73{\cdot}8)$; (b) $x = 69° \, 20'$ and $323° \, 01'$.

38. (a) $1 + x^2 - \frac{1}{2}x^4 - \frac{1}{2}x^6$.

39. (i) $M = \dfrac{19x}{2} - \dfrac{x^2}{32} - \dfrac{x^3}{48} + 78$; (ii) $11{\cdot}84$ ft.

41. (a) $\dfrac{4x + 2}{(1 + x)^3}$; (b) $2\cot 2x$; (c) $e^{x\sin x} (x\cos x + \sin x)$;
(d) $2\sin 2x(\cos^2 2x - 1)$.

42. (c) (i) $\frac{1}{4}$, (ii) $\dfrac{\pi}{4}$; (d) $0{\cdot}268$.

43. (a) (i) $x^2(3\cos 5x - 5x\sin 5x)$,
(ii) $\operatorname{cosec} x(7 - (7x + 3)\cot x)$;
(b) $x(3x + 4)\cos x + (6x + 2 - 8x^2)\sin x$.

44. (a) (i) -27, 15, (ii) $75{\cdot}5°$ and $289{\cdot}5°$;
(b) $5\sin (2x + 53° \, 8')$; (c) 5.

45. $2x\sin x(\sin x + x\cos x)$, $\dfrac{e^x}{1 + e^x}$, $-\frac{5}{7}$, $\cos x(\sin x - 1)$.

46. 1800 sq ft.

48. (a) $\dfrac{1}{x^2 - a^2}$; (b) $\dfrac{2(x + 1)}{\sqrt{(2x^2 + 4x - 1)}}$; (c) $\theta = 15°$ or $75°$.

49. (a) 7·5, 37·2, 160·5, 157·2, 247·2, 277·2; (b) $t = 0.00861$ sec;
(c) 4.73×10^3 units/sec.

50. (a)   (i) $x^2[3 \cos (2x + 3) - 2x^2 \sin (2x + 3)]$,

(ii) $\dfrac{-3x^2 + 2x + 6}{(2 + x^2)^2}$,   (iii) $\dfrac{+5}{2\sqrt{(3 - 5x)^3}}$,

(iv) $4e^{4x} + 3e^{-x} - \dfrac{1}{2\sqrt{e^x}}$,

(v) $\dfrac{2x^2}{2x + 1} + 2x \log (2x + 1)$,

(vi) $1.6x^{0.6} + 5.1x^{-2.7}$;

(b) $\dfrac{dp}{dv} = -1.4cv^{-2.5}$, $\dfrac{dv}{dp} = -0.714c^{1.714} v^{2.4}$;

(c) $\dfrac{dE}{dR} = \dfrac{0.28}{R^{1.28}}$.

51. (a) 238·1 yd;
(b) $i = 5.2 \sin (\theta + 292° 48')$, $i_{max.} = 5.2$, when $t = 0.00127$.

52. Diameter $= 1.349$ in.

53. (a)   (i) $-3x\sqrt{1 - x^2}$, (ii) $\dfrac{6 - 2x^2}{(x^2 + 3)^2}$,

(iii) $e^{3x}(2 \cos 2x + 3 \sin 2x)$;

(b) $R = \dfrac{(x^4 + 1)^{\frac{3}{2}}}{2x^3}$, $R = 4.38$.

54. (a) (i) $\dfrac{3x^2 + 10x}{(3x + 5)^2}$, (ii) $x^2(3 \sin 5x + 5x \cos 5x)$,

(iii) $\dfrac{2(1 - x)}{(6y + 7)}$;

(b) Velocity $= 7651$, acceleration $= -1.289 \times 10^6$.

55. (a) (i) $\dfrac{6x^2 + 20x + 9}{(3x + 5)^2}$, (ii) $4e^{2x}(x + 1)$;

(b) 0;   (c) (3, 1), (−3, −1).

56. (a)   (i) $x^2 + \dfrac{5}{2\sqrt{x}} + \dfrac{4}{x^3}$,   (ii) $\dfrac{6x}{4 - 3x^2}$,

(iii) $2.0 \cos 4x + 1.5 \sin 0.3x$, (iv) $\dfrac{-e^{-\frac{x}{2}}(4x + 11)}{2(4x + 3)^2}$;

(b) $l = 2 + 0.4t$, 4·8 in/hr.

57. $\theta = 60°$.

58. $\sqrt{7} \sin (4t - 49° 7')$, max. at $t = 0.607$, min. at $t = 1.04$.

59. (a) $1 + nx + \dfrac{n(n-1)}{2}x^2 + \dfrac{n(n-1)(n-2)}{6}x^3;$
$+ \dfrac{n(n-1)(n-2)(n-3)}{24}x^4;\ |x| < 1;$
(b) 5·0990; (c) 1%.

60. (i) (a) $7(x + \sin x)^6(1 + \cos x)$, (b) $\dfrac{-2x}{1-x^2}$,
(c) $-e^{-x}(\cos 3x + 3 \sin 3x)$, (d) $x^x(1 + \log_e x)$;
(ii) $\dfrac{dv}{dt} = -\frac{5}{9}$ cm/min.

61. (b) $\dfrac{2}{\cot A - \tan A}$;
(c) $\sqrt{85} \cos(\theta - 12° \ 32')$, $\theta = 61° \ 55'$ and $322° \ 09'$.

62. (b) $R_{max.} = \dfrac{a}{4}$ when $x = \dfrac{a}{2}$. **63.** $x = 4·34$ in.

64. (i) $\sin 15° = \dfrac{\sqrt{3} - 1}{2\sqrt{2}}$, $\tan 15° = \dfrac{\sqrt{3} - 1}{\sqrt{3} + 1}$;
(ii) 45°, 72°, 90°.

65. $\sqrt{58} \sin(\omega t - 1·1688)$.
(i) max. $\sqrt{58}$, min. $-\sqrt{58}$;
(ii) max. $t = 0·871$, min. $t = 1·871$; (iii) $t = 0·5$.

66. (a) velocity, $\dfrac{ds}{dt} = u + ft$, acceleration, $\dfrac{d^2s}{dt^2} = f$;
(b) (i) $\sin 3x + 3x \cos 3x$, (ii) $10x(x^2 + 1)^4$, (iii) $\cot x$.

67. (a) $13 \cos(\theta + 22° \ 46')$, $\theta = 37° \ 14'$ or $277° \ 14'$;
(b) AC = 5·19 ft.

EXERCISE 40
p. 299.

1. (a) $\frac{11}{6}$; (b) 6·19; (c) $\frac{1}{2}$; (d) $\frac{1}{2}$.

2. (1) 8; (2) 16π; (3) 559; (4) 0. **3.** 40·5 tons.

4. (1) 248·8; (2) $\frac{1}{4}$; (3) 64.

5. (1) $\frac{23}{6}$; (2) $\frac{8}{3}$; (3) $-\frac{1}{6}$; (4) $\dfrac{\pi}{2}$; (5) 224·5. **6.** Proof.

7. (a) $4\frac{1}{3}$; (b) 4·87; (c) 0; (d) $\frac{1}{3}$.

8. (1) 30·2; (2) 2·92; (3) $\frac{1}{3}$; (4) 0·2804.

9. (1) 9; (2) 0; (3) $-\frac{13}{3}$. **10.** 87. **11.** 0·094π. **12.** $\frac{122}{3}$.

EXERCISE 41

p. 304.

1. (a) $\dfrac{2}{\pi}$; (b) $\frac{1}{2}$; (c) $\frac{4}{3}$.   **2.** (1) 80 ft/sec; (2) 116.

3. 70 lb/in².   **4.** (a) 345; (b) $86\frac{1}{4}$.   **5.** $\dfrac{2a}{\pi}$.   **6.** 2.

7. (1) $\sqrt{2}$; (2) $\dfrac{3}{\sqrt{2}}$; (3) 0·707; (4) 0·707.   **8.** $\sqrt{\dfrac{a}{2}[c^2 + k^2]}$.

9. $\sqrt{\dfrac{13}{2}}$

10. M.V. $= \dfrac{5 \cdot 5}{\pi}$, R.M.S. $= 3 \cdot 8$, Form Factor $= 2 \cdot 17$.

EXERCISE 42

p. 310.

1. X rect. $= 8,200$ ft², Vol. of flow $= 1,840,000$ gal/min.
2. Period $= 2\pi$, amplitude $= 2$, area $= 4$.
3. (i) Proof, (ii) Area $= \frac{1}{6}$; Vol. $= \dfrac{\pi}{30}$.
4. Area $= 1,370$ ft².
5. (a) Area $= 8\frac{2}{3}$; (b) Vol. 20π.
6. Area $= 5 \cdot 544$, K $= 2$.   **7.** (1) 6·28; (2) 1·09.
8. 209·9 ft lbs.   **9.** $\frac{10}{4}$.
10. 16,040 in³.

EXERCISE 43

p. 324.

1. $(1\frac{2}{5}, 0)$.   **2.** $(1\frac{2}{5}, \frac{3}{2})$.   **3.** $(3, \frac{9 \cdot 6}{5})$.   **4.** $(\frac{2}{5}, \frac{4}{7})$.
5. (1) 28·5; (2) (2·05, 6·78).   **6.** 0·48 in. from centre.
7. (1) $\dfrac{43\pi}{5}$ cu in.; (2) $\dfrac{39}{172}$ in. from face.   **8.** $\dfrac{2\sqrt{3}}{\pi}$.

9. $\frac{7}{9}$ of median from P.   **10.** $\dfrac{3H}{4}$.   **11.** $(\frac{2 \cdot 7}{5}, 0)$.

12. $2\frac{1}{4}$ from centre.   **13.** $\frac{24}{13}, \frac{49}{13}$.   **14.** $n \eqsim 2 \cdot 1$.
15. $3\frac{3}{7}$.   **16.** 18 cu in.; $x\frac{328}{135}$.

EXERCISE 44

p. 330.

1. 24·52 cu in.   **2.** $2\frac{1}{3}$ in. from centre.

3. 240π cu in. **4.** (1) $\dfrac{2a}{\pi}$; (2) $\dfrac{4a}{3\pi}$.

5. $1215\cdot3$ cu in. **7.** Area $\frac{2}{3}a^{\frac{1}{2}}b^{\frac{3}{2}}$, $\frac{3}{8}\sqrt{ab}$. **8.** 281 lb.

EXERCISE 45

p. 347.

1. $\dfrac{h}{3}\dfrac{(2a+b)}{(a+b)}$, $\dfrac{(a+3b)}{36}h^3$. **2.** $36\pi(2\pi-1)$, $6(3\pi-1)$.

3. $\dfrac{14\pi}{3}$, $\dfrac{8\pi}{75\left(\dfrac{\pi}{2}-\sin^{-1}\dfrac{4}{5}-\dfrac{12}{25}\right)}$. **4.** $\dfrac{12}{5\pi}$, $1\frac{3}{4}\sqrt{\frac{5}{2}}$.

5. $\dfrac{2064\pi}{3}$, $\dfrac{16\pi}{3}$.

6. Volume $=\dfrac{3\pi h^{\frac{5}{3}}}{5}$ in.^{3}; (i) Rate $=\dfrac{5}{16\pi}$; (ii) Rate $\dfrac{5}{192\pi}$.

7. $\frac{7}{3}$ in., 468 in.^{3}, $\sqrt{13}$ in.

8. (i) $\frac{256}{3}$; (ii) $(\frac{5}{2}, \frac{64}{3})$; (iii) $\dfrac{32768\pi}{9}$.

9. Area $=\frac{32}{10}$ ($\bar{y}=\frac{20}{32}$, $\bar{x}=\frac{20}{7}$).

10. Vol. $\dfrac{9\pi}{8}-2$, $\bar{y}=\dfrac{9\pi-16}{16\pi(\pi-1)}$.

11. (a) 2; (b) $\left(\dfrac{\pi}{2}, \dfrac{\pi}{8}\right)$; (c) $\dfrac{\pi^2}{2}$. **12.** (a) 100π; (b) $5(\sqrt{5}-1)$.

13. (a) $1\cdot365\times10^{-2}$; (b) $2\cdot33$; (c) $0\cdot2$.

14. $A=24$, $\bar{x}=2\cdot79$, $\bar{y}=\frac{26}{5}$. **15.** $527\cdot5$ lb. ft^2.

16. (a) 144, $\bar{x}=0$, $\bar{y}=\frac{72}{5}$; (b) 49450 ft. lb.

17. $426\cdot9$ in.^{4}, $89\cdot4$ in.^{4}.

18. (ii) $A=\frac{256}{3}$; (iii) $\bar{x}=0$, $\bar{y}=\frac{32}{5}$.

19. (i) 108; (ii) $\frac{27}{5}, \frac{27}{4}$.

20. $\frac{7}{5}$ in. below AB on centre line; (ii) 21 in.^{4}.

21. (a) $\frac{2}{3}-\frac{1}{4}=\frac{5}{12}$; (b) 695π in., $e.g.$ $2\cdot84$ above base on axis.

22. (a) (i) $b\dfrac{(h-y)}{n}\delta y$, (ii) $\dfrac{by^2}{12h}(12h\delta y-66y(y+2\delta y)$,

(iii) $\displaystyle\int_0^h b\dfrac{(h-y)}{h}y^2dy$, $62\cdot5$ in.^{4}; (b) 198 in.^{4}.

23. (i) $\frac{16}{3}$, $(\frac{3}{4}, \frac{8}{5})$; (ii) $\dfrac{256\pi}{15}\left(\dfrac{5}{8}, 0\right)$.

24. (a) $V = \int_0^x A x \, dx$, 12·133;

(b) $\dfrac{\pi a^2}{2}$, (i) $\dfrac{\pi a^2}{4}$, (ii) $\dfrac{\pi a^2}{4}(1 + 4a^2)$.

25. (a) $\frac{32}{9}$; (b) 134·4, 2·73.   **26.** (i) 8·277 in.; (ii) 8·139 in.

27. $n = 1·14$, 126 units, 151 units.

28. (a) $\frac{32}{3}$, $\dfrac{512\pi}{15}$; (b) $\dfrac{4r}{3\pi}$ from 0, $\dfrac{4r}{9\pi}$ from 0.

29. $\frac{17}{11}$ from AF, $\frac{41}{22}$ from AB.

30. (a) (i) 17, (ii) $\dfrac{\pi}{4}$, (iii) 0·805; (b) $\dfrac{W}{EI}\dfrac{l^3}{3}$.

EXERCISE 46

p. 365.

1. (i) $3e^{3x}$; (ii) $-4e^{-4x}$; (iii) $e^{x/3}$; (iv) $e^{-x/4}$; (v) $-2e^{-2x}$;
(vi) $-20e^{-4x}$; (vii) $6e^{3x} + 8e^{-2x}$.

2. (1) $\frac{1}{2}e^{2x}$; (2) $-\frac{1}{4}e^{-4x}$; (3) $20e^{x/4}$; (4) $\frac{2}{3}e^{-3x}$.

3. (1) $2xe^x + e^x x^2$; (2) $e^{2x}(6x^3 + 9x^2)$; (3) $-e^{-4x}(4x^{-2} + 2x^{-3})$;
(4) $e^x(\sin x + \cos x)$; (5) $e^{3x}(3 \cos 4x - 4 \sin 4x)$; (6)
$ke^{ax}(a \sin bx + b \cos bx)$; (7) $-e^{-2t}(2 \cos 3t + 3 \sin 3t)$;
(8) $e^{4x}(4x^{-3} - 3x^{-4})$; (9) $ake^{-kt}(\cos kt - \sin kt)$.

4. (1) $3 \sinh 3x$; (2) $4 \cosh 4x$; (3) $\sinh \dfrac{x}{3}$.

5. (1) $\cos x \, e^{\sin x}$; (2) $6 \cos 2x \, e^{3 \sin 2x}$;
(3) $e^{-x}[(2a - b)x + b - c - ax^2]$.

6. (1) $\log_e a \, a^x$; (2) $\log_e 3 \, . \, 3^x$; (3) $\log_e 16 \, . \, 4^{2x}$;
(4) $-3 \log_e 5 \, . \, 5^{-3x}$.   **7.** (1) $3^5 e^{3x}$; (2) $2^6 e^{-2x}$.

9. 0.

10. $c^2 \sinh \dfrac{a}{c}$.   **11.** (i) $2e + \dfrac{3}{e}$; (ii) $4\sqrt{e} + \dfrac{6}{\sqrt{e}} - 10$.

12. (1) $\frac{1}{2}(e^2 - 1)$; (2) $\left(1 - \dfrac{1}{e^2}\right)$.

EXERCISE 47

p. 372.

1. (1) $\dfrac{1}{x}$; (2) $\dfrac{1}{x - 5}$; (3) $\dfrac{1}{x + 2} - \dfrac{1}{x + 5}$; (4) $\dfrac{3}{3x - 4}$;

(5) $\dfrac{2x + 3}{x^2 + 3x} - \dfrac{1}{x + 1}$; (6) $\dfrac{8x}{4x^2 - 5} - \dfrac{10x}{5x^2 + 3}$.

2. (1) $x(1 + 2 \log x)$; (2) $\dfrac{3x - 6(x + 1) \log (x + 1)}{x^3(x + 1)}$;

(3) $\cos x \log x + \dfrac{\sin x}{x}$; (4) $\dfrac{-3 \log x}{(x + 1)^2} + \dfrac{3}{x(x + 1)}$;

(5) $e^{3x}\left(\dfrac{1}{x} + 3 \log x\right)$; (6) $3e^{-3x}\left[\dfrac{1}{1 + x} - 3 \log (1 + x)\right]$;

(7) $3 \cos 3x \log (x^2 + x + 1) + \dfrac{(2x + 1) \sin 3x}{x^2 + x + 1}$;

(8) $\sec^2 x \log x + \dfrac{\tan x}{x}$; (9) $\dfrac{0 \cdot 4343}{x}$; (10) $\dfrac{0 \cdot 4343(6x + 1)}{3x^2 + x + 1}$;

(11) $\dfrac{2x}{5(x^2 + 1)}$; (12) $\cot x + \dfrac{\sin x}{1 + \cos x}$; (13) $\dfrac{1}{1 - x^2}$.

3. (1) $\log (x + 2) + c$; (2) $-3 \log (2 - x)$; (3) $\tfrac{1}{2} \log (x^2 + 1)$;

(4) $\log (1 + \sin x)$; (5) $\log \dfrac{1}{1 + \cos x}$; (6) $\log (3 + e^x)$;

(7) $\tfrac{1}{3} \log (3x + 2)$; (8) $-\tfrac{5}{3} \log (4 - 3x)$;

(9) $\dfrac{a}{2c} \log (b + cx^2)$; (10) $\tfrac{1}{2} \log (x^2 + 6x + 4)$;

(11) $\tfrac{1}{2} \log_e (x^2 - 2x + 4)$.

4. $3 \log \dfrac{b}{a} + \dfrac{14}{3} (b^{\frac{3}{2}} - a^{\frac{3}{2}})$.

5. (1) $\log_e \tfrac{4}{3}$; (2) $\tfrac{3}{2} \log_e 5$; (3) $\log_e 2$; (4) $\log_e 2$; (5) $\tfrac{1}{2} \log_e \tfrac{11}{4}$.

EXERCISE 48

p. 378.

Remember Consts.

1. (i) $2\sqrt{x + 3} + c$; (ii) $-2\sqrt{5 - x}$; (iii) $\dfrac{2x}{c} \sqrt{b + cx}$.

2. (i) $x - 4 \log_e (x + 4)$; (ii) $\dfrac{x^2}{2} + 4x + 16 \log_e (x - 4)$;

(iii) $2x - 6 \log_e (x + 3)$; (iv) $\dfrac{x}{2} - \dfrac{3}{4} \log_e (2x + 3)$.

3. (i) $\sin^{-1} \dfrac{x}{2}$; (ii) $\sin^{-1} \dfrac{x}{\sqrt{2}}$; (iii) $\dfrac{1}{\sqrt{2}} \sin^{-1} \dfrac{x}{2}$;

(iv) $\sin^{-1} \dfrac{x + 1}{3}$; (v) $\sin^{-1} \dfrac{x + 2}{4}$; (vi) $\dfrac{1}{\sqrt{2}} \sin^{-1} \dfrac{x + 1}{\sqrt{5}}$.

4. (1) $\tan^{-1} x$; (2) $\dfrac{3}{2} \tan^{-1} \dfrac{x}{2}$; (3) $\dfrac{1}{4} \tan^{-1} \dfrac{x}{2}$; (4) $\dfrac{1}{2} \tan^{-1} \dfrac{x + 1}{2}$;

(5) $\dfrac{1}{2} \tan^{-1} \dfrac{x - 2}{2}$; (6) $\dfrac{1}{\sqrt{31}} \tan^{-1} \dfrac{2x + 3}{\sqrt{31}}$;

(7) $\dfrac{2}{3}\sqrt{3} \tan^{-1} \dfrac{2x + 3}{\sqrt{3}}$.

5. (1) $\frac{1}{2}\left(\dfrac{\cos 2\theta}{2} - \dfrac{\cos 6\theta}{6}\right)$; (2) $\frac{1}{2}\left(\dfrac{\cos 2x}{2} - \dfrac{\cos 8x}{8}\right)$;

(3) $-\left(\dfrac{\cos 6t}{6} + \dfrac{\cos 2t}{2}\right)$; (4) $\dfrac{\sin 2t}{2} - \dfrac{\sin 8t}{8}$;

(5) $\frac{1}{2}\left(\dfrac{\sin 8x}{8} + \dfrac{\sin 4x}{4}\right)$; (6) $2\cos\dfrac{t}{2} - \dfrac{2}{3}\cos\dfrac{3t}{2}$.

6. (1) $\dfrac{\sin^4\theta}{4}$; (2) $\dfrac{1}{2\cos^2\theta}$; (3) $-\dfrac{\cos^5 x}{5}$; (4) $\dfrac{\tan^4\theta}{4}$;

(5) $-\dfrac{\cos^4\theta}{4} - \cos\theta$.

EXERCISE 49

p. 382.

1. (1) $\log(x^2 - 1)$; (2) $3\log(x-3) - \log(x-2)$;

(3) $\frac{9}{11}\ln(x+6) + \frac{13}{11}\ln(x-5)$, (4) $\frac{1}{2}\ln(x^2-9)$;

(5) $\frac{2}{5}\ln(x-1) - \frac{1}{15}\ln(3x+2)$;

(6) $3\ln(x-4) - \ln(x-1)$; (7) $2\ln\left(\dfrac{x}{x+2}\right)$;

(8) $\frac{1}{6}\ln\left(\dfrac{x}{x+2}\right)$; (9) $\frac{17}{5}\ln(x+6) - \frac{2}{5}\ln(x+1)$.

2. (1) $\dfrac{1}{\sqrt{3}}\ln\left(\dfrac{x+\frac{1}{2}-\sqrt{\frac{3}{2}}}{x+\frac{1}{2}+\sqrt{\frac{3}{2}}}\right)$; (2) $\dfrac{1}{6}\ln\left(\dfrac{x-2}{x+4}\right)$;

(3) $\dfrac{1}{\sqrt{5}}\ln\left\{\dfrac{\dfrac{x+3}{2}-\dfrac{\sqrt{5}}{2}}{\dfrac{x+3}{2}+\dfrac{\sqrt{5}}{2}}\right\}$; (4) $\dfrac{1}{2\sqrt{3}}\ln\left(\dfrac{x+2-\sqrt{3}}{x+2+\sqrt{3}}\right)$;

(5) $\dfrac{\sqrt{2}}{4}\ln\left(\dfrac{t+1-\dfrac{1}{\sqrt{2}}}{t+1+\dfrac{1}{\sqrt{2}}}\right)$.

EXERCISE 50

p. 387.

1. (1) $e^x(x-1) + c$; (2) $e^x(x^2 - 2x + 2)$;

(3) $\frac{1}{4}e^{2x}(2x^2 - 2x + 1)$; (4) $-\dfrac{e^{-2x}}{4}(2x + 1)$;

(5) $\dfrac{e^{-3x}}{-3}\left\{x^2 + \dfrac{2x}{3} + \dfrac{2}{9}\right\}$.

2. (1) $\sin x - x \cos x$; (2) $x \sin x + \cos x$;

(3) $-x^2 \cos x + 2x \sin x + 2 \cos x$;

(4) $\dfrac{x}{4}(3 - 2x^2) \cos 2x + \sin \dfrac{2x}{4}\left(3x^2 - \dfrac{3}{2}\right)$;

(5) $2x \sin \dfrac{x}{2} + 4 \cos \dfrac{x}{2}$;

(6) $x^2 \sin x - 2 \sin x + 2x \cos x$.

3. (1) $\dfrac{x^3}{3} \ln x - \dfrac{x^3}{9}$; (2) $-\dfrac{1}{4x^2}(1 + 2 \ln x)$; (3) $\frac{1}{2}(\ln x)^2$.

4. (1) $\dfrac{e^x}{2}(\sin x - \cos x)$; (2) $\dfrac{e^x}{2}(\sin x + \cos x)$;

(3) $\dfrac{e^{2x}}{5}(2 \sin x - \cos x)$; (4) $-\dfrac{e^{-2x}}{5}(2 \sin x + \cos x)$;

(5) $\dfrac{e^{3x}}{13}(3 \sin 2x - 2 \cos 2x)$; (6) $\dfrac{e^{4x}}{10}(\sin 2x + 2 \cos 2x)$;

(7) $\dfrac{e^{-x}}{10}(3 \sin 3x - \cos 3x)$; (8) $-\dfrac{e^{-2x}}{13}(2 \sin 3x + 3 \cos 3x)$.

5. (1) $\dfrac{e^{ax}}{a^2 + b^2}(b \sin bx + a \cos bx)$;

(2) $\dfrac{e^{ax}}{a^2 + b^2}(a \sin bx - b \cos bx)$.

EXERCISE 51

p. 398.

1. $63° \ 30'$ (nearly).

2. (1) $R = 4{\cdot}47$, $\alpha = 63° \ 26'$; (2) $R = 3{\cdot}61$, $\alpha = 33° \ 41'$;

(3) $R = 1{\cdot}8$, $\alpha = 33° \ 41'$.

6. $0{\cdot}698$.   **7.** $0{\cdot}48$.

9. $y = 6 \sin \left(\dfrac{2\pi t}{3} + \dfrac{\pi}{3}\right)$, where t is time in seconds.

10. $x = \dfrac{\pi}{2}$ min., $x = 40° \ 12'$ max.   Min. value $= -1$, Max. value $= 2{\cdot}152$.

EXERCISE 52

p. 403.

1. (a) $(2, 3)$; (b) $(-2, +1)$; (c) $(5, 0)$; (d) $(0, -2)$; (e) $(1, -2)$; (f) $(0, 3)$.

2. (a) $-\dfrac{1}{2} \pm \dfrac{\sqrt{7}}{2}$; (b) $\dfrac{3}{4} \pm \dfrac{\sqrt{23}}{4}j$; (c) $0{\cdot}35 + 1{\cdot}4j$.

EXERCISE 53

p. 410.

1. $11 + 7j$.

2. $-\frac{23}{8} + \frac{7}{4}j$.

3. $11 \cdot 2 - 0 \cdot 6j$.

4. 25.

5. $4 \cdot 25$.

6. $5 - 12j$.

7. $-11 + 2j$.

8. $-7 - 24j$.

9. $-10 + 5j$.

10. $40 - 20j$.

11. $\cos 75° + j \sin 75°$.

12. $\cos 30° \mp j \sin 30°$.

13. $\frac{6}{13} + \frac{4}{13}j$.

14. $\frac{5}{17} + \frac{14}{17}j$.

15. $\frac{5}{13} + \frac{15}{26}j$.

16. $-\frac{17}{26} + \frac{3}{13}j$.

17. $-\frac{16}{13} + \frac{37}{13}j$.

18. 1.

EXERCISE 54

p. 414.

1. $5 \,\lfloor 53° \, 8'$.

2. $5 \,\lfloor -53° \, 8'$.

3. $3 \cdot 7 \,\lfloor 71° \, 4'$.

4. $6 \cdot 33 \,\lfloor 161° \, 34'$.

5. $0 \cdot 58 \,\lfloor -149° \, 2'$.

6. $32 \cdot 02 \,\lfloor 178° \, 13'$.

7. $3 \cdot 14 \,\lfloor -9° \, 10'$.

8. $3\sqrt{\frac{3}{2}} + \frac{3}{2}j$.

9. $1 \cdot 71 + 1 \cdot 54j$.

10. $4 \cdot 21 - 3 \cdot 06j$.

11. $4 \cdot 68 - 4 \cdot 22j$.

12. $6 \,\lfloor 45°$.

13. $6 \cdot 72 \,\lfloor 36°$.

14. $3 \cdot 64 \,\lfloor -42°$.

15. $1 \cdot 5 \,\lfloor 30°$.

16. $0 \cdot 75 \,\lfloor 18°$.

17. $1 \cdot 5 \,\lfloor 90°$.

18. $1 \cdot 44 \,\lfloor 45°$.

19. $2 \cdot 32 \,\lfloor 34° \, 6'$.

20. $2 \cdot 24 \,\lfloor -26° \, 34'$.

21. $1 \cdot 53 \,\lfloor 6° \, 8'$.

22. $0 \cdot 53 \,\lfloor -16° \, 51'$.

23. $1 \,\lfloor 45°$.

24. $3 \,\lfloor -45°$.

25. $0 \cdot 67 \,\lfloor 84° \, 47'$.

26. $1 \cdot 3 - 2 \cdot 1j$; $\dfrac{5\sqrt{3}}{2} - \dfrac{5}{2}j$; $\sqrt{79} \,\lfloor 103°$.

27. $1 - j$; $\dfrac{5}{4} - \dfrac{5\sqrt{3}}{4}j$; $\dfrac{5\sqrt{2}}{2} \,\lfloor -105°$.

EXERCISE 55

p. 416.

1. (a) $35°$, $63° \, 26'$, $215°$, $243° \, 26'$; (b) $2 \cdot 24 \, m$A.

2. 3% increase, height 1268 ft, elev. at B $34° \, 2'$.

3. $x = \frac{3}{2} \operatorname{cosec} \alpha$, length $14 \cdot 62$.   4. $0 \cdot 764$ sq in., $\dfrac{4a}{3\pi}$.

5. (a) (i) $0 \cdot 2106$, (ii) $0 \cdot 5038$, (iii) $1 \cdot 62$; (b) $\dfrac{e^k + 1}{e^k - 1}$.

6. (a) 3; (b) $1 \cdot 265$; (c) $v = 15 \cdot 4$, $p = 26 \cdot 75$;
   (d) $60°$, $120°$, $240°$, $300°$.

7. (a) $3 \cdot 11$; (b) $1 - \dfrac{x^2}{2}$.   8. (a) $1 \cdot 493$; (b) $11 \cdot 03$.

9. (i) BD 392 yd, DC $=$ 442 yd, 13·85 acres.

10. 268·6. **11.** 24·9, 67·8.

12. (a) 11° 32′, 168° 28′, 0°, 180°; (b) $r = 9·80$ in., $h = 6·93$ in.

13. (i) $\dfrac{1 - t^2}{1 + t^2}$;

(ii) (1) 244° 12′, 188° 10′, 300° 48′, 351° 50′; (2) 30°, 60°.

14. (a) 90°, 270°; (b) $1 + 5x + \frac{2 \cdot 7}{2}n^2$, 1·28.

15. (a) width 0·0507 in., depth 0·0330 in.;

(b) 2° 56′, width 0·0257 in.

16. (i) $1 - \dfrac{x}{15} - \dfrac{x^2}{225} - \dfrac{x^3}{2025}$; (ii) $1 - \dfrac{2x}{3} + \dfrac{8x}{9} - \dfrac{112}{81}x^3$,

0·96472.

17. (a) $1 - \frac{1}{2}x + \frac{3}{8}x^2 - \frac{5}{16}x^3 + \frac{35}{128}x^4$, 0·99015; (b) 1·719.

18. (i) $(-\frac{1}{2}, -\frac{9}{4})$; (ii) $(-2, 0)$, $(+1, 0)$, $(0, -2)$;

(iii) $y = 5x - 6$, $5y - x = 18$.

19. (a) 2·632 sq in., 2·632 in.; (b) 1·75 in., area 24·2 in.

20. $k = 0·256$, A $= 1$. **21.** $k = 12·59$. **22.** $r = +100$, V $= 230$.

23. (i) $2 + \dfrac{x^2}{12} - \dfrac{x^4}{268} + \dfrac{5x^6}{20736}$, 2·0270; (ii) 0·780 or $-1·8905$.

24. (i) 29·1 in.; (ii) 110° 36′, 212° 20′.

25. $2·79 \sin (120\pi t + 53° 44')$

(i) 0·00168 in.; (ii) 3·69 in.; (iii) $\frac{1}{60}$.

26. (a) (i) $(x - 4)(2x - 3)^{-1}$, (ii) $\dfrac{5}{(2x + 3)^2}$, (iii) $\dfrac{3x}{\sqrt{3x^2 - 1}}$;

(b) $x = 4$ maximum, $x = -1$ minimum.

27. (a) (i) $3x^{-\frac{1}{2}} + 4x^{-\frac{3}{2}}$, (ii) $\dfrac{2 \sin 2x}{1 - \cos 2x}$, (iii) $\dfrac{-3x}{2\sqrt{4 - 3x^2}}$,

(iv) $\dfrac{1}{1 + \cos x}$; (b) $\frac{3}{2}$.

28. (i) 30° 24′; (ii) $3 \sin A \cos^2 A - \sin^3 A$.

29. (i) 150 c.p.s.; (ii) 22·2 in./sec, $-$ 349 in./sec²;

(iii) $\pm 27·1$ in./sec.

30. (i) $\dfrac{2(\sin x - x \cos x)}{\sin^2 x}$, $\frac{25}{5}x^{\frac{1}{2}}e^{\frac{x}{2}}$, $9(\cos 3x + 3 \log_e \frac{n}{3} \sin 3x)$;

(ii) $\dfrac{\pi}{2}$, $\dfrac{\pi}{8}$, $0·515\pi$.

31. (a) (i) $\dfrac{1 - x^2}{(1 + x^2)^2}$, (ii) $\dfrac{2x}{1 + x^2}$, (iii) $3 \sin 2x \sin 4x$;

(iv) $\cos x - x \sin x$.

32. $a = 31·56$, $b = 0·0091$.

33. $k = -3·89 \times 10^{-5}$, $c = 29·61$.

34. $b = 0 \cdot 0491$, $a = 1 \cdot 92$.

35. $r = 3 \cdot 025$, $\alpha = 55° 47'$ (i) $\pm 3 \cdot 025$; (ii) $194° 24'$, $97° 10'$.

36. (b) R $= 14 \cdot 84$, $\alpha = 55° 18'$, $126° 47'$, $343° 49'$.

37. $135°$ minimum, $315°$ maximum.   **38.** $12 \cdot 2°$, $34° 30$.

39. (i) $(t = \frac{2}{5}, 1)$, $y = 10$, -10; (ii) 60 sq ft.

40. (i) $a = \frac{1}{2}$, $b = 0$, $c = -8$; (ii) $y = 0$, $x = \pm 4$; (iii) $(0, -\frac{16}{5})$.

41. $\dfrac{x}{8} (2S - \pi x^2)$, $x = \sqrt{\dfrac{2S}{3\pi}}$, $h = \dfrac{25 - \pi x^2}{2\pi x}$.

42. $-8 \sin \left(\mathrm{wt} - \dfrac{2\pi}{3} \right)$.   (a) $+8$;   (b) $t = \dfrac{13\pi}{6\omega}$, $t = \frac{11}{6}$.

43. $x = 2$ ft, $y = \sqrt{3}$ ft.

44. (a) $\dfrac{9t^2 + 22t^7}{\sqrt{3 + 4t^5}}$, $\dfrac{2[(t + 3) \cos 2t - \sin 2t]}{(t + 3)^3}$; (b) $2ax^2 + \dfrac{2b}{x}$, $2y$.

45. (a) $y = 0$ max. or $-\frac{32}{27}$ min.; (b) Cube, side 6 ft.

46. (a) $\cos \mathrm{A} + \mathrm{B} = \cos \mathrm{A} \cos \mathrm{B} - \sin \mathrm{A} \sin \mathrm{B}$,
$\cos 2\theta = 2 \cos^2 \theta - 1$, $48° 12'$ or $60°$.
(b) 30 ft/sec, -120 ft/sec^2.

47. (a) $\dfrac{8\pi + 6}{\pi}$; (b) $8 \cdot 28$.

48. (i) $\dfrac{2x^2 - 9}{x^4}$; (ii) $\dfrac{2}{(2x - 1)(2x + 1)^3}$; (iii) $2 \cot 2x$;
(iv) $x(2 \cos x - x \sin x)$.

REVISION EXERCISE

p. 431.

50. A $= \dfrac{16a^2}{3}$, V $= \frac{112}{15} a^3 \pi$ $(0, \frac{7}{10} a)$.   **51.** 140.

52. (a) (i) $6 \cdot 33$, (ii) $2 \cdot 84$; (b) $2yx\,dx$.

53. (a) (i) 285, (ii) $1098 \cdot 0009$; (b) $x = 5 \cos 3t - 5$;
(c) $\dfrac{2x}{x^2 + 1}$, $1 \cdot 2813$.

54. (a) (i) $12x^2 - \frac{3}{2}x^{-\frac{1}{2}} - 10x^{-3}$, (ii) $12 \cos 2x - 8 \sin 2x$,
(iii) $8(x^2 - 8)^7(2x)$, (iv) $2x^3 e^{2x}(2 + x)$;
(b) V $= 200 - 8t$, A $= -8$. Starting vel. $= 200$ ft/sec.
2500 ft.

55. (i) $\dfrac{x^5}{32} - \dfrac{5xy^4}{48} + \dfrac{5x^3y^2}{36} - \dfrac{5y^3x^2}{54}$; (ii) $0 \cdot 25\%$.

56. (i) (a) $\dfrac{2x}{(4 - x)^{\frac{1}{2}}} + \dfrac{x^2}{2(4 - x)^{\frac{3}{2}}}$, (b) $\dfrac{12}{(6x - 3)}$;
(iii) $3y = 5 - 2x$.

57. (i) $\dfrac{1}{2(x+1)^{\frac{1}{2}}x^{\frac{1}{2}}} - \dfrac{\sqrt{x}}{2(x+1)^{\frac{3}{2}}}$;

(ii) $2(\sin 2x + \cos 3x)(2\cos 2x - 3\sin 3x)$.

58. $x = 3 \cdot 69$.

59. Turning points $\theta = 0$ or $180°$.

60. (a) $\log_e x$; (b) (i) $2\tan x \sec^2 x$, (ii) $\dfrac{1 - 3\log_e x}{x^4}$;

(c) $\dfrac{1}{\sqrt[3]{1-x}\sqrt{5+2x}} + \dfrac{\sqrt{5+2x}}{3(1-x)^{\frac{4}{3}}}$.

61. (i) $y - 3x + 5 = 0$, normal $x + 3y - 15 = 0$;

(ii) $y = \frac{1}{2}KLx^2 - \frac{1}{6}x^3KL$.

62. $304 \cdot 14$, $t = 0 \cdot 0112$.

63. $(1+x)^n = 1 + nx + \dfrac{n(n-1)}{1.2.}x^2 + \dfrac{n(n-1)(n-2)}{1.2.3.}x^3 + \dots$

$(1-x)^{-n} = 1 + nx + \dfrac{n(n+1)}{1.2.}x^2 + \dfrac{n(n+1)(n+2)}{1.2.3.}x^3 + \dots$

$(1-x^2)^{\frac{1}{3}} = 1 - \frac{1}{3}x^2 - \frac{1}{9}x^4 - \frac{5}{81}x^6 - \frac{10}{243}x^8 - $

$I = 0 \cdot 296944$ to 6 sig. figs.

64. (a) $\cos A \cos B - \sin A \sin B$, $1 - 2\sin^2 A$,

$1 - 8\sin^2 A + 8\sin^4 A$; (b) $I/\sqrt{2}$.

65. $A = 108$ $(\frac{18}{5}, \frac{432}{35})$.

66. (i) $2xe^{2x}(1+x)$, $2x\cos x^2$; (ii) $\frac{2}{3}x^{\frac{3}{2}} + \frac{2}{5}x^{\frac{5}{2}} + K$, $\frac{1}{2}$.

67. $\pi\frac{3}{2}[e^4 - 1]$ $(2 \cdot 44, 1 \cdot 825)$.

68. (i) $\frac{1}{2}mh^2$; (ii) $\frac{1}{6}mh^2$, min. $= \frac{1}{18}mh^2$.

69. $\bar{x} = \frac{1}{4}$, $\bar{y} = \frac{1}{20}$. $V = 3 \cdot 25\pi$.

70. (a) (i) $\log_e 2$, (ii) $\frac{1}{3}x^3 + x^2 + x + c$, (iii) $\dfrac{1}{3\sqrt{2}}$; (b) $0 \cdot 755$.

71. (a) (i) $2 \cdot 5$, (ii) $0 \cdot 549$, (iii) $13 \cdot 375$;

(b) $\dfrac{dy}{dx} = 6(1 - \cos x)$, $y = 6(x + 1 - \sin x)$.

72. (i) $\sqrt{1+2x} + K$; (ii) $\frac{3}{2}\pi$; (iii) $200 \cdot 99$.

73. $r = 4\sqrt{5}$. 537 in.^{3}.

74. (i) $A = \pi\left[-4 + \dfrac{h4}{4} + 2h^2\right]$ $V = 815$ in.^{3}; (ii) $\frac{3}{4}\pi$ in./sec.

75. (i) $A = 5$, $c = 0 \cdot 6423$, $5\sin(\theta - 0 \cdot 64)$; (ii) $2\sqrt[4]{39}$;

(iii) $\dfrac{3\pi}{16}$.

76. (a) $92{,}500$; (b) (i) $\bar{x} = \dfrac{2\pi}{\pi}$, (ii) $\dfrac{4x}{3\pi}$.

77. (a) 1·374 sec, 8·912 ft/sec, 10 ft/sec²;

(b) (i) $\dfrac{4\sqrt{2x}}{3\pi}$ from centre on bisecting radius;

(ii) $\dfrac{4x}{3\sqrt{2\pi}}$ from centre on bisecting radius.

78. (i) $\dfrac{ba^3}{12}$; (ii) (a) 200 in.⁴, (b) 91·68 in.⁴.

79. (a) $\sqrt{12}$; (b) 13·23; (c) $2752\pi^2$.   **80.** (b) 6·08 in.².

81. (i) (a) −1·64, (b) 7·631, (c) $\frac{1}{4}(1 + e^2)$, (d) $\dfrac{\pi}{8} + \frac{1}{4}$;
(ii) $y = 1 + 2x - \log_e x$.

82. (a) $\dfrac{ab^3}{12}$, (i) 106·6, (ii) 286·6; (b) 142·3 × π.   **83.** 1196 in.³.

84. (a) $16x - 5$; (b) (i) $h = \dfrac{32}{\pi x^2}$, (ii) $x = \dfrac{4}{\sqrt[3]{\pi}}$ $h = 2\sqrt{\pi}$.

85. (i) $\frac{80}{3}$; (ii) $\frac{125}{3}$, 68·3, 60·35.

86. (i) V = 60π, A = 48·9; (ii) 24760 lb. in.².

87. (a) (i) $\frac{64}{3}$, (ii) $\frac{26}{3}$; (b) $\dfrac{\pi}{4}(3\pi - 8)$.

88. (a) (i) $\frac{1}{2}Ma^2$, (ii) $\frac{5}{4}Ma^2 = 1500$; (b) 792; (c) $\dfrac{4800\pi^2}{g}$.

89. (i) (1) $\dfrac{1}{2}x^2 + \dfrac{1}{x} + c$, (2) $\frac{2}{3}x^{\frac{3}{2}} + 4x^{\frac{1}{2}} + c$;

(ii) (1) 149·5π, (2) $\frac{32}{3}\sqrt{2}(1 - j)$.

90. A = $\frac{13}{6}$, V = $\dfrac{47\pi}{10}$, $\bar{x} = \frac{147}{130}$.

91. (a) (i) $-\dfrac{L}{R}e^{-\frac{Rt}{L}}$, (ii) $2\sin\dfrac{x}{2} + K$, (iii) $x^{\frac{1}{2}} - \frac{1}{2}\log_e x + C$;

(b) $\dfrac{3\pi}{2} - 4$.

92. (i) (1) +10, (2) 0; (ii) $\dfrac{\pi}{4}, \dfrac{\pi}{2}$, etc.;

(iii) $\dfrac{1}{2a(x - a)} - \dfrac{1}{2a(x + a)}$ 0·14205.

93. (a) (i) $e^x + e^{-x} + c$, (ii) $\log_e x - 2x + c$; (b) 0;
(c) 17·33, $\frac{13}{3}$.

94. (c) $\frac{1}{8}(\pi + 2)$.

95. (a) (i) $4(\frac{1}{3}x^{\frac{3}{2}} - x^{\frac{1}{2}}) + C$, (ii) $\frac{1}{24}(\pi - 3)$;

(b) $\dfrac{1}{2(x - 1)} - \dfrac{1}{2(x + 1)}$, 0·34655; (c) $\frac{2}{3}(1 + x^2)^{\frac{3}{2}} + C$.

96. $\dfrac{2x}{(9 + x^2)}$, 1·03, $\dfrac{4}{2x + 1} - \dfrac{2x}{9 + x^2}$, 3·364.

97. (a) 0·4325; (b) 1·2; (c) $\frac{23}{6}$; (d) $+\frac{1}{4}$.

98. (a) (i) $2j - 5$, (ii) $\dfrac{363 - 81j}{29}$;

(b) $\sqrt{73}\,(\cos 20°\,30' + j \sin 20°\,30')$.

99. $e^x = 1 + x + \dfrac{x^2}{2!} + \dfrac{x^3}{3!} + \ldots \quad e = 2\!\cdot\!7183.$

$e^{-x} = 1 - x + \dfrac{x^2}{2!} - \dfrac{x^3}{3!} + \dfrac{x^4}{4!} - \ldots$

$\tfrac{1}{2}(e^x + e^{-x}) = 1 + \dfrac{x^2}{2!} + \dfrac{x^4}{4!} + \dfrac{x^6}{6!} + \ldots$

100. (a) $-21 + 20j$; (b) $827j - \tfrac{209}{965}$.

EXERCISE 56

p. 449. Classified Questions for Revision

1. (a) $2\tfrac{1}{7}$; (b) $11\!\cdot\!4$. **2.** $972\!\cdot\!9$. **3.** $0\!\cdot\!857$. **4.** $0\!\cdot\!537$. **5.** 18.

6. (a) $0\!\cdot\!4701$; (b) $2\!\cdot\!93$. **7.** $17\!\cdot\!92$. **8.** $0\!\cdot\!385$. **9.** 2655.

10. (a) $0\!\cdot\!062$; (b) $0\!\cdot\!2738$.

11. (a) $x = \pm 3\!\cdot\!02$; (b) $x = 0\!\cdot\!75$; (c) $x = \tfrac{9}{2}$.

12. (a) $x = \tfrac{3}{10}$ or $\tfrac{3}{4}$; (b) $a = \tfrac{5}{4}$, $b = \tfrac{24}{25}$.

13. $a = \dfrac{4}{10^4}$, $b = \dfrac{732}{10^2}$, $c = -160$, $E = 1695$.

14. (a) $x = \tfrac{7}{5}$ or 4; (b) $x = 2\!\cdot\!8$; (c) $x = \pm 1\!\cdot\!123$.

15. (a) $R = 4$; (b) $a = -4$, $b = 256$. **16.** $r = 0\!\cdot\!575$.

17. (a) $x = 7\!\cdot\!49$ taking $\sqrt{x} = 2\!\cdot\!737$; (b) $x = 0\!\cdot\!38$.

18. (a) $x = 1\!\cdot\!142$; (b) $x = 7\tfrac{1}{2}$, $y = -\tfrac{13}{3}$.

19. $c = 9\!\cdot\!712 \times 10^{-7}$.

20. (a) $n = 1\!\cdot\!5$, $k = 0\!\cdot\!4585$; (b) $x = 1\!\cdot\!3$. **21.** $42°\,5'$.

22. (a) $A = \sqrt{a^2 + b^2}$; $\alpha = \tan^{-1}\dfrac{b}{a}$; (b) $0\!\cdot\!0561$.

23. $4\!\cdot\!95\ 30°$ with AB. **24.** (b) $21°\,29'$.

25. $\tfrac{3}{2} + \tfrac{7}{2}\cos 2\theta$, $57°\,41'$, $122°\,19'$.

26. $2\!\cdot\!478$ m.p.h., S. $19°\,33'$ E. **27.** $7\!\cdot\!68$ sq in.

28. $30°$ or $330°$. **29.** $6\!\cdot\!93$ in. **30.** 905 yd.

31. 905 yd. **32.** $4\!\cdot\!53$ in., $6\!\cdot\!88$ in. **33.** $\theta = 270°$ or $62°$.

34. $30°\,58'$, $210°\,58'$. **35.** $116°\,45'$. **36.** 83 ft.

37. $r = 0\!\cdot\!17$, $\alpha = 139°\,46'$. **38.** (ii) $0°$, $45°$, $135°$, $180°$.

39. $25\!\cdot\!3\ 12°\,50'$. **40.** 4903 ft. N. $78°\,29'$ W.

41. $A = 25$, $\alpha = 16°\,15'$ (a) $73°\,45'$; (b) $20°\,37'$ or $126°\,53'$.

42. (a) 1340 yd; (b) 1214 yd. **43.** 2054 ft.

45. $Z = 10\!\cdot\!18$, $\cos \phi = 0\!\cdot\!9829$.

46. (i) $6x^2 + \dfrac{3}{x^4}$; (ii) $e^x(1 - x)$; (iii) $\dfrac{2}{(3x + 2)^2}$; -20.

47. (a) $4\!\cdot\!51 \cos x - 2\!\cdot\!5 \sin x$; (b) $61°$; (c) $7\!\cdot\!01$.

48. Vel. $= 25 + 32t$ ft/sec.　Acc. $= 32$ ft/sec^2.

　　(a) $12\frac{1}{2}$;　(b) $\cos\theta - \theta\sin\theta$.　　**49.** $x = 6$, H $= 180$.

50. (a) $36x^2 + 18x - 4$;　(b) $\dfrac{e^x(2 - x)}{(1 - x)^2}$;　(c) $-(5\sqrt{3} + \frac{3}{2})$.

51. $\frac{3}{2}$, $-\sqrt{3}$, $-\dfrac{2\sqrt{3}}{3}$.　　　　**52.** $2(1 + x)$ (a) 4;　(b) 1.

53. (a) $1 + \log_e x$;　(b) $\dfrac{-2a}{(a + x)^2}$ $13°$;　$23°$;　$144°$.

54. Side $=$ base $= 12$ in.　　**55.** Side $=$ base $= 12$ in.

56. Side $=$ base $= 12$ in.　　**57.** $r = 6\cdot43$ in.

58. (a) 5;　(b) $-\frac{2}{3}$;　(c) $\frac{3}{577}$.　　**59.** (a) $17\cdot21$;　(b) $\frac{5}{6}$;　(c) $\dfrac{10}{\pi}$.

60. $y = x^3 - x^2 - 5x - 3x = \frac{5}{3}$.　　　　**61.** $0\cdot48\log_e \dfrac{10}{Q}$.

62. $\frac{8}{3}$.　　　　**63.** $\dfrac{128\pi}{3}$.　　　　**64.** $7\cdot07$, $7\cdot07$.

65. $y = \dfrac{(10 - x)^4}{144 \times 100} + \dfrac{10x}{36} - \frac{25}{36}$.

66. (a) $\dfrac{10\sqrt{2}}{3}$, $\dfrac{5}{2}$, $\dfrac{10}{\pi}$;　(b) $8\cdot1\pi$.

67. (a) $\frac{7}{6}$;　(b) $9\cdot36$;　(c) 1;　(d) $11\frac{7}{8}$ lb.

68. (a) $\frac{7}{6}$;　(b) $9\cdot36$;　(c) 1;　(d) $11\frac{7}{8}$ lb.

69. $x^3 - x^5 + c$, 18, $\frac{1}{3}$.

70. (a) $\dfrac{13}{3}$;　(b) $\dfrac{x^5}{5} - \dfrac{1}{3x^3} + c$;　(c) $2y = 5e^{x + 1}$.

71. $0\cdot997$, $0\cdot997$.　　　　**72.** $\pm0\cdot02$.

73. 6 in., 1088 in.^{4}.　　　　**74.** $130a + 66$, $l = 3\cdot0385$.

75. 228 in.^{4}, 922 in.^{4}.　　**76.** $(2^6 + 2^5 \cdot 6h)$, $(2^3 + 2^2 \cdot 3h)$, $2\cdot03$.

77. (a) $\dfrac{bd^3}{3}$ in.^{4};　(b) $\dfrac{\pi d^4}{32}$.　　**78.** $\dfrac{ml^3}{3}$ lb. in.^{2}, $\dfrac{ml^3}{12}$ lb. in.^{2}.

79. $3\sqrt{2}$, $45°$.　　**80.** 36 in. 182π.　　**81.** $2\cdot5$, 1.

82. rad. $= 4$ in., BC $= 4\sqrt{3}$, CD $= 2\sqrt{3}$;　(c) $8\sqrt{3}$.

83. $519\cdot6$ cu in.　　**84.** $3\frac{1}{3}$, $\frac{24}{25}$.　　　　**85.** -1, $2\cdot5$.

86. $109°\ 28'$, Max. $= \sqrt{2}$, Hyp. $= \dfrac{10}{1 + \sin\theta + \cos\theta}$,

　　Min. $= 4\cdot14$.

87. (a) $2^5\left[1 + \dfrac{5x}{2} + \dfrac{5x^2}{2} + \dfrac{5x^3}{4} + \dfrac{5x^4}{16} + \dfrac{x^5}{32}\right]$;

　　(b) $1 + \dfrac{x}{2} + \dfrac{x^2}{2} + \dfrac{7x^3}{12}$, $= 1\cdot0208$;　(c) $-\frac{1}{3}x^{-\frac{4}{3}}$

88. $\dfrac{4r}{3\pi}$, $\dfrac{\pi^2}{4}\left(3 - \dfrac{2}{3\pi}\right)$.　　　　**89.** $13°$.